Bow Porcelain

THE FABER MONOGRAPHS ON POTTERY AND PORCELAIN

Former Editors: W. B. Honey, Arthur Lane and Sir Harry Garner
Present Editors: R. J. Charleston and Margaret Medley

BOW PORCELAIN

by
ELIZABETH ADAMS
and
DAVID REDSTONE

The history of England is
The history of private lives

FABER AND FABER
London · Boston

First published in 1981
by Faber and Faber Limited
3 Queen Square London WC1
Filmset and printed in Great Britain by
BAS Printers Limited
Over Wallop, Hampshire
All rights reserved

Also by Elizabeth Adams

Mason Porcelain and Ironstone
(*with Reginald Haggar*)

British Library Cataloguing in Publication Data

Adams, Elizabeth
 Bow porcelain
 1. Bow porcelain
 I. Title   II. Redstone, David
 738.2′3   NK 4399. B7
ISBN 0-571-11696-5

This book is dedicated to Reginald G. Haggar
without whose knowledge, guidance and enthusiasm,
generously imparted to generations of his students,
much that is now known of ceramic history would
be still undiscovered

Foreword

A title on Bow porcelain was envisaged very early on in the planning of the Faber series of Monographs on Pottery and Porcelain. The proposed author, however, died and the project was long deferred. The appearance of the present book is therefore especially welcome as the fulfilment of a long-cherished plan.

Bow was one of the longest-lived and most prolific of the eighteenth-century English porcelain factories, disputing with Chelsea the claim to be the earliest foundation in this field. If Chelsea is generally accepted as the most aristocratic and cosmopolitan of them, Bow endears itself to most English collectors by its own special characteristics of a sympathetic creamy material with a special quality which lends itself well to chunky forms; an exceptionally beautiful violet-toned underglaze-blue; a rich palette of enamel-pigments yielding colour harmonies special to itself; and above all, a certain elusive quality of directness and simplicity peculiarly its own, making it perhaps the most English of all English porcelains. Its body indeed was unique in the history of the ceramic art, being formed by the addition to the paste of a proportion of bone ash. This constituent was in due course taken into use by almost all the other English factories and became the basis of the bone china of the nineteenth century. In this, Bow was a true pioneer, and in a field where there was inevitably much copying of the fashions established by Far Eastern porcelain and the already existing continental factories, Bow—although it certainly copied with the best of them—also stood out by reason of its originality in form and decoration.

In the twenty-five years since a book on Bow was first projected in this series, many new discoveries have been made. In the present book those in the documentary field have been marshalled by Elizabeth Adams, formerly Honorary Secretary of the English Ceramic Circle, who has indeed been herself responsible for many of them. The porcelain itself is dealt with by Dr David Redstone, a collector and connoisseur who was largely responsible for the excavations on the site of the Bow factory which were undertaken in 1969. The finds made at that time have proved an important means of attributing certain models to the factory.

R. J. CHARLESTON

Contents

Colour Plates

Acknowledgements

Our acknowledgement and most grateful thanks are due to many people who have helped us in the production of this volume, and especially to Reginald Haggar, who has encouraged us by his wholehearted support and advice throughout, and by every practical means. The tables in Appendix V were produced by him, and to him we owe the excellent drawings of details and shapes. The index is also entirely his work, and this alone is help for which any author must feel great gratitude. We are glad to thank Mr and Mrs S. Weatherby for details of their family's history, and likewise Mrs Rosemary Pratt and other members of the Peers family who helped us with access to their records.

For other documentary material we would like particularly to thank Hugh Tait, Assistant Keeper of the Department of British and Medieval Antiquities, British Museum, who generously allowed Mrs Adams facilities and unlimited time to work on the Bowcock papers. Great thanks are also due to John C. Austin, Curator of Ceramics at Colonial Williamsburg, Virginia, USA, to Bradford L. Rauschenberg, Assistant to the Director, Museum of Early Southern Decorative Arts, Winston-Salem, North Carolina, USA, and to Clifford J. Larson, formerly Director, Laura Musser Art Gallery and Museum, Muscatine, Iowa, USA. Our special thanks are due to C. R. H. Cooper, Keeper of Manuscripts at the Guildhall Library, who first drew our attention to the Sale notice of 1787 for the Bow factory and to F. B. Stitt, Staffordshire County Archivist, of the William Salt Library, Stafford. We thank the following who have helped us especially with photographs of items in their care: Cleo Witt, Curator of Applied Art, Bristol City Museum; Julia Poole, Assistant Keeper of Applied Art, Fitzwilliam Museum, Cambridge; Elizabeth Owles, Curator, Moyses Hall Museum, Bury St. Edmunds; Kay Staniland, Curator of Costumes and Textiles and Amanda McIlwain, Museum Assistant, reserve Collection, Museum of London; Sheena Smith, lately Assistant Keeper of Art, Norwich Castle Museum; Tiffany Hunt, Deputy Curator, Salisbury and South Wiltshire Museum. John Mallet, Keeper of the Department of Ceramics, Victoria and Albert Museum, has been very helpful with the provision of photographs and advice. Hugo Morley-Fletcher and Anton Gabsewicz of Christie's and Jo Forester, Peter Williams and Sylvia Hunte of Sotheby's have been exceptionally helpful in the provision of photographs, as have Anne George of Albert Amor Ltd., Geoffrey Godden FRSA and Simon Spero; and also H. Gilbert Bradley, Dr Peter Constable and Desmond King. We are also particularly grateful to Vagn Christophers who, along with John Cushion, was responsible for the basic 'ceramic' education of one of us (D.R.) and to Dr Bernard Watney whose chapter on Bow in his book *English Blue and White Porcelain of the Eighteenth Century* was the beginning of an interest in that factory and its wares for the same. We are both very grateful to Pat Redstone for her patience and forebearance and advice and for help with much of the typing. Finally, we thank Dr Alwyn Cox for performing the X-ray fluorescence spectroscopic analysis of some specimens of Bow porcelain, and various private collectors for making their pieces available for reproduction (where no acknowledgements of sources are made in captions to pieces illustrated, they are in private collections). The quotation on the titlepage is taken from 'In a Country Church', from *Tomorrow is My Love* (© Hal Summers, 1978), and is reproduced by permission of Oxford University Press and by kind permission of the poet.

Introduction

English bone china is known today the world over as one of the most practical as well as the most beautiful of ceramic bodies for everyday domestic use. It combines a lovely translucency, brilliant whiteness and the possibility of fine potting with a resilience not possessed by the greyer-toned true hard-paste porcelains. Who has not, at some time, been surprised to find that a bone-china cup from the tea-service has survived a fall from table to floor unbroken? Who has not knocked a bone-china saucer against a tap and yet found the saucer unchipped? This resistance to fracture is the result of the incorporation into the china paste of a quantity of calcined bone, and bone was first employed as an ingredient of a china body by the eighteenth-century east London porcelain factory at Bow. In the first instance, bone was used in an effort to whiten the porcelain paste, but the quality of resilience it gave to the china must have been very soon apparent. The idea of including bone in china paste had spread from Bow to Chelsea by 1758; and the Lowestoft factory, founded c. 1757, employed a china body with bone as a staple ingredient from the beginning. The original aim at the Bow factory was the discovery of a new recipe for a porcelain body, not specifically for bone china, though all subsequent experiments and developments, including those of Neale and Spode, resulting ultimately in the bone china used today, trace back to the first employment of bone at Bow.[1]

This fact alone would be sufficient reason for us to try to set out in as much detail as possible the history of that early seminal factory, and to review its productions, but there are even weightier reasons for such a history. Long before Josiah Wedgwood built his new factory on the Ridge House estate, the proprietors of the Bow Porcelain Manufactory had created their new, extensive and carefully sited works, and had given it the name of New Canton, as

---

1. In a paper published in the Northern Ceramic Society *Journal*, Vol. III, 1979, Geoffrey Godden shows that the porcelain body of a bone china teaset made in the 1780s or early 1790s by Neale & Co. of Staffordshire contained 25% by weight of bone ash, almost exactly the same quantity as a fragment of a Bow coffee cup, plain white with applied prunus sprays, which was analysed by Herbert Eccles and Bernard Rackham in 1922. Neale's bone china therefore antedated Spode's by about ten years, and Godden concludes that Neale & Co. were the pioneers of bone china manufacture in the Potteries.

significant and more relevant to the manufacture of porcelain than Etruria was
for Wedgwood's manufactures of earthenware. If Chelsea was the arbiter of
taste and an Art manufacture, Bow was an initiator of new ideas, new
standards, and the precursor of the modern porcelain industry. The Bow
Manufactory of New Canton was the first ceramic factory that we have
knowledge of, built in England specifically for the manufacture of porcelain. It
preceded Wedgwood's factory at Etruria by nearly a quarter of a century. It
traded throughout the civilized world. In this again it was clearly in advance of
the industrial growth of the Midlands and the building up of the pottery
industry.

A brief chronological summary may help readers to comprehend the pattern
of events and circumstances in the history of the Bow porcelain factory, and the
personalities involved in them. The factory was founded *c.* 1747 by five
partners, chief among whom were Edward Heylyn, a clothier of Bristol, and
Thomas Frye, an Irish artist and mezzotint engraver, well known in his own
lifetime as an able portraitist. The others were John Weatherby and John
Crowther, merchants engaged in the wholesale china and pottery trade and also
with an interest in glass making, and George Arnold, a wealthy liveryman of
the Haberdashers' Company and an alderman of the City of London. In 1749,
the buildings of the Bow porcelain works were established across the River Lea
'in Stratford Road in the County of Essex', as we learn from a fire insurance
policy issued in the names of all the above-mentioned partners, except that of
George Arnold.[2] Previously, in December 1744, a patent to cover a recipe
proposed for the manufacture of a porcelain body had been taken out by
Heylyn and Frye. In 1749, a further patent was issued to Frye alone. This fact
gives substance to the claim made in Frye's published obituary (see
Appendix III) that he was 'the Inventor and first Manufacturer of PORCELAIN
in England'.

A chief aim of the partners was that their porcelain should imitate and
undercut the imports of oriental porcelain, then the staple of the market. They
established their trade in Britain by opening a warehouse in the heart of the
City in 1753, and sending representatives to seek orders and promote their
wares in all parts of the kingdom, as well as arranging auctions of Bow
porcelain, even as far off as Dublin. Overseas trade was largely conducted
through the separate business of Weatherby and Crowther as wholesale china
merchants at St. Catherine's-by-the-Tower, and Bow china was certainly well
known in the American colonies, where George Arnold had particular
connections with Virginia through his relatives. The story of the use of
American clay ('unaker') at Bow may well have arisen by reason of this fact.

By 1760, although George Arnold had long been dead and Edward Heylyn
declared a bankrupt, Bow was the leading commercial producer of English
ornamental and useful china. The factory's decline really began with the death

2. Sun insurance records, Guildhall MS 11936/87 116996 7 July 1749.

of its prime mover, Thomas Frye, after a protracted illness, in April 1761, and was hastened by that of John Weatherby in 1762. Though manufacture at Bow continued under John Crowther's sole management for another thirteen years, the factory gradually lost its pre-eminence, its wares became unfashionable, and the scanty records remaining show the gradual but certain lessening of its prosperity. Finally, closure came in the spring of 1776, the remaining stock and plant were sold to William Duesbury and sent up to Derby, and the factory buildings and kilns were adapted to the production of pitch and tar for maritime uses.

The earliest Bow porcelain was acknowledged by contemporaries to be similar to the French soft-paste manufactured at St. Cloud, but in the course of time Bow china became heavier and much less translucent. Towards the end of the factory's existence its productions were so underfired as often to be opaque and easily mistaken for earthenware.

In the following pages, we hope to show how the methods of manufacture, forms and decoration used at Bow influenced potteries of every sort throughout Britain, and even crossed the Atlantic Ocean before the end of the eighteenth century.

1
Setting the Scene

It is perhaps not necessary to dwell at great length on the influence which oriental wares, imported in ever increasing quantities from the sixteenth century onwards, had on the rise of European ceramic art. The story has been repeatedly told in recent years.[1] But it is certainly important to consider what the oriental trade contributed to European culture. Tea and coffee were imported in quantity, and with the new beverages came vessels used for their consumption. More significant than the decorations that adorned the wares were the forms in which they were cast. Almost every ceramic object of a utilitarian kind had its origin in an Eastern prototype, although it might be considerably modified to bring it into line with Western usage.

The earliest regular trade in Eastern porcelain was that of the Portuguese, who established their stations and routes with some difficulty in the sixteenth century. Imported Chinese porcelain was known as 'carrack' porcelain in Europe, after the type of Portuguese ships which carried it home. The Spaniards were not very successful in establishing an East India trade, but after capturing two carracks laden with porcelain, the Dutch established their own East India Company in 1614. In spite of the fact that the English had founded a Company in 1599, they did not reach China until 1631. Fascinated by imported Chinese wares in various bodies, some decorated in underglaze cobalt blue, which the India Companies imported during the seventeenth century, European potters made great efforts to imitate them, whether in soft tin-glazed earthenware, as in Holland and England, or in a harder material corresponding to the 'red porcelain' (in reality a stoneware) made at Yi-hsing and imported from China. The desire for something even finer in quality and more like the white porcelain from China gave rise to a search for the material from which it could be made, and for the actual recipe by which the 'bones' and 'flesh' of this true hard-paste porcelain might be knit together. Many were the arcanists who hawked their bogus secrets from court to court, or from one prospective patron to another. George Psalmanazar was typical.[2] Hard-paste porcelain was finally

1. See for instance, Hugh Honour, *Chinoiserie, The Vision of Cathay*, 1961, and Oliver Impey, *Chinoiserie, The Impact of Oriental Styles on Western Art and Decoration*, 1977.
2. George Psalmanazar (born 1679, died 1763) was a celebrated impostor and pretender to the secrets of porcelain making whose real name is unknown. Although born in the south of France

achieved at Meissen in 1709 through the work of the Graf von Tschirnhausen and Johann Friedrich Böttger in the service of Augustus the Strong, Elector of Saxony and King of Poland. The secret, however, was rigorously kept, and in England potters turned to the descriptions of Chinese porcelain manufacture sent in letters to Europe by Père D'Entrecolles, a Jesuit resident near the city of Ching-tê-Chên, the chief centre of Chinese ceramic manufacture. They persevered in the search, making use of many extraordinary materials, rather than the requisite china clay and china stone (kaolin and petuntse of the Chinese), and producing various soft or artificial porcelains by their efforts.

England had come late into this excitement and frenzied activity. Although a scheme for making porcelain had been mooted in 1720,[3] and John Dwight had patented a 'transparent earthenware or porcelane' in London in 1693, no real porcelain manufacture began in this country until the fourth decade of the eighteenth century.

The earliest dated pieces of English soft paste known are the Chelsea cream jugs moulded in the form of recumbent goats, one of which carries the date '1745' incised beneath. The Chelsea factory probably does bear away the palm for the earliest founded English porcelain manufacture, but the base of a bowl excavated by Paul Bemrose in 1970 at the Pomona Inn in Newcastle-under-Lyme, the site of the earliest porcelain factory in Staffordshire, is dated '25th July 1746' in underglaze blue, and it shows that the provinces were not far behind.[4] It is true, however, that William Steers, the progenitor of the Newcastle factory, had gone there from London; and Longton Hall, the second Staffordshire porcelain factory, which was founded in 1749, also had London connections, though its original partners were local men.

Indeed, in the earliest years of English porcelain manufacture London occupied a pre-eminent place, and in the products of the two London factories, Chelsea and Bow, controlled and given direction by men of taste and judgement, we see the main characteristics of English porcelain, one undertaking producing primarily art manufactures, the other large quantities of wares for everyday use, as well as figures.

The first signs of the metropolis' second great porcelain factory, Bow, appeared in 1744, when in December of that year the first Bow patent was taken out for 'a certain material whereby a ware might be made of the same nature or kind and equal to, if not exceeding in goodness and beauty, china or porcelain ware imported from abroad'. It is probable that the Bow factory was not yet

---

he gave himself out to be 'a native of the Island of Formosa', and Simeon Shaw recorded that Psalmanazar was reputed to have received a large sum of money from a potter 'in the vicinity of London' for permission to use his name in a projected porcelain manufacture. (S. Shaw, *The Chemistry of Pottery*, 1837). His *Memoirs* were published in Dublin in 1765. See Mankowitz and Haggar, *The Concise Encyclopaedia of Continental Pottery and Porcelain*, 1960, p. 374.
3. William Maitland, *The History of London . . .*, 1756, Book I, p. 528.
4. *E.C.C. Transactions*, Vol 9, Pt. 1, 1973, Paul Bemrose, 'The Pomona Potworks, Newcastle, Staffs, 1745–48', pp. 1–18.

actually in existence, but the first Bow patent leaves one in no doubt that the idea of manufacturing china in east London was definitely under serious consideration.

For years past it has been customary to say that little or nothing is known of the genesis of the early English china factories. Such a statement is no longer true. Certainly our knowledge is still very patchy, but the truth is that so far as the two great London factories are concerned, the origins of Chelsea are a little clearer now, while our knowledge of the rise of Bow is very much more complete. This is due to much devoted research initiated by Hugh Tait of the British Museum, who was responsible for mounting the important Exhibition of Bow documentary pieces at the Museum in 1959–60. His work has since been added to and supported by excavations on the factory site undertaken by Dr David Redstone, and by new documentary research on the part of several members of the English Ceramic Circle. It is now possible to give a fairly detailed and clear description of the buildings of the Bow China House itself, of its London warehouses and of the business undertaken in both places. We also know more of the biographies of the principals in the undertaking, and something of at least a few of the factory workers themselves.

On the continent of Europe, individual porcelain factories were the property of kings or noblemen, and drew their finances from the coffers of their owners. In England, the only porcelain manufacture which may have been supported in this way was that at Chelsea, but no documentary evidence of such support has ever come to light. Ancient rumour connects the name of the Duke of Cumberland with the factory as its patron, and it is a fact that his secretary, Sir Everard Fawkener, was associated with Nicholas Sprimont, manager and later owner of the factory, for a number of years from 1746 until Fawkener's death in 1758. We now know that records in the archives of the Bank of England show that payments of sums of money making a total of £1495 were paid to Sprimont by Sir Everard and his brother William between August 1746 and April 1748.[5] In modern terms this represents a large sum, but whether the monies were paid in support of the Chelsea manufacture by the Duke of Cumberland or by Fawkener himself we have at present no means of knowing. It merely seems most likely that the Chelsea factory arose through aristocratic support, and perhaps one can also read significance into its geographical position. It grew up in a nest of converted dwelling houses in the charming riverside village of Chelsea, just west of the cities of London and Westminster in an area that even today retains its reputation as a very pleasant and fashionable place in which to live.

Very different was the genesis of the China Works at Bow. This was an undertaking entirely commercial in character, and there never was the slightest suggestion that it was in any degree the plaything of a rich man. Except for its

5. *E.C.C. Transactions*, Vol. 10, Pt. 1, 1976, Eric Benton, 'Payments by Sir Everard Fawkener to Nicholas Sprimont', pp. 54–8.

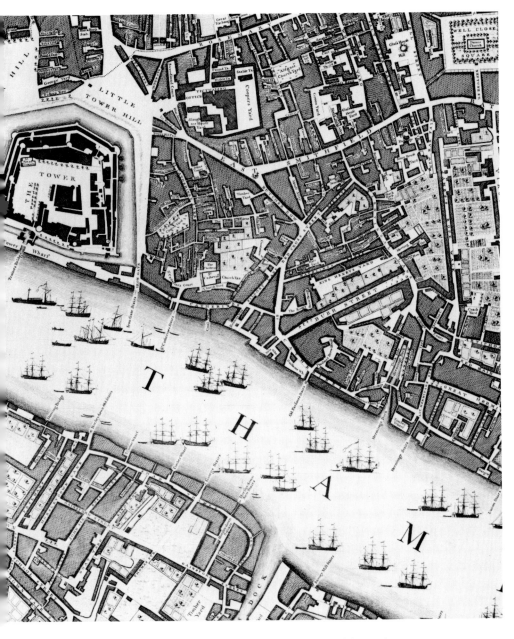

1. Part of JOHN ROCQUE'S MAP OF LONDON published in 1746 (survey 1744–5) showing the Tower and the St. Catherine's area immediately east where John Weatherby and John Crowther were established in a wholesale pottery trading from about 1744 and in a glass works in the East Smithfield area during the 1750s. *Guildhall Library. See pages 22, 26*

genius and first manager, Thomas Frye, a portraitist with a considerable
contemporary reputation, the proprietors of the Bow factory were first and
foremost businessmen with close connections with the City of London, and in
the case of Edward Heylyn with the City of Bristol. It has been suggested that
the earliest efforts of the partners to manufacture china may have taken place in
the village of Bow itself, on the London side of the then county boundary
between Middlesex and Essex, the River Lea, since entries discovered in the
Court Book, 1744, in the Record Office, County Hall, London by Dr A. Ainslie
show that Heylyn acquired a property there in that year, and another before
1750.[6] Whether or not this was so, we now know for certain that the Bow factory
of New Canton was established on the Essex side of Bow Bridge, on the north
of Stratford Causeway, by 7 July 1749. An insurance policy for the factory
taken out on that date not only confirms its situation but also lists the names of
its four proprietors.[7] Two of these, John Weatherby and John Crowther, have
not been considered until now as having anything to do with the founding of
the business, but merely as speculators who in the early 1750s bought their way
into an already well-established concern. In fact, it can be shown that they were
as important members as any of the original consortium. The Bow firm appears
also to have had a sleeping partner, Alderman George Arnold, linen-draper of
the City of London, who undoubtedly provided financial backing and whose
name is given prominence in the West Ham Poor Law Account Books of 1747
and early 1750, where the business is entered as 'Alderman Arnold & Comp.'
Thomas Frye and Edward Heylyn were both concerned with the actual
manufacture of the porcelain, but John Weatherby and John Crowther, who
both had strong family connections with North Staffordshire and the Cheshire
border, the traditional area of the Potteries, already owned a substantial pottery
trading business at St. Catherine's near the Tower (Plate 1).[8] They also had an
interest in a glass manufactory in the same district, and this may well have
given rise to the old story that Edward Heylyn's first experiments in porcelain-
making were undertaken in a glasshouse; there could be a kernel of truth in it.[9]

The Bow factory was set up to manufacture porcelain in imitation of that
imported in such vast quantities from China, and unlike the Chelsea works
concentrated in the beginning on 'the more ordinary sorts of ware for common
uses'.[10] And as Chelsea, the first and greatest English manufacture of luxury
porcelain, had its situation on the fashionable side of the metropolis, so Bow

6. Bernard Watney, *English Blue and White Porcelain of the Eighteenth Century*, 2nd ed., 1973, p. 8, nn. 3 and 4.
7. Sun insurance records, Guildhall MS 11936/87 116996 7 July 1749.
8. *E.C.C. Transactions*, Vol. 9, Pt. 1, 1973, Elizabeth Adams, 'The Bow Insurances and Related Matters', p. 75.
9. *E.C.C. Transactions*, Vol. 9, Pt. 1, 1973, Elizabeth Adams, op. cit., p. 75 and note 6. See also Chapter 2, note 35.
10. *The Case of the Undertaker of the Chelsea Manufacture of Porcelain Ware*, Anonymous, supposed to be by Nicholas Sprimont, 1753, British Museum, Lansdowne MSS No. 839, fol. 21.

with its emphasis on utility and a middle-class market was founded to the east of London, beyond the Tower Hamlets, in an area already known for commerce, and especially given over to those trades liable to cause noxious smells and fumes by their promotion — tanning, glue-making and the like. The district near Bow and Stratford already contained much of eighteenth-century London's industry, so that the effluvia of unpleasant processes could be blown eastwards across open country by the prevailing winds, and not befoul the City. By 1749, and almost certainly for two or three years earlier, the smoke from the first kiln of the Bow Porcelain Works had joined the industrial smog already rising from the shallow valley of the River Lea.

2
The Proprietors of the Bow Porcelain Factory

In 1750 the Port of London was centred in the Pool of London, below London Bridge and overlooked by the Tower. The lesser sea-going ships could make their way up the Thames as far as this last deep anchorage before the way was closed by shallower waters and the narrow arches of the medieval bridge. From the Pool cargoes were lightered to the wharves upstream by barges and smaller sailing boats and the congestion of shipping below the Bridge was severe. It was graphically described by Thomas Pennant in 1787: 'Leaving Billingsgate we were rowed along the mid-channel bounded on each side by vast fleets of all nations and sizes as high as 600 tons, disposed I may say in squadrons with small intervals between them.'[1]

Half a century later Frederick Engels described a similar scene: 'I know nothing more imposing than the view which the Thames offers during the ascent from the sea to London Bridge. The masses of buildings, the wharves on both sides, especially from Woolwich upwards, the countless ships along both shores, crowding ever closer and closer together, until, at last, only a narrow passage remains in the middle of the river, . . . all this is so vast, so impressive, that a man cannot collect himself, but is lost in the marvel of England's greatness before he sets foot upon English soil.'[2]

The quays bordering the Thames's north shore between Bridge and Tower had been specified as 'Lawful Keys' since the time of Elizabeth I, and in the centre stood the Custom House, so placed to control the import of all dutiable goods. Only the largest merchantmen, the huge ships of the East India Company, sometimes of 800 tons burthen, were unable to manoeuvre in the crowded conditions of the Pool. They came up-river no further than Blackwall, and the Custom House had a special officer there to deal with their imports.[3] The goods were removed from them by hoys belonging to the Company 'under

1. Thomas Pennant, *Journey by Water from London to Dover*, c. 1787, copperplate MSS Library of Port of London Authority.
2. Frederick Engels, *The Condition of the Working Class in England*, 1845, English translation, Panther Books, 1969, reprinted 1976.
3. The association of this district (Blackwall) with the East India trade is commemorated in several local street and place names e.g. East India Dock Road, East India Dock Wall Road, East India Dock Basin, though the East India Dock itself was not begun until 1805.

the care of a number of revenue officers attended by others belonging to the ship, and the whole cargo is secured under lock and key'.[4] Different types of goods brought by the East Indiamen were then deposited in particular warehouses, which were listed by Pennant as follows:

At St. Helen's, the most ancient of any . . . Bengal and prohibited goods are lodged.
In Lime Street . . . drugs and baggage.
New Street in Bishopsgate Street, for Madras, Bengal and prohibited goods.
Leadenhall for the same.
Billiter Lane for private trade and drugs.
In Fenchurch Street, Packers Gardens, Whitechapel, Crutched Friars and Tower Hill for tea, china and various miscellaneous goods, and besides these the hired warehouses, as the Three Cranes, and London Wall.

In the eighteenth century the river Thames played an essential part in the life and economy of the City of London. It was the great highway on which the transactions of world-wide commerce depended, and London's greatest internal thoroughfare. The Metropolitan potteries, the individual delftware manufactories of Southwark, Lambeth and Vauxhall on the south bank, and the white stoneware makers at the Hermitage on the north, relied equally on the river for the supplying of their raw materials and the transporting of their finished wares.[5] We know, for instance, of a dealer in flints (one of the raw materials of pottery manufacture, which probably came to the warehouse by barge from Gravesend), who had his premises in Darkhouse Lane, Queenhithe.[6]

It need cause no surprise, therefore, that pottery dealers from 1740 onwards were especially to be found at Fenchurch Street and Tower Hill. The most noted firm near the Tower was that of John Weatherby and John Crowther of St. Catherine's, which was founded c. 1744.

4. Thomas Pennant, op. cit.
5. Mortimer's *Universal Director* published in 1763 lists the 'real Manufacturers of the Blue & White and Plain White, Earthenwares' and three makers of brown stoneware then active in London. Every one of them is within easy reach of the river.
    Addison & Abernethy, Hermitage Street, Wapping
    *Bacchus, Thomas, George Yard, Thames Street
    *Dunbibin, John, Coffin's Yard, St. Margaret's Hill, Southwark
    Griffiths—Lambeth
    Grove, Joseph, Horslydown-lane, Southwark
    Jackson—Vauxhall
    Jones, John, Brown Stone potter, Lambeth
    Sanders & Richards, Vauxhall
    Sanders, Wm, Mortlake
    Swabey, Saml, Vauxhall
    White, Henry, Brown Stone potter, Lambeth
    White, Wm, Brown stone potter, Fulham
*Dealers rather than manufacturers (authors' note).
6. Sun insurance records, Guildhall MS 11936/179 249813 12 October 1767.

Although the Weatherby family was firmly rooted in Staffordshire (and remains so to this day), it had already established a branch in the area of the Tower of London many years before John Weatherby entered into partnership there with John Crowther in the early 1740s. Benjamin Weatherby, John's uncle, had been a cornfactor and brewer with premises at Tower Hill, and had died there in 1708.[7] Family records state that John Weatherby was the first of the Weatherbys ever to have anything to do with the potting industry, and add that before he came to live at King Street near the Tower, he was 'of St. Botolph's, Aldgate, and Sharp's Buildings, Rosemary Lane'. Both these places are not far from the Tower, and one may surmise that John Weatherby first came to London from Staffordshire as a young man determined to make his way in the wholesale pottery trade. In 1744 he and John Crowther became interested jointly in property at St. Catherine's-by-the-Tower, and it was probably from this time that their three career partnerships began. John Crowther's address was given as St. Catherine's-by-the-Tower in an advertisement of 1746, to do with the letting of a pottery adapted for porcelain manufacture at Newcastle-under-Lyme for which Crowther was a London agent.[8] (This was no doubt the advertisement which led to William Steer's tenancy of the pottery equipped to 'burn china' on the Pomona Inn site at Newcastle.)

The wholesale pottery business at St. Catherine's was probably the earliest, and the basic one, of the three businesses in which John Weatherby and John Crowther were engaged, but they were associated with Thomas Frye of the Bow porcelain undertaking at least by April 1748, as is proved in a letter dated in September of that year, written by John Wedgwood, which is preserved in the City Museum at Stoke-on-Trent.[9] In it John Wedgwood refers to information he sought from Weatherby and Crowther, together with Thomas Frye, about the character of Thomas Briand, who purported to know the secret of porcelain manufacture, but whom Weatherby and Crowther plainly considered to be an impostor.

John Weatherby and John Crowther were also partners in a glassworks, the Green Yard Glasshouse at East Smithfield in the Tower area, at least during the 1750s. Insurance policies still extant in the surviving books of the Royal Exchange Assurance Company show that this was a prosperous business,[10] but the partners' most important undertaking was that of the porcelain manufacture at Bow, the factory of New Canton, in which they were joined by

7. Information kindly supplied by Mr and Mrs J. Stuart Weatherby, Alsager, Stoke-on-Trent.
8. William Salt Library, Stafford, *Transactions of N. Staffs. Field Club*, Vol. LV, 1920/21, p. 46, quoted by A. R. Mountford, *E.C.C. Transactions*, Vol. 7, Pt. 2, 1969, p. 87, 'Thomas Briand — A Stranger'.
9. A. R. Mountford, op. cit., p. 91.
10. Royal Exchange Policy Books, Vol. I, No. 29777, 9 July 1754; Vol. IV, 32268, 16 August 1756; Vol. VI, 34583, 5 October 1758. Guildhall MS 7252 (see Appendix I). The glasshouse trade-card is illustrated by Hugh Tait, *E.C.C. Transactions*, Vol. 5, Pt. 4, 1963, Pl. 186.

Thomas Frye and Edward Heylyn, and of which in its earlier years Alderman George Arnold of the City of London was possibly also a member.

The primary importance of the wholesale pottery business at St. Catherine's to what may be termed the empire of Weatherby and Crowther is made clearer by our ability to trace something of it over a period of thirty-six years, the last fourteen of which extend beyond the death of John Weatherby himself in 1762. We know that the undertaking at St. Catherine's probably began in 1744, with the acquisition of property in the area by the two partners. On the 6 July 1749, a fire insurance policy issued to them by the Sun Company described them as 'Dealers in Glass, China and Earthenware' and covered their Stock and John Crowther's Household Goods 'in their Warehouse adjoining Woolard's Wharf, St. Catharine's' for a total of £1000.[11] Associated with this was a policy for the Bow China Manufactory issued on the following day.[12] Eleven years later, on 11 November 1760, a policy was issued to them as 'Glass and China men' of Little Tower Hill for Stock in 'their house at St. Catharine's near Mill Bridge' valued at £500.[13]

John Weatherby died in October 1762. On 1 February 1764, a *William* Weatherby 'of West Ham in the County of Essex' took out a policy with the Sun Company to cover his house 'in his own Occupation near Mill Bridge' for £250, and the stock therein for £800.[14] This was the house the stock in which was formerly insured by Weatherby and Crowther. William Weatherby must have been a relative, perhaps a nephew or cousin, of John, but efforts to settle the relationship have so far proved fruitless. William Weatherby's name first appears in the Sun records on 24 July 1759,[15] and he was then described as a 'Dealer in China, Glass and Earthenware' and was living at a good address, Burr Street, St. Catherine's.

The story is continued through a most interesting document, an indenture between *Benjamin* Weatherby and the surviving executors of a former partner of his, John Higgons.[16] It is dated 8 July 1775, and Benjamin Weatherby is described as 'of St. Katharines in the County of Middlesex, Earthen ware Man'. Benjamin Weatherby 'some time in the beginning of the year of Our Lord One thousand seven hundred and sixty five having an opportunity of

11. Sun insurance records, Guildhall MS 11936/87 116972 6 July 1749.

12. Ibid., MS 11936/87 116996 7 July 1749.

13. Ibid., MS 11936/134 178875 11 November 1760. There is evidence that the potter James Abernethy of Hermitage Street, Wapping was associated with Weatherby and Crowther for a time in the business at St. Catherine's. A notice dissolving this co-partnership was discovered by Francis Burrell in an issue of the *Public Advertiser* dated 24 June 1760.

14. Ibid., MS 11936/152 1 February 1764.

15. Ibid., MS 11936/128 24 July 1759.

16. Aqualate papers, D(W) 1788, P. 10, B. 11, William Salt Library, Stafford. Although Benjamin Weatherby, cornfactor of Tower Hill, John Weatherby's uncle, who died in 1708, is not recorded as having left any children, it nevertheless seems very probable that Benjamin Weatherby 'Earthen Ware Man' and William Weatherby could have been his grandsons. William Weatherby and his wife Elizabeth had a daughter, Fennetter W(h)eatherby, baptized at St. Botolph's-without-Aldgate on 11 April 1740. They were then living at Gravel Lane.

going into the Trade or Business of a Potter (Pottery dealer) applied to and requested the said John Higgons to become a partner with him'. It is possible that the opportunity arose out of the death of William Weatherby, although Benjamin Weatherby's name occurs with the description 'Glass and Chinaman' in the Sun records as early as December 1752. He was then in partnership with a Timothy Pitman, and their address was 'Near Half Moon Street on the North side of the Strand'.[17]

In March 1759, Benjamin Weatherby was on his own at 'St. Catherines Cloysters near the Tower', and styled a 'Merchant', insuring merely his Household Goods and Wearing Apparel for £400.[18] Jewitt mentioned him as bankrupt in 1763; though the *Gentleman's Magazine* listed him bankrupt in February 1764. It seems as if the opportunity of going into the 'Trade . . . of a Potter' in 1765, however it arose, must have been very timely for Benjamin Weatherby. His next policy was dated 28 April 1766, and described him as 'of St. Catherine's near the Tower Merchant'. It covered a stock of glass and earthenware in Rosemary Lane for £300.[19] Just under a year later, his partnership with John Higgons is confirmed by a fire insurance policy issued in their joint names as 'Dealers in China, Glass and Earthenware' of 'the Cloysters, St. Catherine's'.[20] Their stock was valued at £1300. Of this, one hundred pounds' worth was in a warehouse over Millpond Bridge nearby, presumably the same building which had been utilized by both John and William Weatherby previously.

The indenture of 1775 makes it plain that John Higgons provided the capital for the partnership. It gives the conditions under which he became Benjamin Weatherby's partner; he had to 'purchase the Lease of the Warehouse to carry on the said Trade . . . and also advance the whole of the money for the Purchase of a Stock for the moiety of which he the said Benjamin Weatherby would give his Bond'. Arrangements were entered into for the continuance of the St. Catherine's Company in the event of the death of one of the partners, and after John Higgons' decease it continued for a while 'under the management of the said Benjamin Weatherby who was always the acting person in the said Trade or Business'. Higgons's widow Mary, who was one of his executors and a member of the company, remarried in 1772. About that time, creditors began to demand payment from the firm and there was disagreement amongst the executors as to the best way of settling the company's affairs. Arrangements were made to recover monies owed by the firm's debtors, and the list of these attached to the document makes very interesting reading. Most of them were

17. Sun insurance records, Guildhall MS 11936/99 133481 9 December 1752. A bill from 'Weatherby and Pitman opposite the New Exchange in the Strand', preserved in the Library of the Victoria and Albert Museum, was brought to the attention of the authors by Geoffrey Godden. It is dated 16 May 1753, and includes 'Bow China' amongst the wares listed in the heading as being sold by the partners.
18. Ibid., MS 11936/126 167987 27 March 1759.
19. Ibid., MS 11936/168 233218 28 April 1766.
20. Ibid., MS 11936/174 244284 3 April 1767.

dealers and private people living in the south-eastern quarter of England, including London, and especially in Essex, Kent and Sussex; but sums of money were also owing from a number of ships' captains who had bought loads of wares and were bound for foreign ports, half in Europe and half across the Atlantic. In Europe the places concerned were Jersey, Dunkirk (three ships), Bremen, Madeira (with Senegal), Elgin and Carthagena. In the New World Weatherby & Co. had goods travelling to New York (two ships); Jamaica (six ships); Newbury, New England; Philadelphia; Grenada; St. Vincent and Quebec.[21]

In 1770, Benjamin Weatherby's last-known fire policy had described him as a merchant of Burr Street, St. Catherine's,[22] and he was evidently still prosperous then. After the death of John Higgons in 1771 it seems that Weatherby's business sense was not sufficient to keep the firm on an even keel, and the indenture of 1775 was drawn up by consent of all parties to bring the company to an end. Evidence that it had nevertheless been well regarded is given by the account book of the London enameller James Giles, dating between 1771 and 1776, which lists Benjamin Weatherby & Co. along with William Duesbury & Co., Philip Christian & Co., William Davis & Co., and Thomas Turner of Worcester, later of Caughley, as among the firms with which Giles had dealings. Since the other men mentioned were all proprietors of porcelain factories, can the inclusion of Benjamin Weatherby's name be taken to imply that he was representative of the Bow factory in its last years? Or is he simply referred to in his capacity as the pottery and glass wholesaler of St. Catherine's?

It seems extremely likely that throughout most of its existence the business at St. Catherine's was closely linked with the Bow factory as a trade outlet for Bow porcelain, not only supplying dealers at home, but also concerned in shipping Bow wares to other parts of the world.[23] There is little doubt that this was so during the partnership of John Weatherby and John Crowther; and specific reference is made to their business at St. Catherine's in the surviving Bow account book, kept by the clerk of the Cornhill warehouse, John Bowcock, in August 1752:[24] 'Sold out of the Warehouse to Messrs Weatherby & Crowther goods to the value of £26. 0. 6.'

In John Bowcock's memorandum book of 1756 he remarks on 24 July: 'Recd. and gave Mr Beswick receipt for £107. 12s. in full to Sept. 1755 for Weatherby & Crowther. J.B.' This must surely refer to the wholesale firm at St. Catherine's.[25]

---

21. Joseph Ring of Bristol recorded *c.* 1787 in his *Journal* the shipment of his earthenware to Jamaica, Barbados, St. Vincent, Nevis, Virginia, Philadelphia, Bordeaux, Ostend, Rouen, Piscataqua, West Africa and Calais (Hugh Owen, *Two Centuries of Ceramic Art in Bristol*, 1873, pp. 347 and 348).
22. Sun insurance records, Guildhall MS 11936/197 284305 2 May 1770.
23. See Appendix II for list of ships with the 1775 Indenture.
24. British Museum, Additional MS 45905, p. 21.
25. William Chaffers, *Marks and Monograms*, 15th ed., 1964, Vol. II, p. 276.

Like John Weatherby's family, John Crowther's was also one which had its origin in the Cheshire and Staffordshire borders. He was the son of Ralph Crowther of Butley, Cheshire,[26] and possibly related to Robert Crowther, silk merchant, of Stockport, for whom the Bow factory made a set of named and dated blue and white plates in January 1770.[27] Although John Crowther seems to have first lived in London at St. Catherine's, the Bow Land Tax returns show that from 1753 to 1763 at least he resided near the factory. In 1759, he was Master of the Skinners' Company, and in June 1764 his daughter Joyce made an advantageous marriage to a baronet, Sir James Winter Lake.[28]

John Crowther, like Benjamin Weatherby, was listed as bankrupt in February 1764. This fact suggests that both failures may have had to do with the wholesale pottery business at St. Catherine's, and it is interesting to note that there is no further record of any connection of Crowther's with St. Catherine's after that date. The Bow factory itself was apparently not involved, and the only noticeable change in its affairs was the closure of the Bow City warehouse in Cornhill, and the opening of another soon afterwards (certainly before October 1765) in St. Mildred's Court in the Poultry.[29] The new site may have been chosen through the influence of the younger John Crowther, then rector of St. Mildred's, Bread Street. Later the warehouse was moved to St. Paul's Churchyard, and finally closed in 1775.[30]

In spite of the details we have of the younger members of his family John Crowther himself remains a shadowy figure, and is known to posterity chiefly through his participation in the Bow Porcelain Company. He was the last survivor of its original partners, and died, an old forgotten man, in an almshouse for 'decayed London merchants', Morden College, Blackheath, in the autumn of 1790.[31]

The known history of Edward Heylin, the third partner in the Bow factory, is even less than that of John Crowther. Geoffrey Wills published a short paper

26. Bernard Watney, *English Blue and White Porcelain of the Eighteenth Century*, 2nd ed., 1973, p. 26.

27. Elizabeth Adams, *E.C.C. Transactions*, Vol. 10, Pt. 1, pp. 3 and 26, 'Ceramic Insurances in the Sun Company Archives, 1766–1774'.

28. The wedding service at West Ham was conducted by her brother, John Crowther II, who took holy orders in 1758 and later became rector of St. Mildred's, Bread Street. Lady Lake had thirteen children and lived to be eighty-eight years of age. She died in 1834. Descendants of her family are still living, and a portrait of her reputed to be by Reynolds is in their possession. It is perhaps worth noting that she was considered a great beauty in her youth.

29. Sun insurance records, Guildhall MS 11936/164 225572 7 October 1765.

30. It is an interesting point that the creditor concerned in the bankruptcies of both Edward Heylin (1757) and John Crowther was George Harrison of Tottenham, a glassmaker and partner of Weatherby and Crowther in the Green Yard Glasshouse.

31. John Witherington Peers (1745–1835), third son of Charles Peers the first ground-landlord of the Bow Porcelain factory, was ordained in 1769, and became perpetual curate of Chiselhampton and Stadhampton, Oxon., and rector of Morden, Surrey and Ickleford-cum-Pirton, Herts. He was much loved by his parishioners, and a tablet was erected to his memory in Morden Church. It was perhaps he who arranged for John Crowther to retire to Morden College.

about him in the *Connoisseur* some years ago[32] which includes most of the surviving facts concerning him. Edward Heylyn was the third and youngest son of John Heylyn of Wrexham, and was born in Westminster in 1695. John Heylyn was Master of the Saddlers' Company on two occasions, in 1711 and 1721. His sons had diverse careers. John, the eldest, was ordained and became a chaplain in ordinary to George II and first rector of St. Mary-le-Strand. He was also a prebendary of St. Paul's Cathedral and of Westminster Abbey. Henry, the second son, traded as a merchant in copper ore, and died in North Carolina in 1760.

Edward Heylyn was granted the Freedom of the Worshipful Company of Saddlers in October 1718, and the records of the Chamberlain's Court of the City of London mention him as the father of twin sons, Edward and Charles, who were born 'at Wiltshire' in 1722. Both worked as packers in the City for a number of years. The younger Edward, like his grandfather, twice became Master of the Saddlers' Company, in 1779 and 1793. A cryptic reference to Charles Heylyn appears in John Bowcock's papers preserved at the British Museum. In a letter to his brother William Bowcock, an artist then living in Halifax, Yorkshire, dated 30 June 1753, John Bowcock says: 'Mr Berry was Oblidged to make up the Afair for Mr Chas Heylyn or they would have sent to Hallifax. I am surprized at Charles to let anybody know where he was going and I think there was no Necessity for Saing anything.' No further reference to Charles Heylyn is anywhere known.

Edward Heylyn Junior was twice married. Only the two children of his second marriage survived, and the younger of these, Susannah Jane, died at the age of seventy-three in 1837, the year in which Queen Victoria came to the throne. A Henry Heylyn, presumably the child of her elder brother John, died in 1853, and is commemorated by a monument in Battersea Church.[33]

Edward Heylyn the elder was made a Freeman of the City of Bristol in 1731. The relevant entry in the Burgess Books 1705–59 runs as follows: '15 July 1731 Edward Heylin Esq. is admitted into the liberties of this City by order of the Common Council on payment of £no fine and paid he being admitted at the request of Edward Foy Esq. Mayor ... (costs) ... 4s. 6d.'

The minutes of the Common Council of the previous day record that 'Edward Heylin, Clothier' was to become a burgess through the exercise of the Mayor's particular annual privilege of nominating one Freeman without payment of dues. Mr Foy's reasons for choosing Edward Heylyn as his nominee are not known, but it would perhaps be instructive if they could be discovered.[34] Another point worth emphasizing is that Heylyn was listed as a

32. Geoffrey Wills, 'The Bow China Factory and Edward Heylyn', *Connoisseur*, Vol. CXXXIII, 1954.
33. Information from Jim Cox of Morley College Ceramic Circle, Morley College, Westminster Bridge Road, SE1.
34. Perhaps it is worth noting that a well-known London china man, John Fahy (sometimes spelled Foy), whose shop was on the corner of Pall Mall, opposite St. James's Palace, is

clothier. The notion has gained belief that he was in the copper trade like his brother Henry, but this was not so.[35]

A persistent story about Edward Heylyn, quoted by Hurlbutt, is that he fired early experimental Bow porcelain in a glasshouse near Bow Bridge (Plate 2). This may well be an amalgam of two facts, first that his Bow partners John Weatherby and John Crowther were concerned in the Green Yard Glasshouse at East Smithfield, and secondly that there was an experimental 'elaboratory' in the early days of the Bow Porcelain factory. It was listed in the fire insurance policy of 1749 but not thereafter.[36]

That Edward Heylyn was active in the promotion of the Bow undertaking is suggested by two facts. The first and most important is that it was his name which was linked with Thomas Frye's in the first Bow patent of December 1744, for 'a certain material whereby an earth might be made of the same nature or kind . . . [as] china or porcelain ware imported from abroad'. It was in this patent that the kaolinic clay 'unaker' imported from America was listed among the necessary ingredients. The second fact suggesting Heylyn's active participation in the business is indicated in the style of the firm as Edward Heylyn & Co. in connection with certain premises in the parish of St. Leonard's, Bromley-by-Bow *c.* 1752–4. There is no doubt that Heylyn was a partner in the Bow concern from *c.* 1744 right through to his bankruptcy in December 1757. In the *British Chronicle* he was described at this time as 'of

---

mentioned in Duesbury's London account book 1751–3, the *Public Advertiser* 22 March 1756, and in John Bowcock's memorandum book in March and May 1756.

35. Information kindly supplied by Miss M. E. Williams BA, Bristol City Archivist. Miss Cleo Witt, Curator of Applied Art at Bristol City Museum and Art Gallery has kindly informed me that Edward Heylyn was declared bankrupt in Bristol in July 1737, his mother Susannah Heylyn, 'widow of St. George's, Hanover Square', and a glassmaker, John Berrow, being the creditors (*The Trade of Bristol in the Eighteenth Century*, edited by W. E. Minchinton, p. 184, Appendix G. i, in Vol. XX, Bristol Record Society publications). The firm of John Crosse and John Berrow became bankrupt in 1760.

36. Sun insurance records, Guildhall MS 11936/87 116996 7 July 1749. The association of glass-making with earlier efforts to manufacture porcelain in England is underlined by the contents of two letters written to her son, then on the Grand Tour, by Frances Thynne, Countess of Hertford, in December 1743 and January 1743/44. These are quoted by W. A. Thorpe, *English Glass*, 3rd ed., 1961, p. 202. On 4 December 1743 the Countess wrote: 'They have made a great improvement in Southwark upon the manufacture of glass, and brought it so nearly to resemble old white china, that when it is placed upon a cabinet at a convenient distance it would not be easily distinguished by an indifferent judge. They make jars, beakers, flower-pots, sauce-boats, salt-cellars and milk pots of it, which look extremely pretty.' On 7 January 1743/44 she continued: 'The difference between the old china and the glassware is not in the transparency, for the latter is so thick as the former, but from a bluish cast in the white, which is only observable when placed by real china.' Thorpe also gives evidence that white glass was being made in Southwark in the 1740s by at least two firms, and claims that Benjamin Bowles's Southwark glasshouse held a place in English manufacture comparable 'with Bow and Chelsea and with the short-lived enamel works at Battersea'. He quotes advertisements from the *New England Journal* of 24 January 1731/32 and 31 July 1732 to show that 'Fine white Glass Japann'd' and 'Tea Setts of White, Blew and Japann'd Glass' were even so early being imported into America by a Mrs Abbot of Boston.

2. OLD BOW BRIDGE built AD 1110. This view was drawn and engraved by J. Storer and published 1 July 1804 by Vernon & Hood, Poultry, London. The viewpoint, notwithstanding the weathercock, is from the north side of the bridge. Bow Back River is to the extreme left; in the foreground and to the right are two minor inlets and the main course of the River Lea downstream to the bridge is beyond the wooden palings on the right, the perspective at this point being somewhat foreshortened. *Guildhall Library. See page 32 and Appendix XII*

Cornhill, London, Merchant, Dealer and Chapman', though the final dividend notice in the *London Gazette* of 22 January 1763 listed him as 'late of the City of Bristol Merchant'. It was probably from Bristol that he made his way to the Isle of Man, where according to the diary of his nephew, John Heylyn,[37] he died on 16 April 1765. So far it has not proved possible to discover the place of his death and burial in the Island, but it was no doubt to escape the demands of his creditors that he went to Man to spend the last two years of his life. Some years later, after visiting the Island, John Wesley wrote in his *Journal* that it was 'shut up from the world; and having little trade . . . visited by scarce any strangers'. 'The natives are a plain, artless, simple people . . . the far greater part moderately poor; and most of the strangers that settle among them are men that have seen affliction.'

37. Preserved in the Reference Library, Central Library, College Green, Bristol.

The Bow Porcelain Special Exhibition which was arranged at the British Museum in 1959 by Hugh Tait had some interesting consequences which he described in four articles published in *Apollo* the following year.[38] Perhaps the most important of these was the discovery by Mr Saintsbury, then borough librarian of West Ham, of the Poor Law Overseer's Account Books covering the period from 25 March 1749 to 25 March 1752. Under the subheading of 'Stratford Ward' are two half-yearly entries for the Bow Porcelain works listed as 'Alderman Arnold & Comp. (Value) 39 (Payment) 1–19–0.' From 25 March to 29 September 1750 the wording changed to 'Messrs Porcelain Company' and thereafter, until 25 March 1752, when the account books become incomplete, to 'Fry and Company'. The entries of 1749–50 specifically mentioning Alderman Arnold emphasize his association with the porcelain factory which appeared in his obituary notice in the *London Daily Advertiser and Literary Gazette* of 25 June 1751: 'George Arnold Esq., Alderman of Cheap Ward, President of St. Thomas's Hospital and one of the principal proprietors of the Porcelain Manufactory at Bow.'

George Arnold, born in 1691, was the son of William Arnold, a merchant of Exeter. The Arnold family was already established in Devonshire in 1663, and another George Arnold, perhaps William's brother, died in Westminster in 1703. George Arnold the younger was apprenticed in London to a John Heron, and received the Freedom of the Haberdashers' Company in 1718, when he was described as 'of Cheapside Linendraper'. In 1723 he was chosen as a member of the Common Council for the Ward of Cheap, and elected alderman for the same Ward after the death of Sir Joseph Eyles, on 19 February 1740.

Customs Books preserved at the Public Record Office indicate some interest which George Arnold had in overseas trade.[39] In a petition made to the Treasury George Arnold 'sheweth that your Pet^{ner} as surety for James Bradley and Richard Griffin of London Merchants became bound with them to His Majesty ... 17th November 1739 for payment of £4533. 6. 8. to the Receiver General of His Majesty's Customs on 17th May 1741'. Bradley and Griffin owed £2105. 6. 11. to Customs on another undertaking, and privately Bradley owed £46. 7. 9. and Griffin £52. 6. 11. to George Arnold himself and his partners. Further debts to His Majesty of approximately £2577 were too much for Bradley and Griffin. They sold their ship *Hannah*, which was then bound for Virginia under Sam Barnes as master, to George Arnold, and were bankrupted in January 1740/41. Arnold paid off a number of their debts, and the Customs tried to seize the *Hannah* to make up the rest. Bradley and Griffin also owned another ship, the *Elizabeth*, from the profits of whose trading some of the money was raised. She may have been trading from Bristol. The Treasury records mention her return in 'January last', and Lloyds' List

38. Hugh Tait, 'Some Consequences of the Bow Porcelain Special Exhibition', Parts I–IV, *Apollo* (February, April, June and October 1960), Vol. LXXI, pp. 40–5, 93–8, 181–5 and Vol. LXXII, pp. 111–15.
39. P.R.O. Customs Books, Treasury/11/22 fol. pp. 139–41.

No. 560 of 2 January 1740/41 records the return to Bristol of an *Elizabeth* under command of Captain Cheshire, which arrived from Antigua on 31 December.

George Arnold's petition to the Treasury was granted, and he was allowed possession of the *Hannah* 'to be deposed and sold by him as he shall see cause'. A point of interest in the narrative of these transactions is the fact that the *Hannah* was trading to Virginia, for it has recently come to light that George Arnold had a cousin in Virginia, George Yeo, whose will was dated 15 March 1742/43 and proved on 20 April 1743. George Yeo appointed two executors, Cousin John Selden in Virginia, and Cousin George Arnold, merchant in London, in Great Britain. Yeo's specific bequest to George Arnold consisted of 'certain tenements in the Burrow of Hatherly (Devon) commonly called by the names of Wadlands and Finch Parks' and also 'the plate I brought from England'. It is tempting, on this admittedly slender evidence, to wonder whether George Arnold had not something to do with the mysterious supply of American china clay, the 'unaker', the use of which has always been associated with the Bow Porcelain factory. His cousin George Yeo lived in Elizabeth City County, Virginia, near the coast of Chesapeake Bay, a considerable distance from the Blue Ridge Mountains, part of the Appalachian chain, from which the unaker supposedly came. Yet a direct personal link between the Bow factory and Virginia raises tantalizing suggestions.

The inception of the Bow works appears to have occurred in 1744, the year following Yeo's death, when George Arnold and Edward Heylyn jointly purchased land and buildings within the jurisdiction of the Courts Baron of the Manor of Stepney. (The business combination of a linen-draper and a clothier, both perhaps having connection with Bristol, is natural enough.[40]) The first Bow patent, as we have seen, was issued on 6 December that year in the names of Edward Heylyn and Thomas Frye, and was limited to no more than five shareholders by a previous Act of Parliament. From our present knowledge the men in question were Weatherby, Crowther, Heylyn, Arnold and Frye, but it is highly probable that Arnold was always a sleeping partner, though perhaps chief financier to the undertaking.

At any rate, unlike the unfortunate merchants James Bradley and Richard Griffin, he prospered. A single fire insurance policy issued to his firm of linen-drapers by the Sun Company on 28 August 1745[41] is for their stock housed at No. 9 in Cox's Warehouses, Billiter Lane, and worth £2000. (It may be remembered that according to Thomas Pennant warehouses in Billiter Lane were used chiefly for private trade and drugs.) The policy lists the partners as George Arnold, John Serjeant and Thomas Birch. Arnold's firm was recorded as 'in Rood Lane' in 1749. On 21 March 1750 he was unanimously elected

---

40. It suggests familiarity with the city that George Arnold should have ordered fifty or so mourning rings to be distributed to his friends in Bristol under the terms of his will.
41. Sun insurance records, Guildhall MS 11936/74 103209 28 August 1745.

President of St. Thomas's Hospital, of which he had been a governor for nineteen years past. The usual progression after this honour was to the position of Lord Mayor of the City of London, but Arnold's career was interrupted by his sudden death on 23 June 1751. He was buried in Camberwell churchyard, and his tomb erected and epitaph composed by John Serjeant, his partner at Rood Lane, and his 'affectionate relation . . . as a small testimony of the gratitude, esteem and tenderness with which he regards him'. 'After a long enjoyment of uninterrupted health, cheerfulness and tranquillity, in the midst of business, he died as easily as he had lived, for almost without any previous indisposition on the 23rd June, in the year 1751, the 60th year of his age, after having, with his usual domestic ease, entertained a society of his old friends, he retired familiarly from the feast of life and passed gently from this world to a better.'

A man of solid worth, of 'bottom', to use the eighteenth-century phrase, such as Arnold, was exactly the right person to give the nascent porcelain manufacture a firm grounding.

We come at last to Thomas Frye (Plate 3), the artist to whose dedication and tireless work the spirit and actual embodiment of the porcelain produced at Bow must primarily be due.

Frye was born about 1710 'in or near Dublin', and was in fact probably Thomas, second son of John Fryc (1670 1752) of Edenderry, Co. Offaly.[42] Nothing is known of his youth or early artistic training, but about 1734 he appears to have gone to London in company with Herbert Stoppelaer, a portrait painter of no very great ability. In November 1736 Frye was commissioned to paint a portrait of Frederick, Prince of Wales, to commemorate the Prince's acceptance of the position of Perpetual Master of the Company of Sadlers, and it was probably through this assignment that Frye first came to know Edward Heylyn who was already a member of the Sadlers' Company. The portrait was ordered for the Company by Heylyn's uncle, Thomas Sherman, and hung in the Sadlers' Hall for more than two hundred years until it was destroyed in the London Blitz in 1940, together with the building which housed it and most of the Company's historic records. It is now known only through a mezzotint copy which Frye himself made in 1741.

It may well have been through his connection with Heylyn that Thomas Frye was introduced to John Weatherby and John Crowther. Another person with whom he became acquainted in the 1730s was Hillary Torriano whose miniature portrait in oils, painted by Frye, is now in the Victoria and Albert Museum. It is signed and dated: 'T. Frye/Londini/fecit/Sept./1737.' Torriano was at this date a little over twenty-four years old, and came of a family Italian in origin, though settled in England since the early seventeenth century. His father, Nathaniel Torriano, a Freeman of the Haberdashers' Company, had at

42. Michael Wynne, 'Thomas Frye 1710–1762', *Burlington Magazine*, Vol. 114, 1972, pp. 79–84.

3. THOMAS FRYE. From the mezzotint engraving self-portrait
signed with the monogram F and inscribed 'Ipfe' (ipse)
British Museum. See page 36

some time been a supercargo in the East India Company.[43] Hillary followed him in this calling, and after marrying Elizabeth Hardwick, daughter of the British Consul in Lisbon, in 1739, settled at West Ham.

Dr Watney suggests that Thomas Frye went out to West Ham to live, having been a resident of the City of London for some years, in order to engrave original designs for calico-printers, a number of whom had important works established in the neighbourhood of Bow and Old Ford.[44] This is quite possible, but we suggest that it is only one thread in the establishment of the Bow China works in that particular location. Another is the close tie found between the East India Company and the area of Bromley, Bow and Stratford. We have already seen that the great Company ships unloaded much of their goods by the Isle of Dogs, near the mouth of Bow Creek; besides this a local landowning family, the Peers, who possessed large tracts of property in Bromley, Bow and Stratford (including the site of the Bow Porcelain factory itself), numbered at least one director of the East India Company; and Hillary Torriano, Thomas Frye's friend, was by 1750 a supercargo like his neighbour Charles Peers.

It is very likely that Hillary Torriano was instrumental in supplying the proprietors of the Bow factory with oriental porcelains as prototype patterns for the manufacture, and the design of the factory itself, based on one of the Hongs, or national trading buildings in Canton, may also have been suggested by him.[45]

Thomas Frye's obituary was not published in the *Gentleman's Magazine* until 1764, two years after his death on 2 April 1762.[46] It refers to him as 'The Inventor and first Manufacturer of PORCELAIN in England' and states that to perfect it 'He spent fifteen years among Furnaces'. This would agree with the supposition that experiments in porcelain-making began for the Bow consortium in 1744/45, as Frye was suffering from their ill-effects in 1759.

The second Bow patent, taken out in Frye's name only for the manufacture of 'a certain ware which is not inferior in beauty and fineness and is rather superior in strength than the earthenware that is brought from the East Indies' was enrolled on 17 November 1749, and this patent also was limited to no more than five proprietors. The first insurance policy for the Bow works, issued by

43. For details of the responsibilities of the supercargoes see Hosea Ballou Morse, *The Chronicles of the East India Company trading to China 1635–1834*, Oxford University Press, 1926. They were required to manage all the affairs of the Company relating to the buying and transport of the goods carried by the ships to which they were attached, and had a certain licence to trade on their own account, though this was strictly regulated. Among family papers of the Peers family is the record that Mr Torriano, chief supercargo, died on board the *Macclesfield* in Batavia Roads on Saturday, 14 May 1731.

44. The calico-printing works of Richard Emery were situated immediately opposite the Bow China factory on the south side of Stratford Causeway. See Sun insurance records, Guildhall MS 11936/173 240448 18 December 1766.

45. An interesting point is that Frederick Pigou, a well-known supercargo of the Company, had his home in Chelsea.

46. See Appendix III.

4. SHEPHERD AND SHEPHERDESS PAIR symbolic of Liberty and Matrimony.
Height 25.4 cm (10 in) 1753–4
Courtesy of Sotheby's. See pages 39, 191

the Sun Company in July, four months previously, as we have seen, tells us the names of the proprietors, and proves that the factory was firmly established as a commercial concern by the summer of 1749.[47] The obituary notice of 1764 makes it plain that by 1759 Frye's constitution was 'near destroyed' through his intense application and labour in the porcelain factory. He was no sleeping partner. Not only had he discovered and perfected the formula for the porcelain body itself with its revolutionary admixture of bone ash, but he very probably took care to overlook and approve the designs of the wares and figures, at least in the factory's earlier years. Possibly he was personally responsible for some of them. Michael Wynne puts forward the theory, based on the style of the elaborate and theatrical women's head-dresses and coiffures which Frye depicted in some of his late mezzotint portrait heads, that the early rococo Bow porcelain Sphinxes were the personal design of Frye.[48] Could the dramatic and stylish individual figures of the shepherd and shepherdess representing Liberty and Matrimony (Plate 4) be Frye's also? Though it is

47. Printed in full in Chapter 3.
48. Michael Wynne, op. cit.

true that they derive from Meissen originals they have a flair and refinement not normally associated with the rather heavy creations of the anonymous 'Muses modeller' to whom they are generally credited.

Although the obituary speaks largely of Frye's artistic genius, and ends with lines which may seem over-florid to a modern ear, the total effect of it is certainly to recall a man truly loved and respected by all who knew him. John Ellis, Warden of the Scriveners' Company and Dr Johnson's friend, was also a family friend of the Fryes, and executor of the wills of both Thomas and his wife Sarah. The notable portrait of Ellis which Frye engraved in 1761 speaks not only of the sitter, but pays tribute to the personality of the artist also.

Sarah Frye bore her husband five children between 1735 and 1743.[49] Three of them survived to become adult, but Thomas, the eldest, is said to have been a wastrel. Sarah, the second child, and Mary, the youngest, both became china painters in the Bow factory, and both married men who were also china decorators. Sarah and her husband Ralph Willcock (or Wilcox) later worked for Josiah Wedgwood on the famous creamware 'Frog' service which was manufactured for the Empress of Russia, but Sarah received the higher wages. Ralph Willcock had trained as a delft painter with Dunbibin & Co. in Liverpool, and had subsequently worked at William Reid's factory, being still employed there when it failed in 1761.[50]

49. Baptisms of the children recorded in the register of St. Olave's, Old Jewry. They were discovered by Dr B. Watney: Thomas, 10 October 1735; Sarah, 19 March 1736; John, 9 August 1738; Frederick, 5 October 1740; Mary, 27 May 1743. The dates are Old Style.

50. Other relatives of Thomas Frye, besides his wife and children, appear to have lived in the London area. His elder brother Henry was living at West Ham in 1754; Thomas Frye, son of Henry and Jane Frye was baptized at West Ham on 27 October 1754, and Henry, son of Henry Frye was buried at Bow on 23 December 1760. John Bowcock records in his memorandum book for 1758 that on 26 December he 'Dined with Mr H. Frye & family at Stratford'. Another person who was probably related to Thomas Frye (and was perhaps his nephew) was John Fry(e) Jr. (so styled in contemporary records), whose father was possibly a cheese merchant of the same name in Southwark. On 5 June 1749 John Fry 'of the Parish of St. Olave, Southwark, in Surrey, & Elizabeth Eveleigh of the same parish' were married by licence at West Ham. In 1752 a malthouse at Bow which was assessed at £80 appears in the Land Tax returns in the name of John Fry Junior, and from 1753–7 another malthouse at St. Leonard's, Bromley-by-Bow (assessed at £50 Poor Rate in 1753 and 1754) is also ascribed to John Fry Junior. That he was a maltster and not a porcelain-maker as Mr Tait suggested (E.C.C. Transactions, Vol. 5, Pt. 4, 1963, pp. 210 and 211) is proved by a fire insurance policy issued by the Royal Exchange Company on 14 January 1755 in the names of 'John Frye Junr. and Robert Elliott of Bromley in the County of Middlesex Maltsters' (Guildhall Library, Royal Exchange Assurance records, Vol. II, 30455). John Frye's dwelling house, part timber-built and tiled, 'at Bromley aforesaid being his Own Property' was insured for £150. 'Goods in Trade in their Malthouse, Kilns and Granary, part timber built and tiled . . . adjoining the said dwelling house' were valued at £800, and 'Utensils in the Malthouse' at £50, £1000 altogether, a comfortable sum. In 1754 the Poor-rate books at Bromley gave John Frye's partner's name as 'Harwood', not 'Elliott'. From 1754–8 John Frye continued to pay the taxes on these Bromley properties, but probably no longer continued to live at Bromley, for the parish registers at Chelsea hold two entries concerning him: '1754 1st March, Martha, daughter of John and Elizabeth Fry baptized. 1755 16th November, John, son of John and Elizabeth Fry baptized.'

Thomas Frye had died the following year of tuberculosis induced by his strenuous efforts in the Bow China works. His weak health in 1759 had obliged him to seek a complete change, and a prolonged visit to Wales appeared to have produced a cure; but when he returned to London to work and resumed his career as an artist, it was not long before illness returned and took a swift course. Frye was buried in Hornsey churchyard in rural Middlesex on 7 April 1762, and on 24 June 1774, a little over twelve years later, his widow was laid beside him. No trace of the site of their grave remains, and the country churchyard is now surrounded by the suburbs of north London.

3
Lieutenants and Factory

In the previous chapter, we discussed and detailed the lives of the principals of
the Bow Porcelain Manufactory. It is evident that, like Chelsea, and a little
later Worcester, Bow was fortunate to have at its head strong personalities
capable of providing leadership, organization and artistic direction. Less is
known about their subordinates, but two names in particular fall into place
here, those of John Bowcock and Thomas Craft.

John Bowcock did not join the staff of the Bow concern until 1752. Before
that he was a purser in the Royal Navy, which post may have helped in fitting
him to run the business affairs of the Bow Porcelain warehouse in Cornhill, first
opened in February 1753. So far as one can judge it was primarily as a manager
of the warehouse that he was employed, though he also fulfilled some duties as
clerk to the porcelain company, and sometimes acted as an outside
representative and auctioneer. A number of letters written by John Bowcock
have survived, though most of them date from his days in the Navy and throw
little light on his work for the Bow undertaking. They are preserved in the
British Museum, together with Bowcock's memorandum book for 1758, and
an account book covering the years 1751–1755, which includes figures for the
Bow warehouse at Cornhill. This account book was one of the rich legacy of
Bow documents left by Bowcock, which were at one time in the possession of
the great Victorian collector of ceramics Lady Charlotte Schreiber, but most of
which have since disappeared.[1] They were described in the *Art Journal* in
1869: 'In the same collection [were] two books of pencil sketches by a French
artist named De la Cour, of plants, trees, festoons of flowers, rococo scrolls,
cane handles, frames, chimney-pieces, landscapes, (among which is a view of
London), figures, single figures for statuettes, etc. Another book contain[ed]
coloured engravings by Martin Engelbrecht of Nuremberg, of a great variety of
subjects suitable for painting on china; costumes of various nations, ladies and
gentlemen splendidly attired, shepherds and shepherdesses, garden scenes and
summer-houses, palaces, birds, animals and insects, hunting scenes,
musicians, Chinese figures and scenery, interlaced ornaments, etc. A fourth
book, published by Edwards and Darley, 1754, consist[ed] of engraved

1. British Museum, Additional MSS 45905.

5. PART OF A LETTER FROM JOHN BOWCOCK to his brother William, written from Cornhill in June 1753, in which he refers to the possibility of either him or their mother dealing in 'Bow Chiney'. *British Museum. See pages 43, 44*

subjects — Chinese interiors, vases, figures, pagodas, bridges, animals, exotic birds, insects, etc. The Chinese designs [were] mixed up with rococo scrolls and other ornamental work.'

Before their regrettable loss, however, some extracts of accounts etc. had already been made which were first published in William Chaffer's *Marks and Monograms*.[2] They include details of the factory's trade in 1754, and list the cash receipts at Bow from 1750/51–5, which show plainly the great increase in the company's trade at that period. In those five years the receipts of the factory were almost doubled, from £6573 in 1750/51 to £11,229 in 1755. Chaffers also published a very long extract from John Bowcock's memoranda for 1756 which gives the names of a number of dealers and private people who were customers of the factory, and details of some of the wares being produced at the time. These included printed mugs and teawares, conclusive proof that this method of decoration was in use at Bow by June 1756. Mention is also made of pieces of Japanese porcelain borrowed from Lady Cavendish as patterns for the factory, to be kept only for a month; and a partridge required 'alive or dead' presumably also as a model.[3]

John Bowcock came originally from Halifax, Yorkshire, where his widowed mother kept a stocking shop. He made efforts to persuade her and his brother William, a painter, to become agents for the Bow factory, as an extract from a letter to his brother written from Cornhill in June 1753 makes plain (Plate 5):

2. W. Chaffers, *Marks and Monograms*, 15th ed., 1965, Vol. II, pp. 272–6.
3. See Appendix IV.

'Mr Stephenson is on his Journey and will call on Mother as you do not think of dealing in Bow Chiney. I wish he could get some safe customer in Hallifax (sic). Mrs Mercer writ to Miss Sharp as was about it. I sent the method of dealing to her but has heard nothing since.'

John Bowcock was married to Ann Wilkinson, possibly the daughter of a master potter in Wapping or Southwark. Family history relates that he was much distressed by her death, which occurred in 1760 and was brought about by plague during one of his absences on business. Bowcock's memorandum book for 1758 and newspaper advertisements such as those which appeared in the *Norwich Mercury* on 4 and 18 April 1755 show that he travelled widely and sometimes acted personally as auctioneer in provincial sales of Bow porcelain: 'Now Selling in the large Room at the Maids Head, in St. Simon's, Norwich, by JOHN BOWCOCK, from Cornhill, London. A Curious Collection of Ornamental and useful CHINA.'[4]

In 1758 Bowcock spent a large part of the year in Dublin arranging sales which included not only Bow china but some Chelsea wares and a quantity of glass. Some of this last was probably the production of Weatherby & Crowther's Green Yard Glasshouse in London, but some may have been produced in Warrington, where Bowcock had a personal interest in the Warrington Glass Company, owned by Peter Seaman.[5] It was probably on a visit to the north-west in connection with this glass firm that John Bowcock died of lockjaw on 26 February 1765 at Parr, near St. Helen's, Lancashire. It should not be forgotten that it is largely owing to his own enthusiasm for the Bow Porcelain Company and the interest which it engendered among his later relatives, that we have so many details of affairs at the Bow concern during its most prosperous years.

We also owe gratitude to a colleague of Bowcock's, Thomas John Craft, who was one of the principal porcelain decorators at the Bow factory. He left the only known contemporary description of the factory buildings, on a paper pasted inside the lid of the special box made to house the Craft bowl, which was found in a cupboard in the British Museum by Sir A. W. Franks in 1851. There is no record of how it came to the Museum. The bowl was made and decorated in Craft's spare time, about 1760, and used as a christening bowl for 'Miss Nancy Sha', a natural daughter of Sir Patrick Blake, a well-known Essex squire.

The late A. J. Toppin, in a paper read to the English Ceramic Circle in June 1943, suggests that Thomas Craft was at Battersea from August 1753 to

4. Sheenah Smith, *E.C.C. Transactions*, Vol. 9, Pt. 2, 1974, p. 208, 'Norwich China Dealers of the Mid-Eighteenth Century'.
5. Elizabeth Adams, *Some Links between Porcelain Factories of the Eighteenth Century . . .*, Text of a paper delivered at the Ceramics Summer School, University of Keele, 1969. Privately printed.

November 1755, in fact for almost the entire life of the famous enamel factory.[6] Toppin bases this idea on baptismal entries in the Battersea parish registers relating to the three children of Thomas and Anne Craft, only the youngest of whom, Anne, born in November 1755, seems to have survived infancy. Thomas John Craft is first mentioned in the registers at Bow in March 1756, when he and his (? second) wife Elizabeth had their daugher Margaret Rebecca christened. Unhappily, Elizabeth Craft was buried on 15 April 1758. The proximity in date of these two baptismal entries at Battersea and Bow make it appear rather doubtful whether Thomas John Craft of Bow was in fact the same man as Thomas Craft of Battersea.

Later on, Thomas John Craft apparently left the employ of the Bow Porcelain factory, and set up on his own account as a calico-printer. A fire insurance policy taken out with the Sun Company on 20 February 1771 shows that he then had a considerable calico-printing business of his own at West Ham.[7] The total insured was for £1800, and it is interesting to note that by far the greater part of this sum was for Craft's 'Utensils and Stock', valued at £1275. His calico-printing works was housed in timber and tiled buildings worth only £195 in all; his own dwelling house and 'Parlour' nearly equalled the value of the works at £180, and his household goods were worth £150. This was not a business on the scale of the porcelain factory, but Thomas Craft must have kept his affairs comfortably afloat. By 1790, when he wrote the description of the old Bow China works to go into the box with his bowl, he said himself that he was 'the only Person of all those employed there' still to pay an annual visit to John Crowther, the old, retired master of the factory, then an inmate of Morden College almshouse. Craft may have felt that as owner of his own business he had come to be on something of an equal footing with his former employer.

It is worth quoting Thomas Craft's written testimony to the romance and actuality of the Bow China works from the lid of the box of the Craft bowl in full. Clearly the factory meant more to him than a mere industrial undertaking, and although he gave only a few details of its physical structure he certainly managed to transmit a sense of the wonder in a pioneer industry which is entirely lost to us today. When he worked there the technology of the Bow China factory of New Canton was removed by less than the span of a generation from belief in the magic of alchemy.

This bowl was made at the Bow China Manufactory at Stratford-le-Bow, Essex, about the year 1760, and painted there by me, Thomas Craft: my cipher is in the bottom. It is painted in what we used to call the old Japan

6. *E.C.C. Transactions*, Vol. 2, No. 9, 1946, A. J. Toppin, 'Battersea: Ceramic & Kindred Associations', p. 177. Administration of the will of a Thomas Craft 'formerly of Richmond in Surrey but late of the parish of St. George's, Hanover Square', was granted to 'Sarah Craft widow and relict' on 24 May 1796. P.C.C., folio 243, Prob. II 1275.
7. Sun insurance records Guildhall MS 11936/205 294692 20 February 1771.

taste, a taste at that time much esteemed by the then Duke of Argyle; there is nearly two pennyweight of gold—about 15 shillings; I had it in hand, at different times, about three months; about two weeks time was bestowed upon it; it could not have been manufactured, etc. for less than £4. There is not its similitude. I took it in a box to Kentish Town, and had it burnt there in Mr Gyles's kiln, cost me 3s; it was cracked the first time of using it. Miss Nancy Sha, a daughter of the late Sir Patrick Blake, was christened with it.

I never used it but in particular respect to my Company, and I desire my legatee (as mentioned in my Will) may do the same.

Perhaps it may be thought that I have said too much about this trifling toy; a reflection steals upon my mind, that this said bowl may meet with the same fate that the manufactory where it was made has done, and like the famous cities of Troy, Carthage, etc., and similar to Shakespear's Cloud Cap't Towers etc.

The above manufactory was carried on many years under the firm of Messrs Crowther and Weatherby whose names were known almost over the world: they employed 300 persons; about 90 painters (of whom I was one), and about 200 turners, throwers, etc., were employed under one roof. The model of the building was taken from that of Canton in China; the whole was heated by two stoves on the outside of the building, and conveyed through flues or pipes and warmed the whole, sometimes to an intense heat, unbarable in winter. It now wears a miserable aspect, being a manufactory for turpentine and small tenements, and like Shakespear's baseless fabric, etc. Mr Weatherby has been dead many years; Mr Crowther is in Morden College, Blackheath, and I am the only Person of all those employed there who annually visit him.

T. CRAFT, 1790

No painting, drawing or engraving depicting the Bow China factory is known to survive, but it is difficult to believe that none was ever made of a building which must have been famous in its own time. Craft particularly mentions that it was copied from one at Canton (Plate 6), in a style which must have been intended to impress on the public the similarity and superiority of English-made porcelain to the Chinese wares. However we have recently discovered factual descriptions in one way almost as good as, and in another distinctly better than any topographical picture. These are contained in the itemized fire insurance policies for the Bow China works issued by the Sun and the Royal Exchange Assurance Companies. There are five policies dating between July 1749 and January 1767, a period of eighteen years, which included the factory's golden period c. 1752–62.

The discovery of the Bow fire policies is intimately connected with the factory's own manufactures, because it was the name 'Eward Vernon' inscribed on an inkpot (Plate 7) decorated in underglaze blue, that led to the discovery that Edward Vernon was in fact a director of the Royal Exchange

6. THE WAREHOUSES OF THE EUROPEAN EAST INDIA TRADING COMPANIES
on the waterfront at Canton about the year 1730. The English Company's building
is in the centre with the raised middle section. The main building of the Bow
factory may have been based on this design. It is known to have been a two-storied
building with a central archway entrance and was 52.7 m (173 ft) in length. From
plans of Canton the length of the building illustrated was approximately 57 m
(188 ft). (From the *Chronicles of the East India Company Trading to China
1635–1834* by Hosea Ballou Morse, Oxford University Press, 1926.) *See page 46*

7. INKPOT with five pen-holes and central well decorated in early underglaze blue
with Chinese figures in a landscape with stylized flowers, inscribed around the top
'EWARD VERNON ES^qr IULY 1752'. Diameter 8.9 cm (3.5 in), height 6.4 cm
(2.5 in). *Brighton Museum. See pages 46, 106*

Assurance Company.[8] It was not difficult thereafter to see that a search amongst fire policy records might prove rewarding.

The aim of the Bow factory was to produce in quantity 'the more ordinary sort of ware for common uses'[9] in imitation of the porcelains imported by the East India Company, but cheaply enough to appeal to a middle class rather than an aristocratic market. Staffordshire workmen were employed at Bow, and Staffordshire potters have always tended to aim for popular sales.

New Canton is proved by its insurance policies to have been a large factory, as big as any kind of manufactory of its own time, and larger than any other eighteenth-century English chinaworks. Through the agency of the policy books the buildings of which it was composed can be seen in terms of use, value and size in considerable detail, and compared with those of other such factories over a long period of years.[10]

The likelihood that the Bow factory was founded in the last months of 1747, although the first Bow patent was taken out in 1744, is supported by two facts. First, the occupation of 'Potter' begins to appear among the trades mentioned in the Bow baptismal registers early in 1748 (by modern reckoning). Second, an entry referring to the Bow 'Manufactory of Porcelaine . . . lately set up' appears in the fourth edition of Daniel Defoe's *Tour of Great Britain*, edited by Samuel Richardson, which was on sale in June 1748. Hugh Tait draws attention to this in his paper published in the *E.C.C. Transactions* (Vol. 5, Pt. 4, 1963), and he there points out that the 'new facts in the 4th edition must have been gathered by December 1747 or at the latest January or February 1747/48'.

The first policy on the Bow China Manufactory was taken out with the Sun Assurance Company on 7 July 1749.[11]

Edward Heylyn Thomas Fry John Weatherby and John Crowther on Their China Manufactory in Stratford Road in the County of Essex and Utensils and Stock therein Viz.

On a House Elaboratory and Warehouse/Timber/not Exceeding
One Hundred Pounds   100
Utensils and Stock therein only not Exceeding Six Hundred
Pounds   600
One House only adjoining Brick in Mr Frys Occupation not
Exceeding Three Hundred Pounds   300
Household Goods therein only the Property of Mr Fry not
Exceeding Two Hundred Pounds   200
On the Workhouses in one Building 173 feet long Brick not
Exceeding Twelve Hundred Pounds   1200

8. The 'Vernon' inkpot is in Brighton Museum.
9. 'The Case of the Undertaker of the Chelsea Manufacture of Porcelain Ware', 1753, British Museum, Lansdowne MSS No. 829, fol. 21.
10. See the comparative table of some English porcelain factories, Appendix V.
11. Sun insurance records Guildhall MS 11936/87 116996 7 July 1749.

A. TEAPOT with 'banana tree, stork and fence' pattern. Height
12 cm (4.75 in)
1747-52
Bristol Museum and Art Gallery. See page 104

B. INKPOT enamelled in the Kakiemon style and inscribed 'MADE AT NEW CANTON 1750'. Diameter 8.3 cm (3.25 in)
Salisbury and South Wiltshire Museum. See page 117

On Utensils and Stock therein only not Exceeding Three
Hundred Pounds 300
On the Workhouse and Millhouse under one Roof/Timber/situate
West not Exceeding Three Hundred Pounds 300
Utensils and Stock therein only not Exceeding Three
Hundred Pounds 300
On the Kiln House being one Range of Building Brick and
Timber not Exceeding Six Hundred Pounds 600
Utensils and Stock therein only not Exceeding One Hundred
Pounds 100

$$£4000$$

A brief commentary on the terms used in the early insurance policies may be useful.[12] The elaboratory here mentioned is the first reference (and is indeed a rare reference) to a building set apart for experiment and trial *in porcelain manufacture*. Although constructed of timber and therefore of relatively low insurance value (though at £30–£40 worth as much as many contemporary dwelling houses) its contents, described as 'Utensils and Stock', were valued at many times the rate of the building which housed them. £600 is an exceptionally large sum in the circumstances, and argues the elaboratory's great importance to the company. The only comparable term is the reference to a 'Secret room' in the description of the Worcester porcelain factory given in the *Gentleman's Magazine* in 1752, although the purpose of the secret room was not indicated. It may have been a store for materials required for porcelain trials, or a room for experiments.

The brick building 52.7 metres (173 feet) long, which we learn from later references fronted the Stratford Road (Plate 8), contained most of the workhouses, and was no doubt the one to which Thomas Craft referred as being modelled on 'that at Canton in China', and in which '200 turners, throwers etc. were employed under one roof'.

The millhouse, contained with another workhouse under a single roof and built of timber, implies that at this time the Bow company was preparing and grinding its own materials and colours. The windmills depicted in J. H. O'Neale's water-colour (Plate 9), 'taken from behind ye China House at Bow', are nothing to do with the manufactory, but may have been used, as in Holland, for pumping water from the nearby marshes.[13]

12. The inclusion in the text of a brief commentary on the terms used in the early insurance policies was suggested to us by Reginald Haggar. His most generous assistance in the elucidation of the policies and unstinted encouragement of the work on them has been quite invaluable; and we most readily acknowledge it.
13. The windmills are shown on the Chapman and André map of the area published in 1777 (from a survey in 1772), and their relative positions confirm the factory's location behind the artist. The mills are also shown in the same relative positions on the Rocque map of 1744/45.

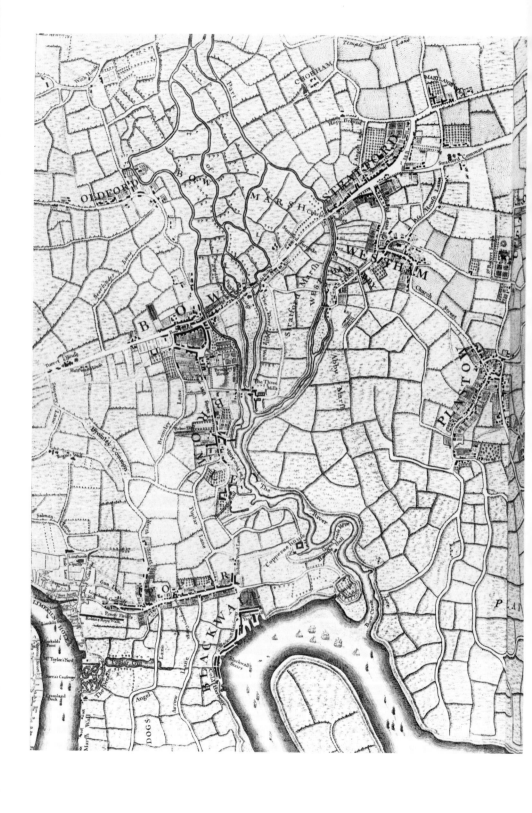

taken from behind ye China House at Bow

9. WATER-COLOUR BY JEFFRYES HAMMETT O'NEALE inscribed 'taken from behind ye China House at Bow'. The position of the factory on the north side of Stratford High Street immediately west of Marshgate Lane is confirmed by the alignment of the three windmills (the nearest is St. Thomas's Mill) in the picture and O'Neale's statement. The position of the windmills is consistent in three maps over the period 1744–77. The cart in the picture was travelling north up Marshgate Lane. The water on the right was one of the many minor channels of the Lea in his area and was known as Pudding Mill River. O'Neale's probable position when he sketched the view is shown in Appendix XII. *Whitworth Art Gallery, Manchester. See also page 49*

8. (*opposite*) JOHN ROCQUE'S MAP of 1746 showing the River Lea (Lee), Old Ford, Stratford, West Ham, Bow, Bromley, Poplar and Blackwall. Bow church (St. Mary-atte-Bow) is situated just below the 'o' of Bow, Bow bridge is immediately east and the road thence to Stratford, one mile away, was the ancient Queen Matilda's Causeway, later Stratford Road or Stratford High Street. The Bow factory site was on the north side of the High Street below and to the right of the letter 'w' of Bow where 'Stratford Diftill House' is marked. The three windmills to the north of Stratford High Street should be noted in relation to Plate 9. The River Lea enters the Thames at Bow Creek, just downstream from Blackwall where the large East India merchantmen anchored. *Guildhall Library See page 49 and Appendix XII*

Only one kilnhouse is mentioned in this 1749 policy. Being of timber and brick, it must have been something of a fire risk, as its high insurance value of £600 shows.

The total value of the building was £2500. Stock and utensils were valued at a further £1500, bringing the whole to £4000. Even at this early stage the Bow concern is proved to have been a remarkably large undertaking, by comparison with other potworks for which we have the insurances.

The insurance policies most nearly comparable with those of the Bow factory are firstly, those taken out in the name of Richard Holdship and Company for the Worcester Porcelain Works and the company's London warehouse, issued on 18 and 19 February 1757 by the Sun Assurance Company; secondly, three for the Chelsea China Manufactory, also taken out with the Sun Company, and dated 27 June 1760, 4 July 1761 and 28 June 1765; and thirdly, those for the Lowestoft Porcelain Factory issued in 1756 and 1765.

In the Worcester Company's first factory policy Warmstry House is included and described as 'their large House in the Parish of St. Alban . . . late in the Occupation of Messrs Miles & Lilly' and no fewer than five kilnhouses are mentioned, everything being of brick and tiled. Even so the total valuation in this policy was only for £1000.[14] The separate policy taken out on 18 February values the wares in the factory and in the warehouse in Aldersgate Street, London, at £1000 for each place.[15] A few days later, on 23 February 1757, Richard Holdship insured his personal stock of porcelain in London House, Aldersgate Street for a further £600.[16] We may note from a policy of October 1763 that the value of the Worcester Company's factory buildings had by then declined from £1000 to £700.[17]

The earliest policy for the Chelsea Manufactory yet discovered, which is dated 27 June 1760, makes it plain that unlike Bow, the Chelsea works had no purpose-built accommodation, but was literally a backyard potworks, with its premises adapted from residential property. They consisted of Nicholas Sprimont's dwelling house, which was built of brick and tiles, valued at £400; and two kilnhouses, a millhouse, a painters' room and a shed, all 'Brick, Timber and Tiled', and together worth only £500. Sprimont's wearing apparel and his stock of china and glass (worth £100 and £1000 respectively) complete the total valuation of £2000.

A year later the value of the stock held at the Chelsea factory had increased to £2000, and the total of the policy to £3000, though the description and valuation of the premises and Sprimont's property remained the same. By midsummer 1765 the list of factory buildings at Chelsea had changed slightly. A kilnhouse, woodhouse, painters' gallery, workshop and stables are now

14. Sun insurance records Guildhall MS 11936/118 156261 19 February 1757.
15. Ibid., MS 11936/118 156249 18 February 1757.
16. Ibid., MS 11936/119 156312 23 February 1757.
17. Ibid., MS 11936/151 203909 27 October 1763.

mentioned, though their total valuation is still only for £500. The policy total remains as before at £3000.[18]

The last policy for the Chelsea Porcelain Manufactory appears in the books in 1771. It was taken out on 10 October by 'William Duesbury and John Heath of the Town of Derby China Manufacturers'. Although the buildings listed remain the same as those given in June 1765, with the exception that the painters' gallery and a separate workshop had become simply 'Painters' Workshops', the value of the property had halved and was only £1500 compared with the £3000 of six years before. The change is accounted for by the omission of any household goods or wearing apparel (Sprimont's personal belongings were valued at £500 in 1765); by the decline in value of the factory buildings from £500 to £200 only, and in the total value of the stock and utensils (including in 1771 those in a house in Butcher Row, London) from £2000 to £1300.[19]

What may have been the earliest phase of the porcelain works at Lowestoft was insured by Obed Aldred on 27 January 1756. The premises consisted of 'Four Warehouses with Chambers over & Kilnhouse adjoining' worth £170; another policy taken out on the same day was issued to 'Obadiah Aldred & —' and covered their 'Stock of Stone Ware in their Four Warehouses'. This was valued at £200. It seems likely that these policies do in fact refer to the Lowestoft China undertaking, and if so provide support for the old belief that earthenware was at one time made in Lowestoft.

Nine years later, on 25 June 1765, Robert Browne, Obed Aldred, Robert Williams and Philip Walker took out a policy which specifically covered the 'Porcelain Manufactory . . . in Lowestoft'. It consisted of 'Seven Rooms and two Kiln Houses with Chambers over, all Communicating Brick & Tiled except a small part which is Stud Brick Boarded and Tiled'. Value: £300.[20]

To return to Bow Canton. Business there continued to increase, and by 22 November 1750 an enlarged insurance policy became necessary. It ran as follows:[21]

Edward Heylyn Thomas Fry John Weatherby & John Crowther. On Their China Manufactury called New Canton situate in Stratford Road in the County of Essex & Utensils & Stock therein as particularly expressed on the back of this Policy Viz.

A Brick House only in the Occupation of Mr. Fry not
exceeding Three Hundred Pounds   300
Household Goods therein only the Property of Mr. Fry
not exceeding Two Hundred Pounds   200

18. Ibid., MSS 11936/133 176294 27 June 1760; 11936/137 183484 4 July 1761; 11936/161 221461 28 June 1765.
19. Ibid., MS 11936/209 303537 10 October 1771.
20. Ibid., MSS 11936/114 150700 27 January 1756; 11936/159 220944 25 June 1765.
21. Ibid., MS 11936/90 123709 22 November 1750.

On the Workhouses in one Building Brick 173 feet long
Fronting the Road not exceed^g Twelve Hundred Pounds 1200
Utensils and Stock therein only not exceeding Six
Hundred Pounds 600
Two Millhouses adjoining Timber built, not exceeding
One Hundred Pounds 100
On the Mills and Utensils therein only not exceeding
Three Hundred Pounds 300
Warehouse and Workhouse over it with three Ground
rooms under the same Timber built not exceeding Two
Hundred Pounds 200
Utensils and Stock therein only not exceeding Two
Thousand Pounds 2000
On the two Kiln houses adjoining in One Range of
Buildings not exceeding Five Hundred Pounds on
Each 1000
On Utensils and Stock therein only not exceeding One
Hundred Pounds on Each 200
Warehouse only adjoining Timber built not exceeding
One Hundred Pounds 100
Stock therein only not exceeding Fifty Pounds 50
Two drying houses and Slip house only adjoining each
other not exceeding Two Hundred (and)
Twenty Five Pounds 225
And a Stables only seperate not exceed^g Twenty
Five Pounds 25
                                                   ————
                                                   £6500

This time the 'China Manufactury' is described by its well-known name of New Canton, and the 'Elaboratory' is no longer specified. These two points perhaps imply that the business was now on a firm foundation, and the famous inkpots with the inscription 'Made at New Canton' and dated between 1750 and 1752 were probably pieces commemorative of the company's status, made to be presented to those who had assisted in some way with its progress.

By November 1750 the value of utensils and stock in the 'Long Workhouse' was doubled from three to six hundred pounds. Two millhouses were listed instead of one, both timber built. Another warehouse was added, with a workhouse over it and three ground rooms beneath, also timber built, and the utensils and stock in this warehouse were valued at the great sum of £2000.

Another kilnhouse also appeared, as well as a drying house and a slip house. Stables, valued at £25 only, were included for the first time. The policy shows that in 1750 the Bow factory was a concern of increased prosperity and considerable size, with buildings valued at £3150 and stock at £3350, making a total insurance value of £6500.

The great expansion in trade implied by the differences between the first and second insurance policies taken out for the Bow Porcelain Company continued for several years. As we have already noted the Account Book records that output and receipts were nearly doubled between 1750 and 1755. In 1753, 1754 and 1755 the value of china sold was over £10,000 each year, and in 1755 the total value of the china sold was £18,115 8s 9d. No doubt it was the increasing demand for its wares that led the Bow China Company to open its City warehouse in Cornhill on 7 February 1753 'for the Convenience of all Customers both in Town and Country; where all sorts of China will continue to be sold in the same manner as formerly at Bow, with Allowance made to Wholesale Dealers'.[22]

On 11 December 1755 the Bow Porcelain concern took out two policies with the Royal Exchange Assurance Company. The first was in the name of 'The Porcelaine Company at Bow', and ran as follows:[23]

On a Brick House situate in Stratford Road in the Parish of Westham and County of Essex, in the occupation of Mr Frye	300
Furniture therein	300
On their Kiln Houses and Workshops adjoining Timber built adjoining the said Dwelling House	1000
Trade therein	400
Utensils in Trade in the same	300
On a new Building adjoining brick built	150
Utensils and Goods in Trade in the same	300
On a Stables timber built situate on the West Side of the said Yard	100
On the Drying Houses, Shed and Compting House adjoining with Warehouses over the same Timber built situate near the said Stable	400
Trade therein	500
Utensils in Trade in the same	700
On the Long Workhouse and Rooms over it, situate fronting Stratford Road in the Parish aforesaid	800
Trade therein	200
Utensils in the same	200
	£5650

Order'd the Word China be ras'd out of the Policy
Agreed the £1400 at 5 p. Cent

22. Aris's *Birmingham Gazette*, 5 March 1753.
23. Royal Exchange Policy Records, Vol. III, No. 31533, 11 December 1755.

There are several differences in detail between this policy and that of 1750. Neither the names of the partners, nor the factory's title of New Canton are given; instead merely the prosaic term 'Porcelaine Company'. Mr Frye's furniture has increased in value from £200 to £300, and the stock and utensils in the kilnhouses from £200 to £700. The stables have increased enormously in value, being now worth £100, and this seems to show that by this time the firm provided all its own transport, in particular for goods going up to the London warehouse, or to St. Catherine's; or for its commercial travellers who visited various parts of the country.

A new brick building is also specially mentioned, containing £300 worth of utensils and goods. The drying houses, now combined with a shed and compting house, and with warehouses over, have increased in value from £225 to £400. The value of the long warehouse however has fallen from £1200 to £800, which may be explained by the ageing of the building; and the value of the trade (or utensils and stock) in it from £600 to £400. The greatest change of value in this later policy, though, is the omission of £2000 worth of stock, formerly listed as in the timber warehouse 'with three ground rooms under'.

This apparent loss is explained by the second policy issued by the Royal Exchange Assurance Company on 11 December 1755, also taken out in the name of the 'Porcelaine Company at Bow'.[24]

On Goods in Trade in their Warehouse brick built (save a small part which is Timber) situate in Cornhill London and late known by the name of the Cross Keys Tavern.   £3000.

The site of the Bow warehouse is almost in the centre of the courtyard which lies before the present Royal Exchange.

The total valuation of the factory buildings at Bow in the 1755 policy was £2750, a drop of £575 on that of 1750. Their contents were valued at £2900, as against £3325, a difference of £425. But the apparent loss of £1000 in value is immediately seen as illusory when the £3000 valuation for the stock in the Cornhill warehouse is taken into account. The two 1755 policies taken together make up a grand total of £8650.

Both the Royal Exchange policies of 1755 bear a note, the first 'Renewed from No. 29145'; the second 'Renewed from No. 29146'. The change from the Sun to the Royal Exchange Company therefore probably took place at the beginning of 1753, but since the company's records up to the end of that year were lost when the Royal Exchange building was destroyed by fire in 1843 this likelihood cannot be verified.

Why did the Bow concern change its insurance agents from the Sun to the Royal Exchange Company? No doubt there was constant effort to cut costs which must have been increasing with the growth in manufacture, and the change in the fabric of some of the factory buildings from timber to brick. The

24. Ibid., Vol. III, No. 31534, 11 December 1755.

most likely answer is that the Royal Exchange offered better terms. Perhaps the situation of the Bow warehouse so close to the head office of the insurance company in Cornhill may have had something to do with it.

Whatever the reason, after the deaths of his partners, Thomas Frye and John Weatherby, John Crowther reverted to the Sun Assurance Company. In July 1763 he insured with them his China Manufactory at 'Bow Canton in Stratford Road' and stock in the warehouse at Cornhill for a total of £4900.[25] The policy ran as follows:

On his China Manufactory situate as aforesaid (Viz^t)
On the House only late Frys not exceeding One Hundred and
Fifty Pounds   150
On the Workhouses only in one Buildings (sic) Brick 173
feet long fronting the Road not exceeding Six Hundred Pounds   600
Utensils and Stock therein only not exceeding One Hundred
and Fifty Pounds   150
Two Millhouses only adjoining each other Timber not
exceeding One Hundred Pounds   100
On the Mills and Utensils therein only not exceeding One
Hundred Pounds   100
Warehouses and Workhouses over with three Ground Rooms
under the same Timber not exceeding One Hundred and
Seventy-five Pounds   175
Utensils and Stock therein only not exceeding Two Hundred
Pounds   200
On the Two Kiln Houses adjoining in one Range of building
not exceeding Four Hundred Pounds   400
Utensils and Stock therein only not exceeding One Hundred
P^{ds} in each   200
Warehouses only adjoining Timber not exceeding One Hundred
Pounds   100
Stock therein only not exceeding Two Hundred Pounds   200
Drying House & Slip house not exceeding Two Hundred
Pounds   200
Stable only separate not exceeding Twenty-five Pounds   25
On the enamelling Kiln Houses adjoining and Communicating
with each other not exceeding Fifty Pounds   50
Three enamelling Killns/Utensils and Stock therein only
not exceeding One Hundred Pounds   100
On the Dipping House only Brick not exceeding Fifty Pounds   50
Utensils and Stock therein only not exceeding One Hundred
Pounds   100

25. Sun insurance records Guildhall MS 11936/148 201347 28 July 1763.

On his Stock in his Warehouse only in Cornhill not
exceeding Two Thousand Pounds 2000

$£4900$

28 July 1763. Pays in Cornhill, at Bow China Warehouse.

This policy most nearly resembles that of 1750, as regards the buildings
which are included in it, though in most cases their value has considerably
declined. The long workhouse at £600 is worth only half of what it was in 1750,
and £200 less than in 1755. The kiln houses at £400 have fallen heavily from
the value they had in previous years. After his death Mr Frye's house is now
worth only £150 instead of £300; why, one wonders? The value of the stables is
back to its 1750 level of £25, perhaps as much as anything an indication of the
contraction of the factory.

On the other hand, some buildings are listed which were not heard of before,
the enamelling kiln houses, containing three kilns, and a dipping house. The
total value of the buildings is now £1050, that of the utensils and stock
(excluding the china at Cornhill) £1850. This is plainly a decline, though the
business is still a very large one by contemporary standards.

John Crowther was declared bankrupt in February 1763, possibly in
connection with the first failure of the wholesale pottery business at St.
Catherine's. The Cornhill warehouse was given up, but Crowther retained the
Bow factory. A policy taken out with the Sun Company in March 1764 shows
that the old warehouse was in the hands of 'Rachael Stephens of Primrose
Street, Bishopgate, Widow' and 'Samuel Gibbs Esq.ʳ'. 'On their House only
called the Bow China Warehouse Brick situate in Cornhill not exceeding Eight
Hundred and Fifty Pounds.'[26] In previous years only its contents had been
insured. This time the empty building itself was covered.

Within a comparatively short time John Crowther reopened the Bow
warehouse in the Poultry. Nathan Davis of St. Mary Axe 'Dealer in Cyder
Spirituous Liquors & China & Glass' took out a fire insurance policy with the
Sun Company on 7 October 1765[27] and included in it were 'Utensils and Stock
not hazardous in a Cellar only under the Bow Warehouse in St. Mildred's
Court in the Poultry, Brick' worth £200. In January 1766 the stock in this
warehouse was insured for £1000,[28] and a year later for £1300.[29] As we have
seen, the Bow warehouse was finally moved to St. Paul's Churchyard, and
closed down completely in 1775.

The policy issued for the Bow China factory on 6 January 1766 ran as
follows:

26. Ibid., MS 11936/152 207349 9 March 1764.
27. Ibid., MS 11936/164 225572 7 October 1765.
28. Ibid., MS 11936/167 229486 6 January 1766.
29. Ibid., MS 11936/172 241537 12 January 1767.

John Crowther of Stratford near Bow in the County of Essex Chinamaker.
On his now Dwelling House only situate as aforesaid
fronting the Road Brick not exceeding One Hundred and
Twenty Pounds   120
Household Goods therein only not exceeding Three Hundred
Pounds   300
Wearing Apparel therein only not exceeding   100
The China Factory only fronting the Road 173 feet Long
Brick not exceeding   300
Utensils and Stock therein only not exceeding   200
Warehouse and Sliphouse only adjoining & Rooms over
Timber not exceeding   50
Stock therein only not exceeding   150
Two Millhouses with a Room only over Timber not exceeding . .   50
Three Mills & Utensils therein only not exceeding   150
Engine House only not exceeding   50
Utensils and Stock therein only not exceeding   50
Stables only adjoining Timber not exceeding   30
Two Large Kiln Houses One Enamelling Kilnhouse &
Warehouses all adjoining Timber not exceeding   300
Nine Kilns & Utensils therein only not exceeding   300
Stock therein only not exceeding   100
Diphouse and Room over only Brick not exceeding   50
Utensils and Stock therein only not exceeding   100
Stock in a Warehouse only Brick in St. Mildred's Court
in the Poultry London not exceeding   1000
                                                            ─────
                                                            £3400

The total value is a decline of £1500 on the valuation of July 1763, even though it includes household goods and 'Wearing Apparel' worth £400, both items which were omitted in the 1763 policy. The main building of the Bow China House, the long workhouse, has come down to a value of only £300, a far cry from the early days of 1749 when it had been worth £1200. Nine kilns are mentioned in this policy of 1766, and from that of 1763 we can deduce that three of these were enamelling kilns, and two glost kilns. One new building makes its appearance in 1766, an engine house, valued at £50. At that date the 'Engine' can only have been an early model of steam pump, probably a Newcomen engine used for drainage merely. That the Bow factory site was low-lying, between arms of the river Lea, and liable to flooding is made plain by the description of the tidal flood of October 1762 discovered in the *Gentleman's Magazine* by Jenifer Frost.[30] 'The China Works at Bow were

30. *Gentleman's Magazine*, Vol. XXXII, October 1762.

overflowed in such manner that the current rushed through the great arch [of the main factory entrance] in like manner as the tide runs through the arches of London Bridge.' In this same flood a gentleman was drowned in his coach on Stratford Causeway, the road which ran past the porcelain works. Evidently loss through water was one among the factors which promoted the Bow factory's slow decline. Yet in the middle sixties matters seem to have mended somewhat, and the policy of 1767 ran as follows:[31]

John Crowther of Stratford near Bow in the County of Essex Chinaman.
On his now Dwelling House fronting the Road Brick not
exceeding Two Hundred Pounds 200
Household Goods therein only not exceeding 300
Wearing Apparel therein only not exceeding 100
China Factory fronting the Road One Hundred and Seventy
three feet long Brick not exceeding 400
Utensils and Stock therein only not exceeding 300
Warehouse and Sliphouse adjoining with Rooms over Timber
not exceeding 50
Utensils and Stock therein only not exceeding 150
Two Millhouses with a Room over Timber not exceeding 100
Three Mills and Utensils therein only not exceeding 200
Engine House Timber not exceeding 50
Utensils and Stock therein only not exceeding 60
Stables only adjoining not exceeding 30
Two large Kiln Houses One Enamel Kiln House and
Warehouses all adjoining Timber not exceeding 400
Nine Kilns and Utensils therein only not exceeding 300
Stock therein only not exceeding 100
Diphouse and Room over Brick not exceeding 60
Utensils and Stock therein only not exceeding 100
The above in Stratford aforesaid
Utensils and Stock in his Warehouse only Brick in
St. Mildreds Court in the Poultry London 1300
                                                        ‾‾‾‾
                                                        £4200

This policy is followed by a note 'See Ind. [presumably Index] No. 13 p. 443'. There is no means of checking this reference. No books of policy indices have survived, but such an entry after a policy usually seems to imply trouble, perhaps failure, for the policyholder—and this is apparently the last of the Bow factory policies.

Nevertheless it leaves us on a more hopeful note than did the previous one. John Crowther's house—the Master's House—and the long warehouse, the

31. Sun insurance records Guildhall MS 11936/172 241537 12 January 1767.

THE

PARTICULARS

OF SUNDRY ELIGIBLE

FREEHOLD ESTATES,

ADVANTAGEOUSLY SITUATE

Adjoining the RIVER LEA, at STRATFORD, near
Bow BRIDGE, in the County of ESSEX;

COMPRISING

THE EXTENSIVE PREMISES FORMERLY

THE BOW - CHINA MANUFACTORY;

Three defirable WHARFS, a MALTING,

Two PUBLIC HOUSES, known by the RED LION, and FOX and HOUNDS;
Ten DWELLING HOUSES and fundry capacious WAREHOUSES;
A commodious Leather Dreffer's Yard, and an Ozier Ground;

IN THE OCCUPATION OF

Jofeph Flight, Efq. Meffrs. *Wight, Dyche, Betts, Bailes, Staines, Pilgrim,
Threfher,* and others:

ALSO,

Two genteel Dwelling Houfes,

Offices, Coach-houfes, Stabling, and Gardens, and an excellent Garden,
walled round, with a Meffuage and Out-buildings,

IN THE OCCUPATION OF

Mrs. *Simpfon*, Mrs. *Sainthill*, and Mr. *Forfter*,

SITUATE

AT WEST HAM, NEAR STRATFORD.

THE WHOLE PRESENT ANNUAL RENTS AMOUNT TO

Two Hundred *and* Twenty-nine Pounds Two Shillings;

THE SUPPOSED YEARLY VALUE

Three Hundred and Ten Pounds:

Which will be SOLD by AUCTION,

By Mr. SKINNER and Co.

On FRIDAY the 22d of JUNE, 1787,

At Twelve o'Clock,

At GARRAWAY's Coffee - Houfe, *'Change - Alley*, CORNHILL,

IN ELEVEN LOTS.

To be viewed till the Sale.

Particulars may be had at the Swan, Stratford; Fox and Hounds, and Red Lion Public Houfes,
near Bow Bridge; at the Place of Sale; and of Mr. SKINNER and Co. Alderfgate-Street.

10. NOTICE OF AN AUCTION SALE held at 12 o'clock on 22 June 1787 in
Garraway's Coffee-House, Change Alley, Cornhill by Mr Skinner and Co. of
various properties at Stratford, near Bow Bridge, Essex, including the former
premises of the Bow China Manufactory. Particulars of the eleven lots are given in
Appendix XIII. *Guildhall Library. See also pages 62–3*

so-called 'China Factory', have both increased in value, and the kilnhouses and timber-built warehouses adjoining have gone up by £100. Most other values remain equal, but the output had plainly increased; stock in the warehouse in St. Mildred's Court in the Poultry was now valued at £1300 instead of £1000.

If we deduct the value of the stock in the City warehouse at St. Mildred's Court, the total value of the Bow China Works in its latter years, lock, stock and barrel, was about £2900, a sum which puts it on the same level of size and importance as the Worcester Porcelain Manufactory when that business was sold by the remaining proprietors of Dr Wall's Company to Thomas Flight of London for £3000 in 1783. Bow and Worcester were the two giants of the eighteenth-century English porcelain industry; though both went into decline it was Worcester which revived and survived. As Thomas Craft lamented in 1790, Bow fell upon evil days.

The manufacture of china at Bow probably ended altogether in 1775, and the company's decease was almost certainly tied to the concurrent winding-up of the wholesale pottery business at St. Catherine's under Benjamin Weatherby. The last City warehouse, run at St. Paul's Churchyard by John Crowther, also closed in 1775.[32]

We learn from another fire insurance policy taken out with the Sun Company that by early 1780 the old Bow factory premises were being used for the manufacture of tar and turpentine by James Parsons, dealer in those commodities.[33] The place was ideal for the purpose, since tar was obtained by heating knots of pine in kilns so that the resin ran down and could be collected, and the residual charcoal could be sold for fuel. The china manufacture's kilns obviously adapted easily, but one can understand and sympathize with Thomas Craft's disgust at this debased use. The tar was of course mainly for the purpose of caulking ships, and Bow was very near the shipyards of the Thames.[34]

Though the legend that William Duesbury of Derby bought up the plant and surplus porcelain of the Bow China Works in 1776 may possibly be true, it can be proved that he certainly did not buy the works themselves. Throughout most of the eighteenth century the ground landlords of the factory were members of the Peers family of Chiselhampton, Oxfordshire, and Bromley-by-Bow, and in 1787 they put their remaining holdings in Bow and Stratford up for sale by auction (Plate 10). The star lot of the sale was Lot V—

32. The Poor Law Overseer's Account Books for West Ham show that taxes were paid for the China House until April 1776, the last few entries being in the name of William Brown, employed at the Cornhill warehouse in 1753.
33. Sun insurance records, Guildhall MS 11936/280 423462 17 January 1780 (this policy was discovered by L. M. Wulcko).
34. For a full description of the process see John Evelyn, *A Discourse of Forest Trees*, 4th ed., 1706, Book II, Chapter III, pp. 149–52.

A Valuable extensive FREEHOLD ESTATE, advantageously situate adjoining the River Lea, at Stratford, and formerly

THE BOW CHINA MANUFACTORY
COMPRISING

A genteel convenient Dwelling House, Offices, and Gardens, capital Warehouses and Store-houses, Distil-house, Cooperage, and numerous other Buildings; capacious Wharf and Yard, and Six Messuages in Front of Road; let to Joseph Flight, Esq. for an unexpired Term of 15 Years from Michaelmas 1787, at a very low Rent of only 63£. per Annum, with a Covenant for an additional Term of 7 Years, if the present Freeholder should so long live, at 68£. per Annum.

The property fetched £1100, but the name of the purchaser is not recorded.[35]

Joseph Flight (whose tenancy had been taken over by his widow by June 1789) was the elder brother of Thomas Flight, who in 1783 had purchased the Worcester Porcelain Company for his two sons. It is unlikely that Joseph Flight entertained any ideas of emulating his brother and nephews, John and Joseph, by reopening the manufacture at Bow. Henry Sandon shows that Joseph was 'a turpentine merchant, tallow chandler and linen draper' and had patented an 'iron liquor' for printing on linen. He also points out that Hanson, another of the elder generation of Flights, owned one of the complex of five mills at Stratford which were London's chief source of flour.[36]

The Flights were men of business, and unsentimental about the former glories of the Bow Manufactory. It was Joseph Flight who transformed the long workhouse into the tenements so deeply deplored by Thomas Craft.

35. We are deeply indebted to C. R. H. Cooper, Keeper of Manuscripts at the Guildhall Library, London, who brought this sale catalogue to our attention, and to Mrs Rosemary Pratt and other members of the Peers family, who have allowed us to use their family papers freely. These are now deposited at the County Record Office, Oxford.
36. Henry Sandon, *Flight and Barr Worcester Porcelain 1783–1840*, Antique Collectors' Club, 1978, p. 12.

4
The Workmen

In 1829, Simeon Shaw published his *History of the Staffordshire Potteries*, and in it mentioned the names of a number of men who were supposed to have gone from the Potteries in 1747 to work at Chelsea: 'Carlos Simpson, 63 years of age, was born at Chelsea; to which place his father Aaron Simpson went in 1747, along with Thomas Lawton, slip maker, Samuel Parr, turner, Richard Meir, fireman and John Astbury, painter; all of Hot Lane; Carlos Wedgwood of The Stocks, a good thrower; Thomas Ward, and several others of Burslem, to work at the Chelsea China Manufactory.'[1]

Although Simeon Shaw has generally been regarded as an unreliable historian, he had one great advantage denied to us—he lived much nearer to the times of which he wrote than we do—and truth has frequently been found embedded in his *History*.

The first proof of his accuracy was provided by Mrs Donald MacAlister, who in 1932 discovered the baptism of 'Careless' Simpson recorded in the register of Chelsea Old Church (St. Luke's) on 4 December 1743, 'Careless, son of Aaron Simpson and Elizabeth his wife.'[2]

Two further children of Aaron and Elizabeth were baptized at Chelsea, Charles on 12 January 1756 and Eleanor on 29 July 1757. On 23 December 1759 Aaron Simpson was buried at Burslem, 'soon after their return' as Shaw said. 'Elizabeth Simpson, widow' survived him until 20 October 1776.

Further evidence of the truth in Shaw's work is given by the discovery in the Chelsea rate books of the name of another of the men he mentions. On 26 September 1754, 'Mr Samuel Parr' was living in a house rated at £11 in Lawrence Street, almost next door to the Chelsea factory, and appears to have stayed there for approximately one year.

Though a number of other names with possible Staffordshire origins can be traced in the registers and rate books of Chelsea, and a number of Staffordshire potters must have worked there, these are the only two whose presence can be proved conclusively by documentary evidence. At Bow the high tally of

1. Simeon Shaw, *History of the Staffordshire Potteries*, 1829, p. 167.
2. Mrs D. MacAlister, *E.C.C. Transactions*, No. 3, 1935, 'Chelsea, the Triangle Period', p. 27. Aaron Simpson was probably the son of Ralph and Mary Simpson, baptized at Burslem on 12 February 1726/27.

C. TRIPLE-SHELL SWEETMEAT on a shell-encrusted base with
simulated coral forms picked out in dark green and brown. The
blue-tinged drab-coloured body painted with flowers in enamel
colours. Diameter 14 cm (5.5 in)

1747–50
See page 118

D. BALUSTER VASE AND COVER decorated in enamels with trailing
peony, stylized 'chrysanthemums' on trailing branches, a phoenix in
flight and reserves painted with a Chinese landscape in sepia on the
body and cover. Mark: a linear scratch. Height 33 cm (13 in)
1748–52
Courtesy of Sotheby's. See page 120

Staffordshire workers is very different from the small one at Chelsea, and incidentally this fact must dispose of the old theory that knowledge of Staffordshire slip-casting techniques in pottery manufacture was exclusive to the Chelsea works. This observation is supported by the evidence of shards found in both earlier and recent excavations on the Bow factory site, which confirm that the slip-casting process was employed there both for useful wares and (alongside press-moulding) for figures.

We now know that although Samuel Parr certainly worked at Chelsea, in the first place he must have been looking for employment in London as a whole (as no doubt were his Staffordshire companions) because his name appears in the earliest instances in the registers at Bow.

It was sometimes the custom in the eighteenth century to add the father's occupation when recording a baptism, and the Revd Thomas Foxley, who was rector of Bow in the 1740s and early 1750s had begun the practice by 1748. In 1751 he entered: 'William, son of Samuel Parr, Potter, and Mary his wife, born 17th February and baptised 17th March.' The identity of Samuel Parr was confirmed by an entry in the registers at Burslem, discovered by Reginald Haggar and communicated to the authors: '1749/50. 1st January, Phebe, daughter of Samuel and Mary Parr baptised.' On 27 March 1753 the Revd Foxley was obliged to include in the burial register at Bow the name of 'Phoebe, daugher of Samuel Parr, a potter, and Mary his wife'. This sad entry makes it quite certain that Samuel Parr of Bow and Chelsea was a Staffordshire man, and is a centrepin in the argument that the Staffordshire Potteries had a considerable influence on the development of the metropolitan porcelain manufactures.

The names of the earlier Staffordshire workers recorded at Bow are as follows (the dates are those of first mention in the parish registers):

December	1746	William Ball
February	1748	Joseph Smith
April	1748	John Smith
June	1749	William Bullock
June	1750	John Stevenson
February	1751	Samuel Parr
March	1751	Richard Ball
August	1752	Gilbert Ward
August	1760	Joshua Astbury
November	1760	Robert Harrison

It can be shown by records and registers that all these men had connections with Staffordshire. On a Bow mug made c. 1750 and now in the British Museum is incised the name of Aaron Tunstall, whose surname is certainly a Staffordshire one, though he was buried at West Ham on 9 September 1754.

It will perhaps be of interest to give the facts, so far as we know them, to do with three of the Staffordshire workmen in particular.

The first is William Ball, whose name was connected with the mysterious Limehouse factory by Mrs MacAlister,[3] and who may well have been the man of the same name who was working in William Reid's Liverpool Porcelain Manufactory after Reid's bankruptcy in 1761.[4] It should be noted that Ball appeared in the Bow register in December 1746 *before* he was recorded at Limehouse. His first daughter Susannah was baptized at Bow.

Thus he was at Bow in 1746, at Limehouse in 1747, is reputed to have returned to Staffordshire after Limehouse's closure in 1748, and finally settled in Liverpool to make porcelain about 1755. He was last recorded as still resident in Liverpool in an insurance policy issued on 4 August 1772.[5]

Ball was apparently a man of some substance, and owned property not only in Bow, rated at £8 per annum, and on which he paid Land Tax of £1 12s 0d annually in 1745 and 1746; but also in St. Leonard's, Bromley-by-Bow, a neighbouring parish, where he paid Land Tax of similar amount in 1744, '45 and '46. This brings out a point worth consideration. The taxes paid by William Ball are very little less than those paid later on by John Crowther, and this underlines the fact that these potters were master craftsmen and quite well off, not unimportant workpeople or labourers.

The second personal history to be examined is that of Joshua Astbury, whose occupation is given in the Bow register at the baptism of his daughter Sarah on 2 September 1760 not as 'Potter' but as 'China Man', that is to say a dealer, possibly a wholesaler, in china wares. So far the name of John Astbury, painter, which was given on Simeon Shaw's list, has not been found anywhere in London, so it is possible that Shaw may have confused John and Joshua. Joshua was the son of the great John Astbury of Shelton, the almost legendary potter, who is one of the most famous figures of North Staffordshire. John Astbury died early in 1744, and Joshua inherited his tools and equipment.

In any case it is fascinating to find a member of this famous Staffordshire potting family in Bow in person, though whether his business was to purchase the products of the London factory or to sell the wares of Staffordshire in the south, or both, it is impossible to say. He evidently did not stay very long; in April 1764 his son Richard Meir Astbury, who also became a well-known potter, was baptized in Stoke.

The third person to be mentioned in detail is William Bullock, 'a potter'. William Bullock and Elizabeth Barker of Great Fenton were married at Stoke on 26 January 1741/42. Their first child Lydia died in the summer of 1748 at the age of thirteen months, and it was after this that they must have come down to Bow. There their second daughter Letitia was born on 6 June 1749, but she was buried only two days later. Whether this second tragedy was the reason for their return to Staffordshire or not we cannot say, but a son, William, was

3. Mrs D. MacAlister, *E.C.C. Transactions*, No. 1, 1933, 'Early Staffordshire China', p. 48.
4. Sun insurance records, Guildhall MS 11936/138 185423 19 October 1761.
5. Ibid, MS 11936/216 314508 4 August 1772.

baptized in Stoke in November 1750, and another named John in June 1753. These boys appear to have lived.

William Bullock's name appears in a list of accounts belonging to John Baddeley, who in partnership with William Reid & Co. of Liverpool ran an earthenware manufactory at Shelton from 1755–8, and there also manufactured porcelain from 1758–61. In 1761, together with William Reid and the two other partners in the company, he became bankrupt. Shelton is the third known eighteenth-century porcelain factory in Staffordshire to be identified, the others being, of course, William Steers's manufacture at Newcastle-under-Lyme, *c*. 1746–51, and William Littler's at Longton Hall, 1751–60. Unfortunately we have so far very little knowledge of the manufactures of Baddeley at Shelton as he appears never to have marked his wares, though they may be similar to Reid's porcelain made at Liverpool.

On 10 June 1758, Baddeley recorded 'Pd. Bullock for Modells, 15s' and on 4 April 1761 'Due to W. Bullock for Modells, £21 19s 6d.' This was only two months before the company's bankruptcy, and shows that William Bullock must have done a lot of work for them as the sum owed him is a substantial one. It also implies that William Bullock was probably one of the earliest modellers to be employed at Bow when he was there during 1749/50.[6]

In a book which was kept by Richard Parrot, a lawyer of Newcastle-under-Lyme, in the 1750s, and which is preserved in Newcastle Museum, Parrot records an unpleasant case in which William Bullock was witness to the adultery of Sarah Beech in August 1758. It is interesting to note that John Baddeley swore an affidavit to the good characters of William Bullock and William Beech, Sarah's husband, and said he had known these two men for fifteen years past. This would mean that Baddeley first met Bullock about 1743, six years before he went to Bow, and leads one to speculate that Bow characteristics might be expected in Shelton porcelain.

In his accounts John Baddeley had another entry, 'Pd. Harrop for Modells 9s' on 25 March 1758. There were two men by the name of Harrop at Chelsea, Joseph and William. The first was mentioned in the baptismal register in 1751, the second in 1753. Perhaps one of these might be the modeller in question. Relevant to the subject may be the information that loads of wood from the Oxfordshire estate of the Peers family were sold to two men named William Harrop and William Bullock in February 1763. Had they returned from Shelton to London? The Peers were, as we have mentioned, the ground landlords of the Bow factory; it would have been quite natural for them to supply some fuel to undertakings in London.[7]

6. Tradition held that John Bacon RA, the sculptor, modelled figures for the Bow factory, and J. T. Smith in *Nollekens and his Times* said that George Michael Moser, later Keeper of the Royal Academy, also modelled for the company, but both suggestions are now disbelieved.

7. MS account book preserved among the Peers family papers, Oxford County Record Office. An advertisement discovered by Geoffrey Wills in the *General Evening Post*, 12 August 1756, No. 3257, proposes that 'any person that has any stacks of oak top wood to dispose of may send their

11. BOWL painted in bright enamel colours with a flowering peony and a bird
perched on a branch. Marks: a script 'G' in brown enamel and a linear scratch,
both on the base. These marks are visible in the outer part of the base but the
bottom of the script 'G' is missing. Aubrey Toppin has suggested that the script
'G' is the signature of John Gazeley. It is also recorded in underglaze blue. The
other letters and numerals are museum index marks. Diameter 12.3 cm (4.8 in)
1750–3. *Salisbury and South Wiltshire Museum. See page 68*

Reference to a John Gazeley, whose name is first mentioned in the Bow
baptismal register in 1749, was originally discovered by A. J. Toppin. Gazeley
is stated specifically to be a 'China Painter' in the register, and had four
children, John, William, Sarah and Elizabeth, mentioned between 1749 and
1753. Sarah may have been the eldest; her burial is recorded in 1752, but no
entry is known for her baptism. John Gazeley evidently stayed at Bow for a
long time (Plate 11). Among John Bowcock's papers is an account dated
September 1761, in which he says that by 'Error Gazeley' was overpaid by £4
12s 6d.

The names of a number of other painters employed at Bow are known. John
Bonner (var. Bonno, Bono) with his wife Elizabeth is first mentioned in June
1750 in the Bow record of the baptism of his daughter Ann. His second child,
Elizabeth, was also baptized at Bow, in December 1751. He seems to have

proposals to the china work at New Canton near Bow Bridge, or the Bow china warehouse in
Cornhill'. The wood supplied from Shenley Brookend by the Peers's was ash and elm. Hugh
Owen, *Two Centuries of Ceramic Art in Bristol*, 1873, p. 310, records that William Cookworthy
and Richard Champion always fired with wood. (Champion noted the fact himself on the plan of
his enamelling kiln.) Owen writes: 'Refuse timber (for Bristol)—root stumps and lop of beech,
oak, ash and elm, was procured in the neighbourhood of Marlborough (presumably from
Savernake Forest) whence it was fetched by wagon.'

moved about in the district, for his son John was christened at West Ham in September 1754, and in February 1756 another daughter, Hester, at St. Leonard's, Bromley. Reginald Haggar suggests that the initials 'J.B.' on the bagpipes of a porcelain figure of a shepherd dated 1757 might be those of John Bonner.

John Philip Angel and Mary Margaret his wife appear in the Bow register in July 1751, when their son John was baptized. This is the only mention of this painter, but he may have been the relative, perhaps the brother, of Benjamin Angel, a calico-printer, who was at Bow in 1754, and by 1763 had works at Old Ford nearby, important enough to be mentioned in Mortimer's *Universal Director*.[8]

In August 1751, the name of Francis Barrs, painter, occurs in the Bow register, and he evidently worked at Bow for some time as he is still mentioned in the Land Tax returns in 1760.

There are three other known painters, William Gadd, recorded in May 1760; John de Lanauze, known only from the polychrome mug which he painted for Mrs Mary Bromley in 1770, and which is now in the British Museum; and Lewis Barber, whom Aubrey Toppin recorded as an apprentice of Edward Heylyn and who was subsequently recorded at Worcester as a china painter in 1761.

Definite evidence of the movement of workers between Chelsea and Bow, apart from that given by a Chelsea worker named Mason which is quoted by Chaffers,[9] is proved by the parish registers of both places. Robert Phenix, a potter, was at Bow from about 1749 until after September 1753, when his second son, John, was baptized there. In 1755 and 1757 his name appears in the Chelsea register in the baptismal entries for his sons Richard and Anthony.

Another man, Henry Pavett, whose occupation was not recorded, seems to have been a native of Bow, as his name appears in the Land Tax returns there as early as 1741 and consistently thereafter; but in 1761 his son William was baptized at Chelsea on 31 May. However, only about eighteen months later, in October 1762, Henry Pavett was buried at Bow and William also, not quite two years old, on 4 March 1763.

James Welch, a painter, and Elizabeth his wife were at Chelsea in October 1750 when their daughter Elizabeth was baptized; but in the summer of 1754 they were at Bow, where their son Walter was christened. Quite by chance a third entry concerning James Welch turned up in the burial register of St. Mary's Church, Hornsey, which almost certainly refers to the same man. '1762. 27th April. James Welch, from Tile Kiln in Edmonton Parish.' Edmonton is about nineteen kilometres (twelve miles) from Bow, travelling directly northwards up the Lea Valley. The Tile Kiln was near Wood Green, not far from the site of the present Underground station. In the eighteenth

8. Knowles Boney records a John Angel, a china painter, living in Frog Lane (Whitechapel), Liverpool in 1760: *Liverpool Porcelain of the Eighteenth Century*, 1957, p. 60.
9. William Chaffers, *Marks and Monograms*, 15th ed., 1965, Vol. II, p. 322.

century Edmonton and Hornsey lay in some of the most beautiful country near London.

The London Tradesman, a guide for the parents of apprentices published by R. Campbell in 1747, mentioned a porcelain factory then apparently existing at Greenwich. There is no other proof of its existence, and nothing is known of its manufacture, but it may have employed at least one worker who subsequently went on to Bow, Christopher Sherwood, a labourer who married Elizabeth Stafford at St. Alfege's, Greenwich, on 25 January 1746/47. On 17 January 1747/48 their son Thomas was christened at Bow, and Christopher Sherwood's name appears in the Land Tax returns for Bow between 1755 and 1760.[10] The type of work implied by the term 'labourer' is suggested by a contemporary description of the workers in a pothouse published in *The London Tradesman*: 'There are several sorts of workmen in a Pot-house; the labourers, who work and prepare the clay, according to the Direction of the Overseer or Master of the Work; those who attend the Mill and Furnace in the Preparation of the Colours; the Potter who forms and fashions the work for burning; and the Drawers who lay on the Colours. The last is the most ingenious Tradesman, and requires the Painter's genius: they are paid by the dozen of pieces painted, and may earn from Fifteen to Thirty Shillings a week. A boy may be bound to this business about Twelve or Thirteen years of age, and requires an education of Drawing, Reading and Writing, etc.'

It can be argued that the Bow factory had a more widespread influence upon eighteenth-century British porcelain manufacture than any other undertaking. Its great innovation, the use of calcined bone ash in the china body, was taken up by almost every porcelain company in the country before the end of the century, and was employed from the beginning by some of those founded later. Bow forms and methods of decoration were also adapted and imitated, in some cases even with an intent to deceive. Some sort of knowledge of the recipe of the phosphatic porcelain body and of the shapes and decoration characteristic of Bow was spread to other works not only by the wares themselves through normal commercial channels, but by interested people who visited the east London factory, or by men who had themselves been employed there. Records of such contacts come from several parts of Britain.

That the methods and some secrets of manufacture used at Bow were familiar to a porcelain-maker in Scotland, even before the Bow works had itself undertaken full commercial production, is apparent from the letters sent by Alexander Lind of Gorgie, near Edinburgh, to Lord Milton, a close political connection of the 3rd Duke of Argyll. The earliest of these is dated 10 April 1749:[11] 'The china made at Bow must be vastly improved since I received the specimen of it from Mr Fletcher, that I thought very little of, it being of the same kind made at St. Cloud but not near so good, it has a pretty Glazeing

10. For a complete list of known workers at Bow see Appendix VI.
11. See R. J. Charleston and John Mallet, *E.C.C. Transactions*, Vol. 8, Pt. 1, 1971, 'A Problematical Group of Eighteenth-century Porcelains', pp. 113–15.

which sets it of, and makes it appear good to those that look only at the outside, but to examine it throughly we must look at the inside and try it not only in the Furnace but likeways by its bearing hot water in cold weather, to see if it stands the sudden transitions from Cold to heat and Heat to cold as the Chinese Porcelain does, by these tryals you wou'd soon find its effects and its glassy constitution but enough of this subject at present.'

A further letter from Lind dated 26 August the same year expresses the hope that he may have the opportunity to use specimens of suitable materials found on the Duke of Argyll's estates in his efforts 'to make some China in the English way', and it continues, 'I had with me about ten days agoe an English Potter from Staffordshire, a very ingenious man, who has been trying Experiments in my way, I shewed him some of my performances, and if you wou'd not think it too much vanity in me to mention it, I wou'd tell you my good Lord, that he thought my Composition far superior to the Bow, and more like the Chinese. In short he is so well pleased with mine, that although he has a considerable bussiness (sic) carrying on in Staffordshire and furnishes all the Country with stone war (sic), he has agreed to come and spend some months with me this Winter in trying Experiments, which will be a great advantage to me; the method of forming his vessels being almost the same with the Chinese. He gave me a very full and accurate account of the Bow China, having made some of it himself, and had a Brother who is an Ennamler and wrought a winter at Bow.'

Sixteen months later, on 18 December 1750, Lind wrote to Lord Milton again: 'I have seen the china manufacturers at Bow and Chelsea his Grace was so good as [to] carry me to both where I had an opportunity of examining everything pretty minutely, I mean the structure of their Furnaces, and the other parts of their manual operations, which were what I cheifly wanted to see, as to the materials they use, Those they keep secret, as far as they can but as I think I know them, and that my own are prefferable, I am the less curious to be informed about them. I should not have seen what I did, I mean their Furnaces etc., if I had not had the honour to have been in company with the Duke of Argyll whose favour and approbation I see they all court, as his Grace is justly looked upon to have a supperiour knowledge in China to every body else, and indeed I am not surprized at his having it, after seeing the great and curious Collection of fine China the Duke has, and knowing the great sums they must have cost him. I bestowed four days in examining them, and find I must bestow double that time in order to view them with the accuracy they deserve to be looked at. As to my opinion about the English china, I must delay giving it untill I see them again, which I expect it wont be long before I have an oppertunity of doing, as his Grace intends to visit them soon.

At Chelsea I luckiely met with Sir Everard Falconer, Lord Hyndford who was alongst with his Grace introduced me to him.'

Lind paid a further visit to Bow with the Duke of Argyll and Lord Hyndford on 10 January 1751, but any further comments he may have made have not survived.

There are in these extracts some interesting pointers to the earliest type of porcelain being made at Bow. The manufacturers' aim of imitating Chinese porcelain was as yet nowhere near successful it seems; about 1748 the body apparently still had a 'glassy constitution' and was 'of the same kind made at St. Cloud' though with 'a pretty Glazeing which sets it of (sic)'; and judging by the remark in the 1748 edition of Defoe's *Tour of Great Britain*, it was mostly in the form of teawares.

Even so, it can be shown that by the summer of 1749 Bow wares were already well known in places as far from London as Scotland and Staffordshire. By 1757 a potter named Joseph Warburton (whose surname suggests a Staffordshire origin) had reached Newcastle-upon-Tyne by way of Bow. The following advertisement appeared in the local *Journal* on 12 February 1757: 'Whereas Joseph Warburton has been employed for some years in making China at Bow near London. He does hereby make known to the Publick that he finds better materials here for the purpose, and to be had at a cheaper rate. Therefore any gentleman willing to encourage such an undertaking may know particulars of the expense by applying to the above Joseph Warburton at Mr Hilcot's Pot-house on the South Shore.'[12]

But with or without knowledge of the manufacture at Bow, it does not seem as if Joseph Warburton's projected China undertaking ever became reality.

When William Littler abandoned the manufacture of porcelain at Longton Hall and went up to Scotland he may have advertised for workers in London, hoping to attract men from Bow and Chelsea. The two following notices at least may have reference to Littler's china and earthenware works at West Pans. The *London Chronicle*, in 1757, noted that, 'Yesterday four persons well skilled in the making British china were engaged for Scotland, where a new porcelain manufactory is going to be established in the manner of that now carried on at Chelsea, Stratford and Bow.'

Several years later, in December 1764, another report appeared: 'We hear from Edinburgh that some gentlemen are about to establish a porcelain manufacture in Scotland, and have already wrote up to London to engage proper persons to carry it on.'

That workers migrated from Bow to the East Anglian porcelain factory at Lowestoft is a tradition of long standing. Legend has it that the recipe for Bow porcelain was stolen by a Lowestoft man — possibly Robert Browne himself, one of the proprietors of the porcelain factory — by means of an early instance of industrial espionage. He is said to have applied for work at Bow, with pretence of being slow-witted, and then to have noted carefully the details of the manufacture, after which he returned to Suffolk to found his own undertaking. Whether this story is true or not, the paste used at Lowestoft from its beginning in 1757 was a phosphatic one, very similar to that employed at Bow,

12. The reference to Joseph Warburton was discovered by R. C. Bell, and quoted by him in *Tyneside Pottery*, 1971, p. 65.

probably formulated by somebody familiar with the secrets of Bow's manufacture.[13]

Three families of workers at Lowestoft had surnames which are recorded at Bow, two of them being sufficiently unusual to give strength to the suggestion that the older members may have travelled on from Bow to Lowestoft. The surnames in question are Mottershead, Redgrave and Stevenson.

The earliest mention of a Mottershead at Bow occurs in 1760, when Sam Mottershead appears in the Land Tax returns. The baptism of 'Anne, daughter of Samuel and Anne Mottershead' on 21 March the same year is recorded in the parish register. Her sister Mary was baptized in April 1763. Aubrey Toppin recorded that James Mottershead was at Bow *c.* 1765-7. William Chaffers lists James Mottershead as a painter at Lowestoft, and gives a letter from a James Mottershead of Hanley, writing back to Lowestoft on 5 November 1793. This was presumably the same man, and the purpose of his letter was to describe his methods in the preparation of gold for gilding purposes. Geoffrey Godden suggests that James Mottershead may have been responsible for the fine flower-painting done at Lowestoft in the 1770s which is usually attributed to the anonymous 'Tulip painter'.[14]

A William Stevenson was recorded in the Land Tax returns for Bow in 1743. Seven years later 'John Stevenson, a Potter and Sarah his wife' were mentioned in the Bow burial register in June 1750 when their daughter Ann died, and other entries in the registers up to 1757 suggest that John Stevenson spent some years in the Bow area, though earlier entries at Burslem between 1743 and 1749 imply that he originally came from the Potteries.

The fire insurance policy taken out by Obed Aldred of the Lowestoft factory with the Sun Company in April 1771 mentions a 'Tenement in Swan Lane Lowestoft in tenure of John Stevenson China Maker',[15] and it seems probable that this was the same man who had presumably gone on to Lowestoft from Bow. Godden records a John Stevenson buried at Lowestoft on 3 September 1777, when he was fifty-seven years of age.

A younger John Stevenson, probably then aged about twenty, married Susanna Barret at Lowestoft in February 1776. With his brother William he ultimately moved on to the Chamberlain factory at Worcester in September 1799. Their names are listed in the wage records in Worcester simply as 'potters'.

There were a number of painters, both male and female, with the family name of Redgrave who worked at Lowestoft, and several well-known Lowestoft patterns are associated with them. Chaffers mentions a James Redgrave as a flower painter, but Geoffrey Godden could find nobody of that name at

13. A story similar to Browne's theft of the Bow secrets is told of Astbury and Twyford who insinuated themselves into the Elers factory by pretending to be half-witted. Other like stories occur on the Continent. They seem to be part of the folklore of ceramic history.
14. G. A. Godden, *Lowestoft Porcelain*, 1969, pp. 40 and 52.
15. Sun insurance records, Guildhall MS 11936/205 297151 30 April 1771.

Lowestoft until 1778, when James Redgrave, son of John Redgrave senior, was born. However the name James Redgrave occurs at Bow in 1747, in the Land Tax returns, though superseded by that of Mary Redgrave in 1752. It could be that this older James had already left the Bow factory for Chelsea or elsewhere, arriving at Lowestoft *c*. 1760.

The migration of workers between Bow and Chelsea has already been mentioned, and though Aubrey Toppin notes that Lewis Barber went on from Bow to work at Worcester, most migrants very probably went on to Worcester by way of the Chelsea factory.

Sarah Willcock, daughter of Thomas Frye, was employed with her husband Ralph as a decorator of creamware by Josiah Wedgwood. She was one of the artists who worked on the famous 'Frog' service ordered by Catherine the Great in 1773.[16] (It is to be noted that Josiah Wedgwood was apparently well aware of the composition of Bow porcelain, and recorded the recipe in his notebook in 1759.)

The widespread influence of the Bow factory on manufactures in Britain is demonstrable, but it can also be clearly shown that Bow was equally well known, and was an influence on porcelain manufacture, in the American colonies. The early transatlantic advertisement for Bow china, 'A Variety of Bow china, Cups and Saucers, Bowls, etc. . . . just imported by Philip Breading and to be sold at his House in Fish Street', which was published in the *Boston Evening Post* on 11 November 1754, is often quoted. No doubt similar advertisements appeared elsewhere, though research in the correspondence of some eighteenth-century American merchants suggests that they did not usually specify which particular English factory they favoured when building up stocks through London agents. Orders were sent asking for 'blue and white penciled English China', 'English Burnt (enamelled) China' or 'black and white penciled English China' (presumably Worcester) as opposed to 'India China' or 'India Burnt China'. These terms are used in a large order sent to Thomas Harris, an agent in London, by James Beekman of New York in April 1767.[17] In the following October Beekman wrote complaining that the goods which Harris had sent over were too dear in comparison with those supplied to other merchants. He included a further list of goods required with this letter, and this time gave note of the prices he would be willing to pay. A list of English blue and white china was included in the order.[18]

---

16. I will not here suggest that 'Tebo', the almost anonymous modeller who apparently worked first at Bow and then at several factories, certainly at Etruria, carried the Bow style about the country, because his history is too incomplete to be proven.

17. *The Beekman Mercantile Papers 1746–1799*, Vol. II, New York Historical Society, 1956.

18. '100   Pint Basons 8d
    48   Sugar Dishes with Covers 9d
    80   Small Milk Pots 6d
    48   Barrel Shape 8d
    6   piece Sause Boats 3/-
    4   Passavant Board Plates and spoons 10/-

Four Masonic punch bowls (Plates 12A and B) of Bow china were ordered by the 'Hallifax Lodge North Carolina' in 1767, and the invoice is still in existence, as indeed is one of the bowls, made to contain a gallon of punch. It is a documentary piece, finely decorated with dishevelled birds, and now preserved by the Masonic Lodge for which it was originally made.[19] Another documentary piece of 'American' Bow porcelain, a teabowl with the inscription 'Ann Target 1754' was recently discovered in Virginia, and had been in its owner's family for generations. A sparrow-beak jug decorated in enamels and inscribed on the base 'A. Target 1754' (Plates 13A and B) came to light in 1961.[20] Two other pieces bearing the name 'Target' are in the British Museum, a cachepot enamelled with floral sprays inscribed 'Thomas & Ann Target July 2th 1754' beneath, and a bowl enamelled with Chinese figures in a landscape, with the inscription in underglaze blue on the underside of the base, 'Thos: Target 1754'. The identical dating and agreement of names on all these pieces stimulates the imagination. We may note that a 'Thomas Targatt, Man' was buried at Woolwich in April 1764.

When Benjamin Franklin sent his wife a present of 'something from all the china workers in England' in 1758, the only two factories which he mentioned by name were Worcester and Bow. 'I send you by Captain Budden a large case and a small box containing some English china, viz: melons and leaves for a dessert of fruit and cream or the like; a bowl remarkable for the neatness of the figures made at Bow near this city: some coffee-cups of the same; and a Worcester bowl, ordinary. To show the difference of workmanship, there is something from all the china workers in England; and one old true china basin mended of an odd colour. . . . Look at the figures on the china bowl and coffee-

18	Large Tea Pots 2/-
6	Barrel Shape 1/6
6	1/9
6	Salled Boules Scolloped Edge 1/6
48	Honey Comb Tea Cups with Handles and saucers $2\frac{1}{2}$
48	Honey Comb Coffee Cups with Handles and saucers $2\frac{1}{2}$
6	Tea Pots 3/6
12	Milk (Pots) 1/3
6	Quart Coffee Pots 7/-
6	Sugar Dishes 1/3
6	Pint Basons 10d.'

Some of these items may well have been of Bow porcelain.

19. Bradford L. Rauschenberg, 'A Documented Bow Bowl Made For Hallifax-Lodge/North-Carolina', *Journal of Early Southern Decorative Arts*, Vol. 1, No. 1, May 1975.

20. Ivor Noël Hume, director of the Department of Archaeology at Colonial Williamsburg, Virginia, very kindly drew our attention to this sparrow-beak cream jug decorated in polychrome with the same peony, bamboo and fence pattern as the 'A. Target 1754' teabowl, and probably a remnant of the same service. It is in the possession of Clifford J. Larsen, formerly director of the Laura Musser Art Gallery and Museum, Muscatine, Iowa, who has very kindly provided the photographs of the jug for inclusion in this book. The jug was first discovered among a collection purchased by a dealer in the small town of New Holstein, Wisconsin, in 1961. Nothing is known of its earlier history.

12A. Interior of enamelled PUNCH BOWL ordered from the Bow factory on 28 December 1767 by the Masonic Halifax Lodge, North Carolina. Diameter 27.6 cm (10.9 in), height 11.6 cm (4.6 in) *See pages 75, 187*

12B. Exterior view of the Halifax Lodge PUNCH BOWL, decorated in enamels with exotic birds. *Museum of Early Southern Decorative Arts, Winston-Salem, North Carolina, USA. See pages 75, 187*

13A, B. SPARROW-BEAK JUG decorated in enamels, inscribed on the base 'A. Target 1754'. Height 8.6 cm (3.4 in). *Collection Clifford J. Larsen, formerly Director, Laura Musser Art Gallery and Museum, Muscatine, Iowa. See pages 75, 124*

cups with your spectacles on, they will bear examining.'[21]

It appears very probable that it was to Bow that Gousse Bonnin and George Anthony Morris turned in 1770, when they were seeking skilled workmen to manufacture 'American China' at their new factory in Philadelphia. On 1 January 1770 they announced the undertaking in the *Pennsylvania Chronicle*: '. . . the proprietors of the China Works now erecting in Southwark . . . have proved to a certainty, that the clays of America are productive of as good porcelain as any heretofore manufactured at the famous factory in Bow, near London.' The 'capital works' of the Philadelphia factory were apparently 'compleated and in motion' in July that year. They were described in later sale notices as consisting of 'three kilns, two furnaces, two mills, two clay vaults, cisterns, engines and treading room'. The example of Bow was followed in Philadelphia by the inclusion of bone ash in the porcelain recipe.

In October 1770 the *Pennsylvania Staatsbote* reported that 'nine master workers have arrived here (from England) for the porcelain manufactory of this city', and two months later the first 'Emission of Porcelain' occurred from the Bonnin and Morris works. Not only the inclusion of bone ash in the paste, but also certain details of the style and decoration of the few surviving Bonnin and Morris pieces which have been identified point to the factory's links with Bow. That the factory in Philadelphia was short-lived was largely due to the collapse of the Nonimportation Agreement, originally set up to protect colonial manufactures from overseas competition. The lure of the cheaper and better imported English wares was too strong for the customers of the struggling Bonnin and Morris factory, and together with the difficulty and high cost of obtaining suitable workmen proved too much.[22]

In 1783, ten years later, Josiah Wedgwood, who objected strongly to the employment of English potters in foreign undertakings which might damage his own overseas markets, published his *Address to the Workmen in the Pottery: On the Subject of Entering into the Service of Foreign Manufacturers*. In it he referred to the former factory at Philadelphia, and underlined the fate which overtook those who sought employment there instead of remaining in English potteries: '. . . another [undertaking] equally fruitless and equally fatal to our people (for *they* were chiefly employed in it) was carried on in Pennsylvania. Here a sort of China ware was aimed at, and eight men went over at first; whether any more, or how many, might follow, I have not learnt. The event was nearly the same in this as in the others; the proprietors, soon finding that they had no chance of succeeding, not only gave up the undertaking, but silenced the just complaints of the poor injured workmen, by clapping one of them [Thomas Gale] into a prison: the rest who had never received half the wages agreed for, were left entirely to shift for themselves. Thus abandoned, at

21. B. M. Watney, *English Blue and White Porcelain of the Eighteenth Century*, 2nd ed., 1973, p. 25.
22. For the full account of the Bonnin and Morris undertaking in Philadelphia see Graham Hood, *Bonnin and Morris of Philadelphia: The First American Porcelain Factory, 1770–1772*, The University of North Carolina Press, 1972.

the distance of some thousands of miles from home, and without a penny in their pockets, they were reduced to the hard necessity of begging in the public streets for a morsel of bread.'

Dr Watney points out that a notice published in the *Pennsylvania Journal* by the Bonnin and Morris factory on 10 October 1771 linked it 'even more closely with Bow. It stated that an apprentice boy named Thomas Frye about 16 years of age had run away from the factory.'[23] An entry in the baptismal register from West Ham dated 27 October 1754 reads 'Thomas Frye, son of Henry and Jane'. Thomas was Henry Frye's eldest son, and nephew to Thomas Frye of Bow.

23. B. Watney, op. cit. p. 26.

5
Materials and Trade

The Bow Porcelain Manufactory was impressed on folk-memory in a most surprising and unexpected way. For many years it was recalled not for its size or efficiency, not even for the charm of its wares, since as the nineteenth century wore on the origins of some were forgotten and others were labelled as the products of different manufactures. What was associated with the name of Bow was the legend that the China Manufactory had made porcelain with clay brought across the Atlantic from England's American colonies. Here is the same sense of romance in industry which Thomas Craft had so clearly felt in 1790, and it sustained the memory of the Porcelain Factory of New Canton above the waves of time for more than a century.

In fact, although 'unaker' was specified as an ingredient of the porcelain body in the first Bow patent issued in December 1744, only one shipment of a material likely to be that clay is known to have been imported into London. It was described as 'earth, unrated', and a quantity of '20 tons, value £5' arrived from Carolina in 1743/44. The Unacoi Mountains, part of the southern Appalachians, are in Carolina. There is no reason to suppose that clay from any other source would have this strange name of Red Indian origin applied to it. It has already been suggested that Alderman George Arnold's direct personal link with Virginia, to the north of Carolina, may have been instrumental in obtaining American clay for Bow. Though the likelihood that Andrew Duché, the potter from Savannah, Georgia, was Bow's supplier has been closely argued by other writers, there is no documentary or other evidence to support the suggestion. Aubrey Toppin introduced the idea that John Campbell LL.D, a contemporary authority on industry and trade and on the European settlements in America, some of whose letters to Arthur Dobbs of Carrickfergus (Governor of North Carolina in 1754) have been preserved, might be the person who sent American clay to Bow.[1]

On 24 June 1749, Campbell wrote: 'I send you in a small box a sample of white clay and the ore intermixed with the vein which has been traced above a mile in Edgecombe county. The clay resembles what I saw at Bow for their china ware which I believe is only a bubble with the undertakers.'

---

1. B. Watney, *English Blue and White Porcelain of the Eighteenth Century*, 2nd ed., 1973, pp. 9–13.

E. SPARROW-BEAK JUG decorated in enamels with Chinese figures
in a landscape. Height 8.5 cm (3.3 in)
1753–5
See page 126

F. SQUARE DISH with indented corners decorated in underglaze blue and overglaze red and enamels and gilding after a Japanese original. Seal marks. Width 15.2 cm (6 in)
1752–5
See page 126

The wording suggests that Bow had already employed American clay, but that Campbell thought its use there to have been no more than an experiment. He was endeavouring to find something similar to Bow's experimental clay, but not necessarily, it seems to the authors, for the purpose of supplying it to the Bow factory.

'This clay' (from Edgecombe County), continued Campbell, 'is near water carriage, and if worth anything enough might be had.' As things turned out, Edgecombe clay was evidently never exported, and the single load of unaker which arrived in London in 1743/44 was sufficient to give the Bow factory a more than transient fame.

In 1758, Robert Dossie stated in *The Handmaid of the Arts* that kaolin was discovered 'in some mountains on the back of Carolina in great abundance; whither the proprietors of a work near London sent an agent to procure it for them; but he neglecting it for other pursuits, I believe no quantity has hitherto been brought from thence'. The 'work near London' is almost certain to have been Bow, and perhaps the early Bow porcelain with a 'glassy constitution' of which Alexander Lind spoke was made with American clay. The Bow china body seems to have been stabilized into the phosphatic formula by mid-1749, and one can suggest that from then on the materials employed in its manufacture were supplied from English sources.

And from where in England did the Bow factory draw its raw materials? In 1759, Wedgwood noted what he believed to be the Bow porcelain formula in his Experiment Book: '4 parts bone ash; 4 parts Lynn sand; a $\frac{1}{4}$ part of gypsum plaster or alabaster; a $\frac{1}{4}$ part of blue ball clay. This is the composition of Bow china but I am not certain of the proportions. In the early period of the manufactory they used to frit the bone ashes, sand and gypsum mixed up together and made into bricks, but have for some time past omitted that process and used them crude.'[2]

Little attention has hitherto been given to the suppliers and auxiliary trades of eighteenth-century ceramic manufactures; the main sources of our information on the subject are the accounts and notes kept by John Baddeley of Shelton in the middle of the century, and these are now preserved among the Aqualate papers housed in the William Salt Library in Stafford.[3] It is noteworthy that though John Baddeley's works were in North Staffordshire much of the supplies he needed came through dealers in London, and it seems very probable that local London factories would have been among their customers also.

The source of ball clay for potters' use is in South Devon, near Teignmouth, and in Dorset, not far from Poole, and in the eighteenth century several Dorset families ran a regular trade in exporting it to London and elsewhere by sea.[4]

2. Ibid., pp. 12 and 13.
3. Extensively quoted by John Mallet, in 'John Baddeley of Shelton', Pt. I, *E.C.C. Transactions*, Vol. 6, Pt. 2 1966, and Pt. II, *E.C.C. Transactions*, Vol. 6, Pt. 3, 1967.
4. For the details of the exporting of clay from 'Dorset in the seventeenth and eighteenth centuries

Gypsum and alabaster are the products of mines in Derbyshire, and Lynn sand, as its name suggests, was supplied from King's Lynn (Lynn Regis) on the Norfolk coast. Edmund Elsden, a merchant of Lynn, supplied John Baddeley with the sand, and it can be seen from Elsden's insurance policies that he was in business selling both sand and Baltic timber at least from 1753 to 1767.[5] It seems highly likely that he would have shipped sand to Bow also; the sea journey down to London was a comparatively short one from Lynn, and the Bow factory had its own wharf on the Lea. Another source of potters' sand was the Isle of Wight.[6]

Bones may have been obtained direct from the knackers' yards of east London (as the hides were supplied to tanners), and calcined and ground at the factory, or mills nearby. The Bow Porcelain works could also have obtained its supplies of 'virgin earth' from Newdick & Nicholas of Cornhill. That this firm supplied 'Bone Ashes' to John Baddeley can be seen from his accounts, and the carriage charges on this commodity between London and the Midlands were heavy.[7] Loads of bone ash, like potters' sand, were delivered to North Staffordshire by water, and the nearest navigable point to the Potteries in the 1750s was Winsford in Cheshire, on the river Weaver. From there the journey

see J. P. M. Latham, 'Dorset Clay to Staffordshire Pot', *E.C.C. Transactions*, Vol. 10, Pt. 2, 1977. Mr Latham has discovered that Captain Joliffe, Thomas Hyde and John Calcraft MP were foremost in the business in the middle and later eighteenth century, and quotes from 'Capt. Joliffe's Account of ye clay pitts near Wareham and Poole', now in Dorchester Record Office. It dates from *c.* 1756. 'Clay at this time yeilds from 14s to 18s ye ton in London. The freight to London is 7s per ton—seldom under. . . There are no clay merchants that buy ye cargoes from ye shipps and retayle it out to ye potters and pipemakers. The Potters and pipemakers buy from ye shipps and that which is not bought off in 6 days is putt in a cellar and sold out.

'They buy at all times of ye yeare, but credit must be given frequently which more than anything is attended with loss, and resulting, though not often, ye ship and cargo are lost. There must be an agent kept always in London to dispose of ye clay before it is sent up and to attend ye clay cellar.' It seems that like other London potters the undertakers at Bow would have bought their ball clay direct from the shippers at wharves in the City.

5. Sun insurance records, Guildhall MSS 11936/103 136866 2 August 1753; 11936/162 223974 28 August 1765; 11936/175 245634 13 May 1767.

6. Flints are not mentioned in Wedgwood's Bow recipe though Thomas Frye referred to them in the second Bow patent, and many flints, both calcined and raw, were found in the most recent excavations on the Bow factory site. They are of course not geologically native to the lower part of the Lea Valley. It is possible that the use of ground, calcined flint in the china body was suggested at Bow by John or Joshua Astbury, or at least by Staffordshire employees. John Astbury was credited in Staffordshire with the discovery of flint as an important ingredient in a fine earthenware body. Flints were and are found and calcined at Gravesend on the Thames estuary, and might have been supplied to Bow through such a dealer as Edward West, No. 3 Darkhouse Lane, Queenhithe, 'Victualler and Dealer in Flints' (Sun insurance records Guildhall MS 11936/179 249813 12 October 1767). In his book, *Two Centuries of Ceramic Art in Bristol*, 1873, Hugh Owen records that Joseph Ring, commencing the manufacture of Queen's ware in Bristol in 1786 obtained 'ground flints' from Bell & Griffin of Stone, Staffordshire, and 'sopphora' (zaffre) from John Salte of London.

7. See John Mallet, op. cit., *E.C.C. Transactions*, Vol. 6, Pt. 2, 1966, Appendix A, 'Account Book Showing Transactions Undertaken by John Baddeley on behalf of Messrs Reid & Co.', Aqualate papers, D. 1788 V. 94; and 'Account, written in John Baddeley's handwriting, submitted to Thomas Fletcher in 1763, evidently concerned with Porcelain', Aqualate papers, D. 1788, p. 14 (2), 'John Baddeley of Shelton', Pt. II, *E.C.C. Transactions*, Vol. 6, Pt. 3, 1967, Appendix F.

was completed by road until the opening of the Trent and Mersey canal later in the century.

As Dr Watney points out, the term 'virgin earth' as applied to bone ash, had a definite meaning for eighteenth-century chemists.[8] It occurs in a book which had considerable importance at that time, *The Elements of Chemistry* by Herman Boerhaave MD (1668–1738), director of the Botanic Garden at Leyden, which was translated into English by Dr Timothy Dallowe of London in 1735. Boerhaave postulated that after the calcination, grinding and washing of various natural substances such as bones or forms of limestone, the resulting fine sedimented 'earth' was a 'simple, hard, friable, fossil body, fixed in the fire but not melting in it, nor dissoluble in water, alcohol or air'.[9] It could be thought of as the basic material of creation, and the contemporary attitude of the potters to its use shows how very near alchemy and the chemistry of pottery were to being confused in the eighteenth-century porcelain-makers' minds. Thomas Frye himself described the process thus in the specification for the second Bow patent, which was enrolled on 17 March 1749/50: 'As there is nothing in nature but by calcination, grinding and washing will produce a fixed indissoluble matter, distinguished by the name of virgin earth, the properties of which is strictly the same whether produced from animals, vegetables or . . . all fossils of the calcarious kind, such as chalk, limestone etc.; take therefore any of these classes, calcine it till it smokes no more, which is an indication that all the volatile sulpherous parts are dissipated, and that the saline are sett loose; then grind and wash in many waters to discharge the salts and filth, reiterate the process twice more, when the ashes or virgin earth will be fit for use'.

Newdick & Nicholas supplied others of the potters' needs, including lampblack and smalts (diluted cobalt, in the form of a finely pulverized glass used for underglaze-blue decoration). John Baddeley obtained some of his smalts from them, but he was also supplied by one Sanders, and by James Smallwood, almost certainly a local man living in Newcastle-under-Lyme. One of Baddeley's chief suppliers of smalts however was Frederick Teush, a merchant who had a smalt mill and snuff mills at Sewardstone, Essex, but whose London warehouse was in Star Court, Bread Street. Teush's fire insurance policies show that he was in business for very many years.[10] It seems very likely that his supplies of smalts would have been imported from Saxony, and therefore of the best quality; and it must be a strong probability that Teush also supplied smalts to Bow, which could almost be considered as his local

---

8. B. Watney op. cit., pp. 12 and 125.
9. Jonas Hanway in '*A Journal of Eight Days Travel from Portsmouth to Kingston upon Thames* . . .', London, 1757, recommended virgin earth as a suitable soil dressing for herbs, in the same way as rose growers employ bone meal today. It was evidently already available as an article of trade.
10. Sun insurance records, Guildhall MSS 11936/80 109334 28 August 1747; 11936/99 132607 13 October 1752; 11936/120 159467 13 October 1757; 11936/125 164960 12 October 1758, etc. to 313088 4 July 1772.

china factory, and one which made so great a speciality of blue and white wares.

John Baddeley's Shelton accounts suggest that he made china decorated in colours as well as blue and white, since enamels are mentioned, and indeed in December 1758 he himself travelled to the glass-making centre of Stourbridge in Worcestershire to collect 80 lb of enamel. The journey cost him £1 10s and the hire of a man and horse for transport 10/6. Enamels for use at Bow could have been supplied by a number of London dealers, but again Newdick & Nicholas are among the most likely, though a business supplying colours was run by the Noy family near St. Catherine's for a considerable number of years. In 1767 its owner was Hannah Noy, widow or daughter of its founder Thomas.[11]

It has been suggested that Bow bought cheap gold in Sheffield for gilding, but there seems little foundation for this assertion.[12] Chaffers records that payments for powder gold and grain gold appeared in the Bow accounts for 1757 and 1758, now lost, but does not note to whom they were made. Lead for glaze was probably obtained through merchants such as Newdick & Nicholas.

Having gathered together the necessary materials, and combined them in the manufacture of its wares, the China Factory of New Canton was faced with the need to dispose of them in trade, and the indications are that from its earliest years it did so on a very large scale. It has already been suggested in Chapter 2 that John Weatherby and John Crowther engaged in the manufacture of porcelain at Bow as part of their threefold commercial interest in the production and distribution of ceramics and glass. They appear to have been first of all entrepreneurs in the pottery trade, acquiring their premises at St. Catherine's in 1744,[13] and listed as merchants there in *The Complete Guide to London* from 1744 onwards. By 1748 their correspondence with John Wedgwood of Burslem on the subject of the would-be porcelain-maker Thomas Briand, shows that they were in close contact, if not already in partnership, with Thomas Frye. It seems to have been primarily through the wholesale firm at St. Catherine's that Bow wares were shipped abroad to many parts of the world, including the American colonies; dispersal in London, and Britain as a whole, was directed chiefly from the Bow City warehouse, though some sales were always made from the factory itself.

A copy of the notice announcing the opening of the first Bow warehouse in the City of London was discovered by J. E. Nightingale FSA and published by him as long ago as 1881.[14] He found it in *Aris's Birmingham Gazette* of 5 March 1753, and noted a nearly similar entry in the *Derby Mercury* of the following

11. Sun insurance records, Guildhall MS 11936/177 248983 22 September 1767. A Mrs Noy is included amongst those owing money to Benjamin Weatherby & Co. in 1775.
12. G. Bernard Hughes, *English Pottery and Porcelain Figures*, 1964, pp. 56, 57; and William Chaffers, *Marks and Monograms*, 15th ed., 1965, Vol. II, p. 274.
13. Land Tax Books, Guildhall Library, London.
14. J. E. Nightingale, *Contributions towards the History of English Porcelain*, privately printed, Salisbury, 1881, page XLV.

9 March. Another announcement had appeared in the *Norwich Mercury* on 24 February:[15]

Bow China Ware

Was opened on Wednesday the 7th February, near the Royal Exchange in Cornhill, with a Back Door facing the Bank, in Threadneedle-street, for the Convenience of all Customers in both Town and Country; where all sorts of China will continue to be sold in the same Manner as formerly at Bow, with Allowance made to Wholesale Dealers.

A bill, by coincidence also dated 5 March 1753, and made out to the 'Honb!e Gen. Clayton' of Great Brook Street, by William Brown on behalf of the 'Porcelaine Comp.y' survives, together with a corrected copy of the same date, made after William Brown had discovered that he had overcharged on one of the items.[16]

1753	Bought of the Porcelaine Comp.y from the Bow China Warehouse Cornhill				
5th March	6 fine Parteridge handled Cups	2/-	£	12.	6
	1 blue Pickle Stand Imperfect			12.	—
Charg'd 4/-	10 fine Enameld Dysart Plates	2/-	1	0.	—
before	4 fine Blue Oblong Dishes	4/-		16.	—
being a	1 fine Parteridge Tea pot			5.	6
Mistake	1 Sprig'd Enameld Water Cup & Saucer			4.	—
	4 Enameld Water saucers			8.	—
	3 Artichoak Cups	2/-		6.	—
	2 Enameld Parteradges	4/-		8.	—
	1 pair Enameld Ballad Singers			12.	—
	1 pair D.o fluter & Companion with Tabor			9.	—
	1 fine Enameld fesant Dysart Plate			4.	—
			£5	16.	6.

15. Notice in the *Norwich Mercury* discovered by Sheenah Smith. See *E.C.C. Transactions*, Vol. 9, Pt. 2, 1974, p. 207. 'Norwich China Dealers of the mid-Eighteenth Century'.
16. Our attention was drawn to this corrected bill by John C. Austin, Assistant Keeper of Collections, Colonial Williamsburg Foundation, Colonial Williamsburg, Virginia, USA, to whom we are much indebted. General Clayton may have been amongst the earliest buyers of Bow porcelain. A bill made out to n. 2, — Clayton Esq. by John Taylor of Pall Mall is preserved among the papers of the late A. J. Toppin CVO. It includes a 'Bow ware sugar dish' at 4s od, sold on 21 February 1748/49.

By Mistake in Chargeing four shillings instead of two for the Dysart Enameld plates I took Twenty Shillings too much for which I Crave your Lady S^{ps} Pardon and have with this Sent it back.

Objects similar to the first two listed items are illustrated in Plates 14 and 15.

Bow's second porcelain warehouse in London was opened on The Terrace, St. James's in 1757, but closed only about a year later. It is possible that this may have been as a consequence of the bankruptcy of Edward Heylyn. The following notice from the *Public Advertiser* was discovered by J. E. Nightingale.

To be Sold by Auction

By Mr LAMBE

At his House in Pall-Mall, St. James's, on Monday the 10th of April 1758 and the five following Days, (by order of the Proprietors of the Bow Manufactory of Porcelain).

All the intire Stock of their Warehouse, on the Terrass in St. James's Street, they having intirely quitted the same; consisting of fine Epergnes, Chandeliers, Branches decorated with Flowers and Figures, fine Essence Pots, beautiful Groups, and other figures of Birds, Beasts, Jars, Beakers, Bottles, etc. Service of Dishes and Plates, Sauceboats, Bowls, Compleat Tea and Coffee Equipages, a large Assortment of fine Enamel and fine Partridge Sets, which are most beautifully painted by several of the finest Masters from Dresden, made up in Lots proper for the Nobility and private Families.

There is a large quantity of the Chelsea Manufactory among the Stock.

The whole to be viewed at the Time to Sale, which will begin each Day punctually at Twelve.

We know from John Bowcock's surviving papers that efforts were made to establish agents for Bow China in provincial towns, and also that outriders—or salesmen, in modern terms—travelled through the country to take orders, and supply goods to china dealers and shopkeepers. Bowcock sometimes fulfilled this role himself. In the earlier part of 1758 he was in Dublin, engaged in arranging auction sales which, like the sale in the notice quoted above, included Chelsea productions as well as Bow wares, and also a quantity of glass. On 22 August however, according to his memorandum book, he was 'At Nottingham. Called on Mr Rigley; he says he was used ill about some figure Thorpe sent, not to order, and has done (with us).'[17]

---

17. British Museum. Thorp was evidently an unsatisfactory employee for the Bow concern. An advertisement to do with him appeared in the *General Evening Post* of 12 August 1756: 'This is to give notice to all those it may concern that as Joseph Thorp has been employed by the Porcelain Company at their Warehouse in Cornhill, as their Rider in the Country, in both Situations he has

14. COFFEE CUP ('handled cup') decorated in red and blue enamels and gilt with the 'partridge' pattern, nowadays called the 'two quail' pattern, after a Kakiemon original. Height 5.9 cm (2.4 in). 1752–5.
See pages 85–6, 120, 122

15. TRIPLE-SHELL 'PICKLE STAND' decorated in underglaze blue with the 'desirable residence' pattern inside the shells and a cell diaper border. Height 12.7 cm (5 in). 1753–6. *See page 85–6, 127–8*

Bow wares were also disposed of in large quantities by auction sale, a method of dispersal apparently begun by the Chelsea factory, which continued well into the nineteenth century and was employed by several later manufactories, most notoriously by that of Charles James Mason in the 1830s and 40s. J. E. Nightingale was unable to find a notice for an auction sale of Bow porcelain earlier than 24 March 1757, but such sales may have commenced at least by early 1755. The Bow account book for the years 1751–5 preserved at the British Museum records a sale held in Dublin on 20 February 1755,[18] and an advertisement presumably for a sale of Chinese porcelain which appeared in the *Norwich Mercury* on 6 September 1755 contained a note, 'No Bowe (sic) Manufactory in this Collection' which suggests that Bow wares had already been auctioned in Norwich and were considered inferior to the oriental.[19] On 3 and 10 June 1758 respectively the two following notices were published in Norwich. 'To be Sold by AUCTION on . . . the 9th of June and the following Days. A Large and Valuable Collection of ENGLISH CHINA, consisting of Dishes, Plates, Sauceboats, Tea and Coffee Equipages, both blue and fine enamel'd, with great Variety of curious Groupes of Figures, of Birds, Beasts, Jars, Beakers and Branches, ornamented with Flowers; the whole made up in proper Lots for publick or private use . . . Catalogues to be had at the place of Sale.' On 10 June: 'To be sold by AUCTION on Friday the 9th instant and the Eight following Days, at the Great-Room in the late Sir Benjamin Wrench's Court, in Cockey Lane, Norwich. A large and Valuable Collection of English CHINA, of the Manufactory of Bow. Consisting of Epergnes, fine Branches ornamented with Flowers, beautiful Groups of Figures, Jars, Beakers and Bottles, finely enamel'd; Dishes, Plates, Sauceboats and Bowls; Compleat Tea and Coffee Equipages; Several Pieces of China for Desarts, as Baskets, Shells, Leaves, Apples, Mellons, Lettices, Colliflowers, and other curious Shapes; and are put in proper Lotts for publick or private Uses, which will begin each Day at Ten o'clock. CATALOGUES to be had at the Place of Sale. N.B. The Publick may depend on the said Goods to be Sold without Reserve, the Proprietors leaving this Sale intirely to the Mercy of the Company. AARON LAMBE, AUCTIONEER. A large Parcel of empty BOXES, to be sold.'

It is apparent from the notices above, and from those for the auction sales in London held in February and April 1758, and also conducted by 'Mr Lambe, At his House in Pall-Mall, St. James's' that outside auctioneers were

---

been unpowered to receive money for the said Company, but as he has been discharged from the service of the said Company, all those Dealers with the said Company are desired not to pay the said Thorp any Money on their Account, as it will not be allowed by the said Company.'
18. British Museum, Add. MS 45905.
19. This information and the following advertisements were discovered by Sheenah Smith, and published by her in her paper, 'Norwich China Dealers of the mid-Eighteenth Century', op. cit., pp. 206–8. An early advertisement mentioning Bow china was published by a retailer, John Sotro, Goldsmith and Toyman, at the Golden Heron on the North Side of St. Paul's Churchyard in the *Daily Advertiser*, on Thursday, 9 January 1750: 'Note, this China is now come to so great a perfection that it is not inferior to old Japan . . .'

sometimes employed by the Bow factory. (Early in 1758, of course, John Bowcock was busy in Ireland.) In the spring of 1757 Bow had employed 'Mr Cock and Co. at their New Auction Rooms in Spring-Gardens, leading into St. James's Park'. In 1755 and 1756 Chelsea's public auctioneer had been Mr Ford 'At his Great Room in the Haymarket'. Chelsea also employed Mr Gelley 'At the Great House in Great Marlborough-street', and from 1759, David Burnsall of Berkeley Square.[20]

Bow china was also, of course, carried among the stock of many chinamen 'both in Town and Country'. The names of several of the more important London dealers occur in John Bowcock's memorandum book of 1756—Mr Fogg, Mr Fahy, Mr White, Mr Vanderkiste, Mr Hunter, Mr Morgan, Mrs Bernardeau and Mr Baxter among others. Charles Vere, perhaps the richest and best-known china dealer in eighteenth-century London, whose premises were at the sign of the Indian King (no doubt an intentional pun) on the corner of Salisbury Court, Fleet Street, was honoured by the Bow Manufactory in having a pattern named after him—Bowcock lists '1 pair sauce-boats Mr Vere's pattern 4s' in March 1756, but which pattern it was has unhappily been forgotten.

Research among contemporary directories, insurance policies and similar sources has produced information about a considerable number of pottery and porcelain dealers all over the British Isles. Of those mentioned above, Robert Fogg was a well-known and fashionable chinaman, whose shop was in Bond Street. An example of his trade-card, giving his sign 'At the China Jarr' still exists in the collection formed by Sir Ambrose Heal which is now in the British Museum. Fogg's son of the same name continued in the Bond Street premises, but Robert Fogg the elder died at Reading at the advanced age of ninety in 1806.

Mr Fahy (or Foy) of St. James's, has already been mentioned in these pages (Chapter 2); Joseph Vanderkiste was recorded c. 1750 at 379 Strand; in 1763 he had removed to Southwark and was listed there as a chinaman. His name also occurs in John Baddeley's accounts as a supplier of cullet and glass in 1757, 1759 and 1761. Crushed and ground glass was an ingredient for a porcelain body included by some manufacturers, sometimes together with ground oriental china. The latter may have been tried for a time at Bow, though Wedgwood's version of the Bow recipe does not mention it.

'Mr White' was identified through the discovery by Alwyn and Angela Cox of a bill issued in December 1756 to 'The Right Hon[ble] the Marquis of

20. David Burnsall was a wealthy man, and a close associate of Nicholas Sprimont of Chelsea. After Sprimont's death in 1771 a lawsuit was brought against Burnsall by William Duesbury, the new proprietor of the Chelsea factory, for porcelain said to have been unlawfully sold to Burnsall by Sprimont's manager, Francis Thomas. Burnsall apparently took over the western part of Monmouth House, Lawrence Street, from Sprimont in the second half of 1767, improved it and let or sold it to Dr Michael Arne, son of the composer, a year later. See J. V. G. Mallet, 'The Site of the Chelsea Porcelain Factory', E.C.C. Transactions, Vol. 9, Pt. 1, 1973, p. 123.

Rockingham': 'R. White, At the Golden Jarr opposite to the Kings Arms Tavern in New Bond Street, London, Who sells all Sorts of China Ware, Great Variety of Glass Cut & Plain, Fine Delft & Staffordshire Stone Ware; Likewise India Pictures, Japand Dressing Boxes and Bow Porcelain at the very Lowest Prices.'

The Marquis's purchase of seven Nankin mugs, and 'A Fine White Plate' cost a total of £2. 3. 0. The items were bought at Christmas time 1756, but the bill was not settled until 3 June 1757.

Dr and Mrs Cox also discovered among the Rockingham papers an account including the purchase of a 'complete set of White Sprigged tea china' of Bow manufacture, at a cost of £2. 2. 6. with its packing box 6d extra. This was dated 16 April 1753. Another bill of 18 November 1754 gave '4 Bow milk jugs' at 6/-, or 1/6 each.

A fire insurance policy was taken out with the Royal Exchange Assurance Company by William Hunter, chinaman, of Queen Street, Mayfair on 17 October 1754,[21] and it seems reasonable to assume that this was the man whom Bowcock noted on 4 May 1756 as desiring 'to have some mustard ladles as the cream ladles, only small boles and long handles; [and] 6 enamelled roses, 2 pr. green leaf candlesticks, 4 white leaf candlesticks'. However there was another William Hunter, who may have been the person meant, a goldsmith and jeweller, of 51 Lombard Street, there from 1732–62. On the whole, the chinaman seems the more likely.

Mr Kentish, requiring 'a mandril coffee-pot', is most likely to have been John Kentish, goldsmith, jeweller and toyman at 18 Cornhill from 1758–93. Thomas Williams and Thomas Morgan were both London chinamen of importance. Mr Morgan's name appears frequently in William Duesbury's London account book, 1751–3. Thomas Williams's shop was in St. James's, and he was the man mentioned in one of Horace Walpole's letters as having had the impudence to put up the price of a cracked china vase because it had been damaged in the earthquake which caused such a furore in London in 1750.

Baxter, with whose orders Bowcock seems to have taken particular trouble, may have been Dudley Baxter of 6 Bedford Row, his address from 1757–68. Elizabeth Baxter followed him there as ratepayer from 1768–73.

1756
18 June   . . . 2 double doz^n of lace and 2 double of doz^n dysart rose
               pattern knife handles: to be mounted and sent in Baxter's
               parcel . . .
24 July   . . . Goats, swans and every other sort of toys to be sent in
               Baxter's order, flat drawers to be made on purpose, and
               each kept separate . . .

21. Royal Exchange Assurance, policy No. 31356, 17 October 1754, Guildhall Library.

The thought of Bow 'toys', scent-bottles, seals and the like, is a curious and intriguing one.

Mrs Bernadeau, to whose order for knife handles of the 'wheatsheaf' pattern Bowcock referred on 24 July 1756, was the wife of James Bernadeau, one of the best-known cutlers in London, whose premises were at Russell Court, Drury Lane. The Bernadeaus supplied knives with handles of silver and semi-precious stones, as well as of porcelain, and notice of their business was included in Mortimer's *Universal Director* in 1763.

Besides the names of some china retailers, John Bowcock also mentioned some of the firm's private customers, not only as purchasers, but sometimes as sources of models for the china manufacture. Lady Cavendish for instance lent pieces from her own collection to be copied at the Bow factory, as Sir Charles Hanbury Williams did at Chelsea.

1756
28 May   Patterns received from Lady Cavendish, a Japan octagon cup and saucer lady pattern; a rib'd and scollop'd cup and saucer, image pattern; a basket bordered dysart plate.

Bowcock mentioned these pieces again at the end of November, with the addition of 'a Japan bread and butter plate' and the note 'To be returned in a month, May 28th 1756'. It seems they did not get home until the end of the year.

In Ireland, in April 1758, Bowcock noted in his memorandum book, 'Lady Freik shew'd me two tureens she brought from France, moulded from a full-grown cabbage', and gave a sketch of one.

The name of the Duke of Argyll is specially noteworthy among those of the customers at Bow. He was extremely interested in the whole business of porcelain manufacture,[22] and as Alexander Lind remarked in 1749, 'his Grace is justly looked upon to have a supperiour knowledge in China to everybody else, and indeed I am not surprized at his having it, after seeing the great and curious Colection of fine China the Duke has, and knowing the great sums they must have cost him.' On 20 May 1756 John Bowcock noted that the duke's account with Bow stood at £207 5s 0d, a truly phenomenal sum, much of it perhaps for pieces decorated in 'the Old Japan taste' which Thomas Craft remembered that the duke so much esteemed.[23]

The prices of Bow china at the time it was being produced, seem to our eyes magically cheap. The following are the prices quoted in Bowcock's Notebook of 1756.

22. John Mallet is not convinced that the duke did not put capital into the Chelsea undertaking. See R. J. Charleston and J. V. G. Mallet, 'A Problematical Group of Eighteenth-century Porcelain', *E.C.C. Transactions*, Vol. 8, Pt. 1, 1971, p. 115.
23. In today's terms this would perhaps be twenty times the amount.

Wares   A sprig'd sallad vessel 12s
                 1 pr. sprig'd boats 6s
                 1 pr. sauce boats, Mr Vere's pattern 4s
                 1 pr. large rib'd boats 4s
                 1 sprig'd upright tea-pot 3s
                 1 enamelled partridge coffee pot 9s
                 12 setts blue teas at 2s 10d
                 2 square & enamelled desserts 15s
                 1 blue dolphin pickle stand 5s
                 1 white basin & cover 3s
                 1 pint printed mug 5s
                 ½ pint ditto 3s 6d
                 1 fine plate 4s
                 1 partridge handled cup and saucer 3s 6d
                 Octagon dysart partridge plate 3s 6d
                 4 white leaf candlesticks 2s 3d
                 1 sprigged teapot 4s

Figures   16 Cooks, 2s each (abated) [Plate 16]
                 2 harlequins 7s
                 9 gentlemen and ladies at 9s £4 1s
                 1 enamelled pero 6s
                 1 shepherd, imperial 7s
                 1 shepherdess, 9s
                 1 pr. Dutch dancers 9s
                 1 gentleman and lady 18s
                 1 cook 7s
                 1 boy and girl 12s
                 1 Paris cries 6s
                 1 woman with chicken 7s[24]

A few further prices are given in an advertisement published in the *Norwich Mercury* on 4 April 1761, which announced a sale of 'Ornamental and Useful CHINA' conducted by John Bowcock. The origin of the china was not

24. The blue dolphin pickle stand was probably a smaller item than the 'Blue pickle stand Imperfect' for which General Clayton was charged 12s in 1753. The printed mugs seem to have been relatively expensive, probably reflecting the fact that this was an entirely new method of decoration. The price of blue teacups and saucers appears to have risen between 1756 and 1761, though it may be that the 1756 price was a wholesale one and those for 1761 were retail. It is difficult to see from the few surviving prices which we have what 'abatement' was made for dealers, or to know whether private customers received any allowance for immediate cash payment, and so on.

16. THE COOKS. The male figure is taken from Bouchardon's *Cris de Paris*. He holds a dish with two trussed ducks and she holds a dish with a leg of mutton. Height 17.1 cm (6.75 in). 1754–7. *Courtesy of Sotheby's.* *See page 92*

mentioned, but it must have been from the Bow Manufactory. Although most of the items were not priced (it seems not to have been an auction sale), it included 'Blue teacups and saucers at 3s, 3s 6d, and 4s per set: [and] Large Breakfast ditto at 4s and 5s per set'.[25]

There is no doubt that every early English porcelain factory must have kept accounts. Every principal engaged in so risky an undertaking as porcelain manufacture was well aware of the extreme thinness of the knife edge that lay between success and failure, and Sir Everard Fawkener of Chelsea expressed this clearly when he wrote to Sir Charles Hanbury Williams on 25 August 1751.

25. Sheenah Smith, op. cit., *E.C.C. Transactions*, Vol. 9, Pt. 2, 1974, p. 208.

Sir Charles had already assisted the Chelsea factory by lending some of the pieces of the magnificent Meissen service presented to him by Augustus III of Poland, Elector of Saxony, so that they might be copied at the Chelsea works, and Sir Everard now approached him with another request: 'I have been desired to move you for a further favour on behalf of this new manufacture . . . which is, that you would be pleased to let them know the prices at the whare houses of the Royal Manufacture of the several things you have indulged them with the sight & use of. They are sensible that the extent and success of their manufacture will depend upon the price, yet, as they have been at an immense expence to bring it to this point of perfection they would have such a price for their ware as to re-imburse them & leave some advantage. They are without any light to guide them in a matter of this moment, and wd. therefore be extremely thankful for the assistance they might receive, from knowledge of how those at Dresden govern. They met with encouragement last spring, tho' they had little but separate pieces to sell, except Tea and Coffee services.'[26]

All the early English porcelain manufactures probably started in a small way with limited capital and a small labour force. We are given a glimpse of the scale of finance involved, and the number of workers necessary to start such a manufacture in an unpublished letter sent to an English nobleman by three discontented French potters who were anxious to establish a porcelain manufacture and try out their skills in this country.[27] The letter, which, from internal evidence, must have been written c. 1746–9, is accompanied by a schedule of initial capital outlay and recurring costs for wages, fuel and raw materials. We do not know where or from whom these Frenchmen got their information, or how it was worked out, but the schedule is sufficiently detailed, and the wages sufficiently close to those paid in the English mid-eighteenth-century pottery industry to be worthy of consideration. A 'total prime cost' of 11,100 livres is given for the furnace, the construction of a water-driven or horse-powered mill, potters' wheels and other equipment, and an initial supply of materials for paste and glaze. Reckoning the livre at 10d in old money we have a capital outlay of £462 10s 0d.[28] Nothing, however, is allowed for buildings other than the oven and mill, nor is there any indication of the capital needed to cover overheads, losses (always heavy at a porcelain factory), experiments and other non-productive work. The figures are skeletal and need

26. Quoted by Norma Perry, in her monograph on Sir Everard Fawkener, Vol. 133, 1975, in the series *Studies on Voltaire and the Eighteenth Century*, edited by Theodore Besterman; and also by Eric Benton, 'Payments by Sir Everard Fawkener to Nicholas Sprimont', *E.C.C. Transactions*, Vol. 10, Pt. 1, 1976, p. 56.
27. Based upon a paper by Reginald Haggar, *E.C.C. Transactions*, Vol. 10, Pt. 5, 1980. We are deeply grateful for an opportunity to study this paper in advance of publication.
28. *The Shorter Oxford English Dictionary*, 1947, Vol. 1, 'An old French money of account . . . about equal to the present franc.' If 2s 6d is the equivalent, as George Savage suggests (*Eighteenth Century French Porcelain*), multiply by three. This makes the wages excessively high.

considerable filling out.[29] An initial labour force of twenty-five is allowed for,[30] including turners, finishers of ware, moulders, modellers, painters, ornamenters and labourers, involving a monthly wage bill of 1770 livres, or £77 18s 4d per month, making a total outlay of 3640 livres or £151 13s 4d per month. In many ways this letter is tantalizingly uninformative. We have no means of knowing what answer was given, if any; who the workmen were, or whether, if their letter brought a favourable answer, they were able to get away from France. So many French workers did try to escape, and only ended up in a bastille.[31]

Yet in spite of the importance of the monetary and commercial side of the porcelain-making industry, scarcely any records or accounts from the English factories have come down to us. Those belonging to Bow, preserved until the latter end of the nineteenth century, were the most complete known, but have now almost entirely disappeared, except for one or two items, and a few references and quotations in the works of Llewellyn Jewitt and William Chaffers. The Bow account book for 1751–5, as mentioned earlier, is preserved in the British Museum (Add. MS 45905).

Chaffers gleaned from it a table of 'The Weekly Account of Trade etc. at London and Bow' covering the first three months of 1754, which shows at a glance that far more goods were sold at a discount (presumably to dealers and wholesalers) than for straight credit (no doubt to private persons).

The same observation holds good for the annual account for 1754, which Chaffers quotes in full; and as one would expect, sales were highest in the summer quarter. The bare recital of the actual cash receipts at Bow and London (Cornhill) 1751–55, shows the steady increase of the business at the time, and ties up neatly with the early insurance policies, which tell the same story.

1750–1	£6573	0	8
1752	7747	4	8
1753	10114	11	6
1754	10965	6	3
1755	11229	15	2

A table of the weekly production of biscuit ware at Bow during part of 1754 is particularly interesting, because it indicates the value of ware produced before being decorated and glazed. This table shows the number of biscuit kilns in operation each week for the first six months of the year, and one can

29. Sir Everard Fawkener, between August 1746 and April 1748 had to supply Sprimont with sums of money amounting in all to nearly £1500 (Eric Benton, *E.C.C. Transactions*, Vol. 10, Pt. 1, 1976, pp. 54 and 55).
30. Vincennes employed fifty-two workers, including women and girls, *c*. 1750 (E. S. Auscher, *A History and Description of French Porcelain*, 1905).
31. A search of the archives gives no clue as to whether the letter was answered. For escaping workers see X. de Chavagnac and A. de Grollier, *Histoire des manufactures Françaises de porcelaine*, 1906, p. 133.

work out that a single kiln held about £60 worth of ware for each firing. Unfortunately we have no knowledge of what losses were incurred, nor do we know how these figures were arrived at, or what they represented in relation to costs of labour, raw materials, fuel and firing, or what profits were made.

No kilns were listed at all until the fourth week in February, and then two kilns weekly until the fourth in May, after which there were three in operation which continued throughout June. In the fire insurance policy of 1766 two large kilnhouses, one enamelling kilnhouse and nine kilns are listed. One would imagine that this meant that Bow ended up with six biscuit and gloss and three enamelling kilns, even though its output of porcelain in its later years was very much diminished.

Chaffers speaks of a cash account book for 1757 and 1758 showing receipts and payments at a London branch of the Bow factory; this was probably Cornhill, not St. Catherine's, as the names of individual customers were given, with the ready money taken daily and the cash received from St. James's Street etc. It came to about £120 a week, most of which was paid to John Weatherby (at St. Catherine's?) but sometimes to 'Mr Crowther'.

Some details of the wages paid to the agents at the Cornhill warehouse are also given by Chaffers. 'Mr Brown'—William Brown who had overcharged General Clayton by more than his own week's wages in March 1753, and who is recorded as paying the rates for the old China Works from 1774–76[32]— received 18s a week in his days at Cornhill. 'Mr Sandys' had 12s; Hugh Williams, 12s; (John?) Stephenson, 12s; 'Burnett', 10s. By comparison with the prices charged for the chinaware this remuneration was not high, and yet it compared favourably with the payment cited in 1747 by Campbell in *The London Tradesman* for a ceramic decorator, 'the most ingenious Tradesman . . . paid by the dozen of pieces painted, and [who] may earn from Fifteen to Thirty Shillings a week'.[33]

The lost cash account book of 1757–58 mentioned one or two small sums paid to Edward Heylyn, and frequent payments varying between £15 and £30 were made to Thomas Frye, perhaps in connection with the running expenses of the factory. A complete picture of the financial structure of the Bow undertaking may well be forever lost to us, but from the fragments that remain we can glimpse it as one of the largest, and in its middle years one of the most successful, commercial manufactures in eighteenth-century England.[34]

32. Poor Law Overseer's Account Books for West Ham, 1747–76.
33. Arthur Young, in *A Six Month Tour Through the North of England*, 1770, gave the following list of wages paid in the Staffordshire Potteries at that time:
    Grinders (of flint), 7s per week
    Washers and breakers (of clay), 8s per week
    Throwers, 9s to 12s
    Engine lath men, 10s to 12s
    Gilders, men, 12s women, 7s 6d
    Painters, 10s to 12s.
34. See Appendix VII.

G. FAMILLE ROSE DECORATION on Bow tablewares
and a miniature coffee cup (*left foreground*)
1752–8
See page 126

H. KITTY CLIVE as 'The Fine Lady', after Charles Moseley, and
HENRY WOODWARD as 'The Fine Gentleman', after Francis
Hayman. Height 24.4 cm (9.75 in) and 27.3 cm (10.75 in)
respectively
1750
Godden Collection. See page 134

6
Early Underglaze-Blue Decorated Useful Wares

The existence of a distinctive group of underglaze-blue decorated useful wares made at the Bow factory has long been recognized but, with one exception,[1] it has received little attention from ceramic historians. The notable feature of the group is the particular colour employed, which is a bright royal blue with considerable variation in intensity from piece to piece. This particular shade of blue was not used on Bow wares after about 1752, and it has no counterpart on other English porcelain of the period. It does, however, resemble the colour of underglaze blue used on earlier St. Cloud porcelain. How the particular blue colour came about has never been satisfactorily explained. Some aspects of the use of cobalt compounds for ceramic decoration are considered by Watney.[2] Zaffre (zapher), one of the cobalt ore products,[3] is mentioned in the 1744 patent along with lapis lazuli and lapis armenis as a possible material for blue decoration. It is highly improbable that either of the latter minerals were used, on account of their scarcity, and probably they are mentioned only to mislead potential competitors. The use of 'smalt or zaffre as is required to be deeper or paler' is mentioned in the 1749 patent.

Many factors would have influenced the final colour tone achieved, including fuel type,[4] firing temperature, firing atmosphere (oxidizing or reducing) and interaction of the pigment with body and glaze. In addition, the particular pigment source, its method of preparation and final particle size would have been important.

1. Bernard Watney, *English Blue and White Porcelain of the Eighteenth Century*, 1st ed., 1963, p. 19.
2. Ibid., ch. 1, in 1st ed., 1963, and 2nd ed., 1973.
3. Cobalt occurs naturally as the ores cobaltite and smaltite which are essentially cobalt arsenical compounds. The ores invariably contain trace amounts of other metals including iron, nickel, copper, manganese, antimony and bismuth. The relative amounts of these contaminants, *inter alia*, influenced the final colour achieved but were more or less constant in ore from a particular vein. Ore products which are usable for ceramic decoration are zaffre (calcined cobalt ore fused with sand) and smalt (zaffre fused with potassium carbonate), the resulting compound being a complex potassium aluminium cobalt silicate. The process resulted in a workable dilution of the intense pigment and, when fired, a blue colour of exceptional stability.
4. Wood is mentioned as kiln fuel for both biscuit and glost firing in the patents of 1744 and 1749, but quantities of coal and clinker were found among wasters on the factory site in the 1969 excavations.

Schneeberg in Saxony was the most important European source of cobalt in the eighteenth century and over a long period only smalt was exported thence to maintain a monopoly. The high cost of imported Saxon smalt induced the Society of Arts after its foundation in 1754 to offer a prize of £50 for the discovery of a British source, though various finds had been made in Cornwall from 1744 on. The award went to Francis Beauchamp in 1755 for the discovery of cobalt ore in a mine near Truro. The amount of smalt imported into England rose year by year from 1747 to 1754,[5] and the contribution of British smalt to the supply at this time and later is uncertain. A large quantity of imported cobalt would have been needed in the seventeenth and eighteenth centuries for the decoration of tin-glazed earthenwares. It is possible, therefore, that the distinctive blue tone in this group of Bow useful wares was due to the use of cobalt obtained from an unusual source and that the supply was not maintained. No evidence has been found as to the identity of this source.

There is no doubt that this group of porcelain represents some of the very earliest products of the Bow concern. That is supported by the limited range of shapes and decoration and by the primitive qualities of the potting, painting and glaze. Most of the shapes in the group also occur among the enamelled wares attributed to the period 1747–50 (see Chapter 8) but were subsequently discontinued.

The characteristics of this class of ware are typified by the bowl illustrated in Plate 17. The pattern, a Bow version of the so-called 'fisherman' design, is quite common in the group, particularly on small cylindrical objects such as coffee cans. The fisherman stands in a boat holding, outstretched, a rod and line. The pattern always features another figure who sits cross-legged under a tree. Indeed, the pattern is sometimes called the 'cross-legged Chinaman'. A notable feature of the design is a group of willow fronds hanging down from the rim without obvious attachment to branches—a daring and effective device. The inside of this bowl is decorated with three rocks within a circular reserve. The rocks appear to be sticking up out of water and they are a common feature of Chinese riverscapes on English eighteenth-century porcelain. Sometimes designs featuring such rocks are called, somewhat inappropriately, 'cannonball' patterns.

The body used at the time is the least primitive feature. It is dense and the potting thick so that the pieces are surprisingly heavy for their size. Where the body is reasonably thin it is quite translucent, a tungsten filament lamp giving a medium straw colour. The remarkable toughness of this body is evident from the number of large flatwares and uncracked teapots that survive. The toughness and stability is a direct result of the inclusion of bone ash in the body composition. No chemical analysis of the body of a typical royal-blue decorated piece has been published. However, analysis of a biscuit waster with a scratch 'R' mark (see Appendix XI) shows that it is a bone-ash porcelain with a relatively high proportion of silica.

5. Royal Society of Arts manuscripts, Dr Templeman's transactions, Vol. 2, 1754–8.

17. BOWL with the Bow 'fisherman' pattern. The design on the reverse is the 'cross-legged Chinamen'. Diameter 16.6 cm (6.5 in). 1747–52. *See page 98*

The characteristics of the glaze on the bowl and on most, but not all, pieces in the Bow early blue class are noteworthy. The glaze is full of very small bubbles so that under magnification it has a fine granular appearance. That is not an unusual feature in the lead glazes used by eighteenth-century English potters and can still be detected, where the glaze is thick, on wares from other factories dating from the very end of the century. But on this early Bow ware it is especially prominent and sometimes gives areas of the surface a semi-matt appearance due to the minute bubbles bursting at the surface. Occasionally the glaze may also have an orange-skin appearance. It tends to pool in the bottom of vessels and bowls where it reveals considerable tinting with cobalt. This was done in an attempt to whiten the glaze but it frequently fails to do so. The glaze distributes itself rather unevenly, particularly on the undersides of the pieces where it tends to gather. It has been suggested[6] that the glaze on these pieces sometimes appears to be in two layers. That is the case on the bowl where, on the vertical outer part of the footrim, the 'top coat' of glaze, which is heavily tinted with cobalt, has only partly covered a thinner clear 'undercoat' glaze. The double-glaze appearance is also prominent inside the footrim where the outer tinted glaze lies on top of the clear glaze like an applied patch. At first glance, it has the appearance of glaze 'pegging'[7] as practised at Worcester but closer inspection reveals the presence of the thinner clear glaze in the inner angle of the footrim. Some technical development evidently occurred within this class because some of the wares show no evidence for the double layer and

6. Bernard Watney, op. cit., 2nd ed., 1973, p. 15.
7. This refers to the Worcester practice of removing dried glaze powder from the inner angle of footrims by means of a wooden peg to reduce the possibility of adhesion to the saggar during glost firing.

indeed have a much better controlled glaze. If a double layer of glaze was used, what then was the motive for it? One possibility is that the 'undercoat' glaze was used to fix the painting to the body as was, and is, done at Worcester in the so-called 'hardening-on' firing. The virtual absence of 'running' in the cobalt painting of this group lends some support to this idea and contrasts with the frequent occurrence of such a fault in another group of early Bow underglaze-blue painted wares of which the Martin bowl[8] is a good example. Another possibility is that the piece was reglazed to correct imperfections in the first glazing. A further frequently observed feature of this group is the occurrence of turquoise spots in the glaze. It appears to be an accidental contamination of the cobalt used to 'blue' the glaze. However, the absence of other colour contamination suggests an association between the cobalt source and the turquoise pigment, probably a copper compound.

One of the earliest designs (Plate 18) in the group is a Chinese river scene where the landscape is given a rough wash with the deep vivid blue colour. There is a single-storey house near the centre of the design and three kinds of tree scattered over the landscape. One of the tree designs is highly stylized with flat tops and two main branches each side and shorter branches under. Trees drawn in such a way are not found on any other English porcelain of the period. Presumably they have an oriental origin but they are uncommon. However, they are seen on English tin-glazed earthenware of a slightly earlier period. Like most tin-glazed plates, Bow plates of the early blue class were fired face upwards. That can be discerned from the long marks under the rim where the three pegs used to support the stack of plates in the saggar made contact. Not infrequently, part of the peg remains on the plate due to adhesion with the glaze. This practice was changed soon afterwards and thenceforth nearly all Bow plates and other flatwares were fired face downwards. It had the effect of minimizing the disfigurement caused by contact with the sloping support pin. These support pins and the pierced saggars were among the finds of all three excavations on the Bow site (see Appendix XIV). The vast majority of these pins are of round section but quite a number are triangular with corresponding shaped holes in the saggars. Triangular pins, but not round ones, were used to support flatwares manufactured by the tin-glazed earthenware potters including those of Southwark and Lambeth. Despite the co-existence of the large ceramic industries on the north and south banks of the Thames, few parallels between them have come to light. One such parallel is the large round plate illustrated in Plate 19. This design is known as the 'scroll' pattern from the central rectangular reserve representing a partly unrolled scroll painted

---

8. Bowl decorated in underglaze blue in the Chinese style with a bird standing amongst rushes and rockwork with flowering peonies below a narrow border of flower sprays divided by diaper. The interior carries the inscription 'William & Elizabeth Martin. November 20 1750'. Hugh Tait, *Bow Porcelain 1744–1776*, Catalogue of the Bow Porcelain Special Exhibition, 1959, Cat. No. 26. Also illustrated by Watney, op. cit., 2nd ed., 1973, Pl. 2c.

18. PLATE with Chinese landscape design with unusual stylized trees also seen on tin-glazed earthenware. Diameter 22.7 cm (8.9 in). 1747–52. *See page 100*

19. PLATE with the 'scroll' pattern, an exact copy of a Chinese original. Diameter 26 cm (10.2 in). 1750–2. *See page 100*

with peonies, bamboo, rockwork and a fence. The unrolled part of the scroll is represented at one corner of the rectangular design. The Chinese emblem for a 'Musical Stone of Jade' is represented above and below the scroll amidst foliage. The border design is unusual with abstract diamond lozenges alternating with stylized flowers in reserves. The pattern is an exact copy of a Chinese original and exactly the same pattern was used by the tin-glaze potters of the south bank. Some examples of the pattern are finely drawn and of pale colour. As mentioned before, the second Bow patent implies some degree of control over the depth of blue colour by the use of either smalt or zaffre and in the Bowcock memorandum book for 1756 is an entry specifying pattern, colour and shade requirement for particular orders, 'the bordered Image—blue and pale as you please' and '12 Dragon breakfast cups and saucers with good deep colour'.

The opposite ends of the rather short development spectrum of the Bow early blue might be represented by the two plates illustrated in Plates 20 and 21. The plate with the pair of rather disconsolate fishermen—one has given up and is making off—is thickly potted and the glaze or double glaze shows many of the characteristics already described. In addition, a large area of glaze on the front has gathered into bumps and discoloured. A similar plate, formerly in the possession of the late A. J. Toppin, was exhibited at the English Ceramic Circle 1927–48 Commemorative Exhibition and is illustrated in the Catalogue, No. 152. The plate with the two mandarins (Plate 21) in the Fitzwilliam Museum, Cambridge, is a more elegant design and the potting and glazing are much more accomplished.

Plate 22 illustrates what seems to have been a favourite design for sauceboats although it is also found on sparrow-beak jugs and on cups. At the spout end there are tall trees with arrow-shaped tops, centrally there is a large realistic rock formation with 'telegraph poles'[9] arising from it, and on the right is an attractive two-storey house of decidedly European appearance with a chimney at the gable end. The same pattern with some variation is seen on an early silver-shape three-footed sauceboat[10] with lion mask and paw feet. It is one of the popular early patterns that was carried on, still on sauceboats, into the 1760s. The bell-shaped mug with a bold divided strap handle (Plate 23A) carries a pattern often found on cylindrical shapes such as mugs, tankards and coffee pots. The main design features are large rocks rising from water and a pavilion with tall pointed roof supported by two pillars sited on sloping

9. Watney, op. cit., 2nd ed., ch. 2, p. 17, coined the phrase 'trees that look like telegraph poles' to describe this particular stylization. Though a familiar feature of the landscape for the first sixty or so years of this century, telegraph poles have almost entirely disappeared over the last two decades with the routing of telecommunication cables underground or via microwave radio transmission. Likewise 'trees resembling masts' will be archaic for future generations of connoisseurs and collectors notwithstanding the pleasure such phrases have given the present. The occasional updating of such imagery would be appropriate; otherwise it too becomes antique.
10. Victoria and Albert Museum.

20. PLATE with the
'disconsolate fisherman'
pattern. Diameter 26.5 cm
(10.4 in)
1747–52
See page 102

21. PLATE with the
'mandarins' pattern.
Diameter 22.5 cm (8.8 in)
1750–52
*On loan to the Fitzwilliam
Museum, Cambridge, from the
collection of the late Dr and
Mrs H. Statham.
See page 102*

22. SAUCEBOAT with the 'desirable residence' pattern. Length 15.7 cm
(6.2 in). 1750–2. *See page 102*

ground. Long tendrils with flowerheads trail upwards across the scene. But the striking feature is the distinctive lower border pattern consisting of alternating arcades of half flowerheads and trellis. That pattern is on the remarkable coffee pot in the Victoria and Albert Museum which is also used as the frontispiece illustration in Bernard Watney's *English Blue and White Porcelain of the Eighteenth Century*. Based on a design originally for metal, the handle and spout of this coffee pot are virtually at right angles. Bow seems to be the only English factory of the period to attempt such a bold, or even rash, arrangement. At least three other surviving examples of Bow porcelain coffee pots with the same handle/spout disposition are known.[11]

The mug described above and the coffee pot in the Victoria and Albert Museum both have potters' tally marks incised on their bases. The marks are a linear scratch (Plate 23B) and an incised 'R' respectively. These marks also occur on well-potted early white and enamelled wares. A biscuit waster with an incised 'R' was found on the factory site during the excavations in 1969. Painters' marks as opposed to potters' marks are relatively unusual in the early blue group. A script 'G' and a capital 'B' in blue are recorded.[12]

A further example of a building in a Chinese landscape is illustrated in Plate 24. The design seen on the coffee can is crude but quite effective and seems to be used only on small cylindrical shapes. Adjacent to the handle, there is a rocky island with two 'battleship mast' trees arising from it. A small sailing boat separates the remainder of the design, which consists of rocks, a tree with branches above and large leaves below and a two-storey building of highly improbable design looking like two primitive shelters placed one on top of the other. The coffee can in Plate 24 is shown next to a waster coffee cup found on the factory site during the 1969 excavations. It is of the same pattern and is painted in the same vivid blue colour. Apparently, the cup became a waster because of faulty glaze. This pattern was carried on through the 1750s well beyond the early blue period.

All known Bow early blue designs are oriental in origin and most, if not all, are close copies and not chinoiserie, that fanciful European vision of China. The fidelity of the copying is illustrated in Plate 25, which shows a Chinese export porcelain plate of about 1720 on the left and the Bow version of this peony and bamboo pattern on the right. The scroll pattern is another example of a closely copied Chinese design. Locating the oriental originals is the major difficulty here but there are probably many more examples to be found.

The range of shapes found in this group is strictly limited to useful wares and most of these are of Chinese origin such as the typical small globular teapot shown in Colour Plate A with the 'banana tree, fence and stork' pattern. Some miniature teawares in the early blue are recorded.[13]

11. Catalogue of the Ainslie Collection, Sotheby's, March 1961, lot 156. Another example, with enamelled Kakiemon decoration, was formerly in the Spero Collection. See also Catalogue of the Caldwell Collection, Sotheby's, 7 October 1969, lot 3.
12. Watney, op. cit., 2nd ed., ch. 2, p. 17.
13. Catalogue of the Ainslie Collection, Sotheby's, March 1961, lot 126.

23A. MUG decorated with
pavilion in Chinese landscape
and unusual lower border
design. Height 14.8 cm
(5.8 in)
1747–52
See pages 102, 106

23B. LINEAR SCRATCH
MARK on the base of the mug
illustrated in Plate 23A.
Disfigurement of the footrim
is due to removal of material
for chemical analysis
See page 104

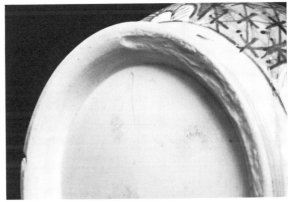

24. (*right*) COFFEE CAN with 'two-storied shelter' design. Height 6.4 cm (2.5 in);
(*left*) WASTER COFFEE CUP with the same design recovered in the 1969 excavation.
Height 6.0 cm (2.4 in). 1747–52. *See page 104*

25. (*left*) Chinese export porcelain PLATE of first quarter eighteenth century; (*right*) Bow copy. Diameter 22.5 cm (8.8 in) both. 1747–52
See page 104

It is difficult to say precisely when the vivid blue group comes to an end but there seems to have been about two years' overlap during which the early blue and the typical later inky blue were both used.[14]

One of the best known examples of the early Bow blue porcelain is the inkpot (Plate 26) in the Colchester Museum. It has 'MADE AT NEW CANTON 1750' in capitals around the top and a blue capital 'B' on the base. It is generally assumed that the series of New Canton inkpots dated 1750 to 1752 was made to celebrate and advertise the opening of the new factory building in 1750. This large building must have given the factory a considerable increase in production capacity and it would have needed increased turnover to justify the capital expenditure and higher running costs. It is noteworthy that the Martin bowl[8] dated 20 November 1750 is not painted in the vivid blue so characteristic of the group. The glaze on this bowl is also of much better quality than usual and there is no suggestion of double glazing. The price paid for the improved glaze seems to have been an increased tendency for the blue to run. A few pieces in the early vivid blue colour have the improved glaze but the painting does not run. The mug illustrated in Plate 23A is an example. Apart from the possibility that the Martin bowl is antedated, it seems likely that 1750 or 1751 marks the end of the early blue as a coherent group. In all the writings about the

14. The inkpot of generally similar form to the 'New Canton 1750' example inscribed 'Eward Vernon Esqr. July 1752' (see Chapter 3, Plate 7) is decorated in the typical vivid early blue colour but the painting style of the latter is decidedly more fussy. It is in the Brighton Museum.

products of the Bow factory there has been a great reluctance to ascribe pieces to the period late 1747 or early 1748 to 1750. There is no justification for such a view with regard to the early blue group, and there seems to be no good reason why the early blue should not have been made and sold from the commencement of marketing of Bow products early in 1748 at the latest.

26. Five-hole INKPOT with central well, inscribed 'MADE AT NEW CANTON 1750'. Diameter 8.3 cm (3.25 in) *Colchester Museum. See page 106*

7
White Porcelain

M. L. Solon, in his *Brief History of Old English Porcelain*,[1] is enthusiastic
about the merits of Bow white porcelain decorated with the 'may-flower
pattern in relief'. He mentions its origin — 'the Chinese white porcelain of Fuh-
Kien' (sic) and how the pattern was 'so constantly reproduced' by St. Cloud,
Dresden and Chantilly before its use at Bow. But 'none of the productions of
these factories had ever equalled, in charm and perfection, a fine example of
Bow manufacture. Whenever such a specimen is introduced in a general
scheme of decoration it never clashes with its surroundings: the mellowness
and unctuosity of its substance make all other white china appear crude and
harsh by its side.' Such lavish praise might be justified by the quality of some of
the early very translucent white prunus-decorated (see Plate 36) porcelain (often
with incised 'R' mark) but not by the general standard of these wares which were
made over a long but undefined period of the factory's history.

White porcelain has a rather curious history. It reached an early zenith in
China with the classically simple shapes emanating from the kilns at Ting-chou
in Chihli province during the later Sung dynasty (960–1279). It was one of the
first true porcelains made in China. It has orange translucency and a glaze that
tends to collect in drops, particularly on the exterior of bowls—the so-called
'teardrops'. Many wares were fired facing downwards[2] and the rims are either
unglazed or bear support marks. The colour of the finest wares (*pai ting*) is
ivory-white in contrast to later Ch'ing copies which are chalk-white in colour.
The severe limitation on textural interest of plain white porcelain was fully
realized by the Ting potters who, with great subtlety, carved, incised or
moulded floral designs before glazing. Coloured glazes were developed during
the Sung dynasty, blue decoration followed in the Yüan dynasty (1260–1368)
and was vastly developed in the subsequent Ming dynasty which also saw the
introduction of coloured enamels. It is tempting to think of the next
development in white porcelain as a reaction to this long-lasting blaze of
colour. It occurred towards the end of the Ming dynasty at Tê-hua in Fukien

1. M. L. Solon, *A Brief History of Old English Porcelain and its Manufactories*, Bemrose and
Sons, limited edition, London, 1903.
2. The three characteristics of Ting ware mentioned form a curious analogy with the products of
Bow which, at different times, displayed the same.

province, where the kind of white porcelain known in Europe as *blanc de chine* was made. The great virtue of this Fukien porcelain was the peculiar and attractive creamy glaze once described as like 'milk-jelly'. It appears that a high proportion of the output was devoted to small figures such as the Buddha, Kuan-yin, Kuan-ti and other Buddhist deities. The modelling is extremely crisp and attractive and these figures have been and still are widely copied. The range of useful wares seems to be rather limited but bottles, dishes, writers' and artists' accessories and libation cups are all found. Small flared beakers and sacrificial cups, the latter resting on three tree-stumps, both with prunus blossom in relief, reached Europe in considerable numbers during the seventeenth century.

In England, Queen Mary II[3] acquired some notable Fukien wares for her large collection of oriental porcelain at Hampton Court. Later, Augustus the Strong of Saxony developed a taste for the white wares and, as well as acquiring a vast collection, initiated the production at Meissen of numerous white figure models including birds and large animals, and a range of domestic china. A great deal of the latter was decorated with prunus blossom in relief. This must have met with success because nearly every continental factory followed suit as did the English porcelain factories in their turn. Differences in the end product between the hard-paste oriental and Meissen wares and the soft-paste continental and English factories now emerge. As would be expected, the brilliant tight-fitting glazes of the hard-paste bodies conceal much less detail than the thicker bubble-filled soft-paste glazes. There is considerable variation in the glazes, probably due to poor control in the firing. Sometimes the effect is disastrous, especially with figures, but there are numerous examples of lead-glazed soft-paste porcelain with excellent glaze quality. At Bow, there seems to have been a rapid learning process with notable improvement in the glaze between 1748 and 1752. Cobalt was not used to tint the glaze of white porcelain which in some instances has a decidedly yellow tinge. The body used for the early white wares is the dense, tough, often surprisingly translucent one common to the factory's products of the years 1748–54. Where variation occurs, it appears to be more in the firing than in the basic body composition. Eccles and Rackham report the body analysis[4] of an early sauceboat which, though gold-decorated in this case, is often seen in the white. It is based on a silver original and was produced with various handle forms. The analysis is strikingly similar to that of the body composition of the scratch 'R' waster reported in Appendix XV, that is, a bone-ash porcelain with a relatively high silica content. At some time during the mid-to-late fifties, the quality of the body deteriorates. This applies to all the domestic wares, coloured as well as white. The most striking change is in the decreased

3. Bevis Hillier, *Pottery and Porcelain 1700–1914*, Weidenfeld and Nicolson, London, 1968, ch. 12, p. 265.
4. H. Eccles and B. Rackham, *Analysed Specimens of English Porcelain*, Victoria and Albert Museum, London, 1922.

translucency, which may be due to underfiring; but the possibility of some change of body composition cannot, on present evidence, be excluded (see Appendix XV). It is probable that white porcelain was made over the whole period of the Bow factory's existence although the range of shapes seems to decline progressively from about 1760. In contrast to most other contemporary English porcelain factories, the Bow concern produced the complete range of domestic wares in white porcelain including all types of tableware (Plates 27–9, 31–4, 38–9) and containers for toiletries. Of all the useful wares mentioned in the Bowcock memorandum book, about thirty-five per cent are in white porcelain. Centrepieces were a speciality. They were all based on single or multiple shell forms (Plates 30 and 37). One of the 1750-dated Bow pieces is a single-shell salt.[5] These shell forms are an expression of the important rococo theme of water, indeed the word itself derives from the French *rocaille* which meant rockwork for the construction of grottoes. Such centrepieces are assembled on a sculpted base structure from individual mouldings of shells taken from life. A variety of marine life is represented including seaweed, coral, snails, sometimes seagulls' nests complete with eggs and, rarely, a crab. The centrepiece shown in Plate 37 is less usual. It is in the form of a shell-encrusted stand for six accurately fitting shell cups each with pouring lip and spiral stem forming a handle.[6,7] A single shell is mounted high on a central pillar. About six examples are known, one blue decorated, one white and the rest enamelled. The true purpose for these objects has not been discovered. The serving of flummery or oysters has been suggested. The small bucket illustrated in Plate 28 was probably intended to hang from a table centrepiece which has not yet been identified in Bow porcelain, although it may have a counterpart in later creamware[8] which indicates the general design if not the exact usage.

Many white porcelain tablewares were also produced with enamelled or underglaze-blue decoration. An example is the large oval basket[9] (see Plate 56) with moulded exterior, rope twist handles and rim, and female-mask handle terminals. It is based on a Meissen original[10] and Bow versions are either enamelled or white.

A decorative innovation at Bow was the use of coloured enamels on sprigged white porcelain. The best-known example is the Target flowerpot[11] (Plate 49), the base of which carries the inscription 'Thos & Ann Target July 2th 1754'. The application of enamelled flowers in *famille rose* or *famille verte* style is seen

5. British Museum. Described and illustrated in Hugh Tait, *Bow Porcelain 1744–1776*, op. cit., Cat. No. 32.
6. Hugh Tait, *Apollo*, August 1958, p. 49, Fig. VI.
7. Geoffrey Wills, *Apollo*, March 1959.
8. Wedgwood creamware catalogue 1774, design 52. Illustrated by Wolf Mankowitz, *Wedgwood*, Spring Books, London, 1966, ch. 2, plate 10.
9. Sotheby's, sale catalogue for 20 May 1969, lot 299.
10. Michael Newman, 'English Adaptations of a Meissen Basket', *Antique Collector*, June 1965, p. 113.
11. British Museum. Illustrated in Hugh Tait, *Bow Porcelain 1744–1776*, op. cit., Cat. No. 62.

27. PEACH-SHAPED CREAMBOAT with applied prunus decoration. Length 14.6 cm (5.75 in)
1750–4. *See page 110*

28. BUCKET with applied prunus decoration and twisted grooved handle probably intended to hang from a table centrepiece. Height 8.0 cm (3.1 in)
1752–5. *See page 110*

29. EGGCUP with applied prunus decoration. Height 7.1 cm (2.8 in)
1752–5
See page 110

30. SHELL SWEETMEAT DISH. Apart from shell forms Bow white porcelain without applied decoration is rare. Length 14.0 cm (5.5 in)
1750–4
See page 110

31. BELL-SHAPED MUG with applied prunus decoration. The handle shape is unusual. Height 12.1 cm (4.8 in)
1750–5
See page 110

32. THREE-FOOTED SAUCEBOAT with applied rose decoration.
Lenght 21.0 cm (8.3 in). 1750–5. *See page 110*

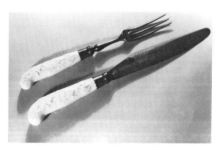

33. OCTAGONAL PLATE with applied
prunus decoration. Recessed base.
Diameter 22.8 cm (9.0 in)
1750–5. *See page 110*
34. KNIFE AND FORK with prunus-
moulded handles. Knife blade is
stamped 'GRAY'
1750–60. *See page 110*

35. BISCUIT WASTER CANDLE
NOZZLE with applied prunus
decoration, found in 1969 excavation.
Height 5 cm (2 in)
1752–8. *See page 114*
36. MOULD for prunus sprig found in
1867 excavation. *See page 108*

37. CENTREPIECE with six removable shell cups with spiral twisted stems. Height 17.8 cm (7 in) 1752–5. *See page 110*

38. POMADE POT with applied prunus decoration and acorn knop. Mark: incised 'R'. Height 13.4 cm (5.3 in) 1750–5 *See page 110*

on a variety of useful shapes.[12,13,14] This type of decoration is also mentioned in the Bowcock memorandum of 1756, thus: 'May 20. Duchess of Leeds. 2 square enamd. and sprig'd. desst. 15s.'

The pair of lizard candlesticks illustrated in Plate 40 are more or less faithful copies of Fukien originals. The feet are of the lion mask and paw type and the tail of the rather fierce lizard spirals up the column to support the drip pan. An earlier version with some colouring is illustrated by Hurlbutt.[15] Lizard candlesticks are referred to in William Duesbury's London account book 1751–3: 'Dlevred 24 (Feb. 1753) A pr. of Lizard candlesticks 0.1.6.' It is not known exactly why Duesbury had them but it seems probable that they were enamelled there and fitted with ormolu mounts for porcelain flowerheads or flowerhead candle nozzles.[16,17] There is a curious echo of this design among the Bowcock papers in the British Museum which include a few drawings by Bridget Bowcock, John Bowcock's niece. One of them[18] is of a small round bottle-shaped vase with a square base and a cat-like creature clinging to it attacking a snake which is coiled round the object. In the Bowcock memorandum, white leaf candlesticks, white branch candlesticks and white biscuit candlesticks are all mentioned, although we cannot be sure exactly what Bowcock meant by these terms. Candlesticks were an increasingly popular product at Bow with a widening range of designs appearing from the late 1750s to the end. However, the candlestick design which used the candle nozzle illustrated in Plate 35 has not come to light. This biscuit waster was recovered from the factory site during the 1969 excavations. White vases are very uncommon,[19] the majority being enamelled or blue decorated. A white wall bracket representing two cupids, one dressed as Britannia, is in the British Museum[20] and a similar one is in the National Museum of Ireland, Dublin. An important aspect of the use of white porcelain was the production of a large range of figures including animal models. Those products are considered in Chapters 9 and 13.

12. Frank Hurlbutt, *Bow Porcelain*, London, 1926, Pl. 13a. Pl. 13b is also of interest in the context of white porcelain, being a composite picture of white wares from a variety of sources including oriental, continental and English.
13. Sotheby's, catalogue of the Ainslie Collection, 7 March 1961, lot 9.
14. Christie's, catalogue of 5 December 1966, lot 141.
15. Frank Hurlbutt, op. cit., Pl. 6.
16. Hugh Tait, 'Some Consequences of the Bow Porcelain Special Exhibition', Part IV, *Apollo*, October 1960.
17. Sotheby's, sale catalogue, 15 March 1966, lot 150.
18. British Museum. Hugh Tait, *Bow Porcelain 1744–1776*, op. cit., Cat. No. 152, Fig. 55.
19. Sotheby's, sale catalogue, 14th May 1974, lot 108.
20. Hugh Tait, 'Outstanding Pieces in the English Ceramic Collection at the British Museum', *E.C.C. Transactions*, Vol. 4, Pt. 3, 1957, p. 53.

39. GLOBULAR TEAPOT with applied rose decoration.
Height 12 cm (4.75 in). 1752–5. *See page 110*

40. Pair of three-footed (lion-mask) CANDLESTICKS with a lizard curling around
the stem. Some examples are surmounted with ormolu branches supporting a
candle nozzle. Height 12 cm (4.75 in). 1747–52. *See page 114. Courtesy of the Royal
Ontario Museum, Toronto, Canada*

8

Earliest and Middle Period
Enamelled Wares

Pre-1750

The reluctance of many earlier writers to attribute any Bow porcelain to the period 1748–50 is understandable in view of the uncertainties about the factory's commencement and the lack of pieces dated prior to 1750. The very concentration of pieces dated 1750 (at least nine) has focused attention on that date as the one representing the beginning of trading. This is untenable since Tait's[1] discovery of the reference to the Bow 'Manufacture of Porcelain' in Samuel Richardson's fourth edition of Daniel Defoe's *Tour of Great Britain*[2] dated 1748, and the indexing of that work in the Register of Books published on the last page of the monthly *Gentleman's Magazine* for July 1748. This evidence is supported by the mention of 'potter' as an occupation in the Bow baptismal registers early in 1748 (see Chapter 3). From the available evidence it appears reasonable to assume that the Bow factory was operating commercially from late 1747. That was nearly two years prior to the granting of Thomas Frye's second patent on 17 November 1749, which was intended to protect the use of bone ash in the Bow porcelain body. To the extent that specimens have been analyzed, all of what we know today as Bow porcelain is a bone-ash porcelain.[3] It has been assumed that porcelain made to the bone-ash formula would not have been sold prior to the granting of the patent. Tait[4] thinks this is unlikely and the assumption is unwarranted on two grounds. Firstly, patent protection traditionally arises from the application date regardless of the

1. Hugh Tait, 'The Bow Factory under Alderman Arnold and Thomas Frye', *E.C.C. Transactions*, Vol. 5, Part 4, 1963.
2. Daniel Defoe, *Tour of Great Britain*, edited by Samuel Richardson, 4th ed. 1748, Vol. 1, p. 2. 'The first village we come to is Bow: where a large Manufactory of Porcelaine is lately set up. They have already made large quantities of Tea-cups, saucers, etc. which by some skilful persons are said to be little inferior to those which are brought from China. If they can work this so as to undersell the Foreign Porcelain, it may become a very profitable business to the Undertakers, and save great sums to the Public, which are annually sent abroad for this Commodity.'
3. Sir Arthur H. Church, *English Porcelain of the Eighteenth Century*, 1911. Church analyzed some of the (presumably) biscuit wasters found in the 1867 excavation, which took place about 30 metres (100 feet) south of the actual factory site but which turned up undoubted Bow specimens. He remarks (pp. 40, 41): 'The number of specimens free from bone ash was quite insignificant.' This implies that there were some. Quoted by Hurlbutt, op. cit.
4. Hugh Tait, 'Some Consequences of the Bow Porcelain Special Exhibition', Pt. III, *Apollo*, Vol. LXXI, p. 182.

granting date. The application date is not known for Frye's second patent but could have been as much as a year before the date of granting. Secondly, what a commercial concern does in practice and what patents it applies for or holds are not necessarily the same thing. Perhaps the proprietors were just slow in getting the application in or it was judged that the likelihood of a rival concern's discovering the use of bone ash was low, and a short-term risk worth taking at a time when sales were the important thing. The research for non-phosphatic Bow porcelain has been neither systematic nor extensive and obviously should be pursued using modern analytical techniques. Thomas Frye was resident in West Ham at the time of the first patent (granted 6 December 1744) and, as we have seen, there is documentary evidence that by 25 March 1749, the factory was operating on what was its finally established site on the north side of Stratford High Street, with a frontage probably exceeding sixty metres (two hundred feet) immediately west of Marshgate Lane.

The Bow Porcelain Special Exhibition held at the British Museum from October 1959 to April 1960, *inter alia*, focused attention on the earliest wares of the factory,[5] comprising a small group of enamelled wares including three triple-shell dishes,[6, 7] a single-shell salt,[8] a three-footed sauceboat[9] and a tankard (Plate 41).[10] These six pieces have in common a body and glaze colour recalling that described by Hurlbutt as 'greyish-drab'.[11] Such an appearance is quite distinctive and appears to be due to glaze tinting, possibly with cobalt or other pigment. On some pieces, the glaze is slightly opaque as well. The enamel palette is also distinctive, the colours used being maroon, red-brown, yellow, blue, emerald green, blue-green and black. This palette, in part, is the same as that used on the enamelled 'New Canton' inkpots, the least familiar of which is illustrated in Colour Plate B. The greyish-drab appearance does not occur in that or other 1750-dated pieces, or on other wares which, on various grounds, are attributed to later periods. In addition, the shapes are not continued. The shape of the tankard (Plate 41) appears to be unique and very few sauceboats similar to the one illustrated in Plate 42 are known. Another example with the

5. Tait, *Bow Porcelain 1744–1776*, op. cit., Cat. Nos. 1–8, including two fragments recovered from the site.

6. These triple-shell dishes are referred to as shell salts in the catalogue in contrast to the usual practice of referring to multiple-shell dishes as sweetmeat dishes. It is presumed that the ground for so doing is relatively small size. It should be noted that, in his memorandum book, Bowcock refers to a 'dolphin pickle stand'. See Plate 53.

7. Two of these are illustrated by Tait, *E.C.C. Transactions*, Vol. 5, Pt. 4, 1963, op. cit. Plates 190, 191.

8. Sotheby's, catalogue of the Ainslie sale, 7 March 1961, lot 175.

9. Formerly Toppin Collection. Illustrated by Tait, 'Some Consequences of the Bow Porcelain Special Exhibition', Pt. I, *Apollo*, LXXI, February 1960, Fig. VI. Sotheby's catalogue of the Toppin sale, 19 May 1970, lot 46. A similar sauceboat with upstanding handle is illustrated in the catalogue of the Ainslie sale, op. cit., lot 67.

10. Illustrated in Tait, *Bow Porcelain 1744–1776*, op. cit., Fig. 2; also in the catalogue of the Ainslie collection, Sotheby's, 7 March 1961, lot 158.

11. Frank Hurlbutt, op. cit., Plate 16b and p. 95.

drab body (Plate 43) is decorated in underglaze blue and overglaze red. The shape is closely based on a silver original with, for ceramic material, an entirely unpractical handle with acanthus moulding. It is noteworthy that the underglaze-blue decoration on the piece is of the 'early blue' kind (see Chapter 6). This sauceboat differs in three respects from the one included in the Bow Porcelain Special Exhibition. The handle of the latter is a more conventional loop with thumb rest and the sides have applied flower sprigs which are enamelled. The disposition of the feet is different in the exhibition sauceboat which has two at the handle and one at the spout end. The triple-shell dish illustrated in Colour Plate C is a hitherto unrecorded example of its kind and is similar in all respects to the one included in the Bow exhibition, illustrated by Tait[7] (also illustrated in the catalogue of the Ainslie collection, lot 174).

The only wares noted by the observer in Defoe's *Tour of Great Britain* (see note 2) are 'tea-cups, saucers, etc.' but no mention is made of decoration. There is no doubt that early blue and plain white sprigged tewares fulfil the greater part of this requirement but it is surprising that there are few, if any, surviving enamelled teacups, teabowls or saucers which can be confidently attributed to this early period. Another apparent omission from this period is enamelled flatware, which is surprising in view of the mastery of the kiln-support problems of flatware indicated by the successful firing of the early blue and plain white plates and dishes. The deficiency was soon to be remedied. Like most of the chronological subdivisions of Bow wares any particular year is seldom a satisfactory dividing line. It is particularly true of 1750, dominated as it is by the concentration of dated pieces.

1750–1758

The small but notable range of coloured wares produced at Bow between 1748 and 1750 is evidence of a determination to succeed with this more difficult and costly product. It should come as no surprise therefore to find a rapidly increasing range of enamelled useful and ornamental wares from the early 1750s onwards. As with underglaze-blue decorated wares, shapes used were either from European silver or of oriental origin, but the decoration was predominantly oriental, with Japan rather better represented than China. Herein lies a difficulty, for Chinese designs were sometimes derived from the Japanese and in a particular case it may be very difficult to know which tradition the Bow painters were following. That applies to much of Bow underglaze-blue/overglaze-red and gilt decoration,[12] at least some of which appears to derive from a class of rather fussily decorated export wares known as 'Chinese Imari'. There is a strange irony in this because the first Japanese porcelain, made soon after 1600, itself derived from the Chinese tradition, the

---

12. This common type of decoration is strictly speaking neither underglaze blue nor enamelled but, as it contains elements of both, is mentioned in the appropriate sections.

41. TANKARD of rare,
possibly unique, shape
enamelled in the *famille rose*
manner. Drab-coloured body.
Height 13.3 cm (5.25 in)
1747–50
Formerly Ainslie Collection.
Courtesy of Sotheby's.
See pages 117–8

42. SAUCEBOAT with drab-
coloured body, three lion-
mask and paw feet, the
outside moulded with a
trailing flower-stem picked
out in enamels, the interior
with enamelled flower sprays.
Length 16.5 cm (6.5 in)
1747–50
Museum of London.
See page 118

43. SAUCEBOAT of similar
material and form to Plate 42
without exterior moulding
and decorated in the early
underglaze blue with
overglaze *rouge de fer*. Length
20.5 cm (8 in)
1747–50
See page 118

secret of its manufacture having been brought from Ching-tê-chên some time
before. The first kilns were established at Arita in Hizen Province and very
soon two distinct styles emerged, both destined to be of great importance in the
decoration of European ceramics. They were the style associated with the
family of Sakaida Kakiemon[13] and the style known as Imari.[14] It was the
success of the latter wares in the European market which prompted the
Chinese to copy it from about 1700, and hence the problem of identifying the
cultural origin of decoration of this kind.

The red and blue wares excepted, there is no difficulty in deciding the origin
of the decoration, as in the plainly Chinese style of the plate in Plate 44 with
the rather crowded design and sketchily drawn chrysanthemums and birds
enamelled in purple, blue, green and black, dating from the early 1750s. A
similar design is seen in Plate 45 which is earlier and rather more common,
enamelled in a typical Bow *famille rose* palette. This narrow-rimmed plate was
known as a 'nappy' plate (from 'knapping' or trimming the border to half
width) designed for use away from the table, as in travelling where the smaller
diameter took up less room on a tray.[15] The baluster vase (Colour Plate D)[16]
dating from about 1752 is very effectively decorated with a mixture of Chinese
and Japanese motifs. The naturalistic trailing peony contrasts with the stylized
flowerheads on woody stems. The sepia monochrome reserves are painted with
Chinese landscape designs. The trailing lotus painting is seen on at least one
other Bow vase.

The Japanese Kakiemon style, however, predominated on enamelled wares
of the early fifties. This decorative style is one of the most successful ever used
in ceramic decoration and it would be difficult to improve on George Savage's
summary of it:[17] 'The keynotes of Kakiemon decoration are simplicity, a great
feeling for the value of the white porcelain surface which is balanced very
effectively with the painted areas, and a carefully judged asymmetry which is
typical of Japanese art as a whole.' Perhaps the best known of all Bow
enamelled Kakiemon designs is the 'partridge' pattern, Plate 46, referred to as
such in the Bowcock memorandum.[18] That design was adapted to a wide range
of shapes from knife and fork handles to the largest dish and was a popular
pattern for large dinner and tea services. It seems to have been used over a very

13. Soame Jenyns, 'The polychrome wares associated with the potters Kakiemon', *Transactions
of the Oriental Ceramic Society*, 1937–8.
14. Imari was the port of shipment for Arita wares.
15. Frank Hurlbutt, op. cit., p. 102.
16. Formerly McGuire and Winkworth Collections. Sotheby's, 23 October 1974, lot 194.
Thought to be Italian porcelain at one time. The painting of the trailing lotus is similar to that on
a Bow vase in the Passmore Edwards Museum, Stratford, London E17.
17. George Savage, *Porcelain Through the Ages*, Cassell, London, 1961, p. 91.
18. See Appendix IV. The pattern is often referred to as the 'two-quail' pattern. This
terminology is apparently more recent. Opinion is divided as to what the two birds represent but
a recent ornithological opinion favours the partridge, as in the original Bow nomenclature
(Bowcock), although there is obviously considerable artistic licence in their representation.

44. (*left*) PLATE decorated with chrysanthemums, foliage, rocks, and two birds in purple, blue, green, and black enamel colours. Diameter 22.5 cm (8.8 in). 1750–3. *See page 120*

45. (*right*) NAPPY PLATE decorated with *famille rose* enamel colours with flowers, bamboo and two exotic birds. Diameter 19.5 cm (7.7 in). 1748–52. *See page 120*

46. FLUTED DISH decorated in enamels with the 'partridge' pattern. Diameter 24.1 cm (9.5 in). 1752–8. *Albert Amor Ltd. See page 120*

long period at Bow, perhaps for the entire life of the factory. It was used at the other contemporary English factories, notably Worcester and Chelsea, as well as all the important continental factories, and has continued in use up to the present time. The characteristic trailing red leaf border, often divided up with four-petal flowerheads in gilt, was common to a number of Kakiemon designs and was used for non-Kakiemon decoration as well. A notable Kakiemon design (Plate 47B) used at Bow and elsewhere was the so-called 'wheatsheaf' pattern (correctly called 'banded hedge') which appears on all four enamelled examples of the dated 'New Canton' inkpots.[19] A waster of a lobed dish with the design was found in the 1969 excavations (Plate 47A). This dish had reached the stage of underglaze-blue painting with appropriate areas left blank for the later enamelling and had been glazed. The fault which spoilt the piece at that stage is clearly visible as a large gas pocket in the glaze overlying the 'wheatsheaf'. The finding of wasters with enamel decoration is uncommon due to the late stage in the production process at which the enamel firing is done. Only the gilt firing came later. The majority of wasters, both at Bow and Worcester excavations, derive from the biscuit firing.

Most continental manufacturers used Kakiemon-style decoration. As might be expected from their early contact[20] with the Orient, reinforced by the trading monopoly with Japan obtained in 1641, the Dutch soon brought the Kakiemon wares to Europe and used these designs on their tin-glazed earthenware.[21] However, it was sometimes difficult for the European painters to maintain the restrained discipline of the Kakiemon originals and elaborated designs occur as well as copies of great fidelity. The continental porcelain-makers who preceded the English factories all used the Japanese style[22] and the question is sometimes asked whether the painters at Bow used the originals or European copies as models. The matter can seldom be resolved on the basis of direct comparison because so often the design and indeed the palette are identical to the original, whether the copy be from St. Cloud, Chantilly, Meissen, Bow or Chelsea. The Japanese wares had been imported in quantity over a long period and on the ground of likely availability it seems more probable that the Bow and indeed other English porcelain painters were using the Japanese originals as models. Variations on the Kakiemon patterns, such as the addition of Chinese decorative themes, occurred at most of the European porcelain factories and the Meissen *indianische Blumen* style of flower painting, especially when combined with a yellow ground, is a highly

19. British Museum, Fitzwilliam Museum, Salisbury Museum and Victoria and Albert Museum.
20. The Dutch East India Company was founded in 1614, fifteen years after the foundation of the English one, but the Dutch seem to have been the first to reach China and Japan. The Portuguese had established trading links with the Orient even earlier.
21. A comprehensive permanent exhibition of Dutch polychrome-decorated tin-glazed earthenware (Delftware) can be seen at the Rijksmuseum, Amsterdam.
22. A selection of similar Kakiemon designs from various European porcelain factories, including the English ones, is also on permanent exhibition at the Rijksmuseum, Amsterdam.

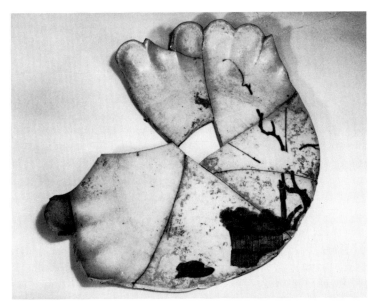

47A. WASTER OF A SCALLOPED DISH decorated with the 'banded hedge' pattern. The decoration has proceeded only to the stage of underglaze-blue painting and glazing. The dish would have been presented to the enameller in this (undamaged) state for filling in the Kakiemon design. The fault which led to this plate being discarded can be seen over part of the 'banded hedge'. 1752–8. *Recovered during the 1969 excavations. See page 122*

47B. SCALLOPED DISH similar to the waster shown in Plate 47A decorated in enamels with the 'banded hedge' pattern. 1752–8. *Albert Amor Ltd. See page 122*

successful evolution of the Kakiemon original. At Bow, the Kakiemon style did not evolve in the true sense and any variation tended towards over decoration with scattered flower sprays, or expansion of the area occupied by the design, so diminishing one of its principal virtues.

A notable Kakiemon design faithfully reproduced at Bow (and Chelsea), always on octagonal shapes, consists of panels left mainly in the white alternating with panels with iron-red fretted scrolls and ground colour giving the impression of white decoration on a red ground (Plate 48). There are usually two scrolls in each panel separated by a stylized flowerhead in gilt. The white panels are decorated with a single flower or a Chinese *pa pao* symbol of two books overlaid with a fan. An apparent omission from the Bow Kakiemon range is the 'hob in the well' pattern, based on a Chinese legend and regularly used at Chelsea. The few Bow examples of the 'lady in a pavilion' pattern may represent replacements. Known Bow Kakiemon patterns in a similar vein are the 'tiger and wheatsheaf', a kylin and a running man pulling a bunch of flowers on a string,[23] the 'wheatsheaf' and two exotic birds[24] and the 'flaming tortoise'.[25]

A stage in the development of enamel decoration at Bow can be seen in the application of floral sprays on white wares decorated with relief prunus or other flower sprigs. The flowerpot with the inscription 'Tho[s] & Ann Target July 2th 1754' (Plate 49) shows how early the technique was used but it does not seem to be markedly successful and is hardly true to the spirit of the original white wares. It occurs mainly on tablewares and there is a reference to it in the Bowcock memorandum (Appendix IV): see page 114. The name Target and the date 1754 appear on three other pieces of Bow porcelain. A sparrow-beak jug, decorated in *famille rose* enamels with a Chinese design of a peony, bamboo and a fence, is inscribed on the base 'A. Target 1754' 'Plate 3 A and B).[26] A teabowl[27] is similarly decorated and inscribed and is evidently from the same service. A bowl with enamel decoration inscribed 'Thos. Target 1754' is considered below.

A Chinese design[28] used extensively on Bow teawares of the middle 1750s is illustrated in Plate 50 on a teabowl, together with the original design on a Chinese coffee cup. The central feature is an island with rocks in brown enamel picked out in gilt. On the island stands an open-sided barn, supported on four pillars, on each side of which are two kinds of tree, one with red and the other with green foliage. At the base of the trees on the left is a bush with large red leaves. The reverse shows a smaller island with four large trees, alternately

23. Christie's, 21 April 1969, lot 101, also 16 November 1970, lot 130.
24. Frank Hurlbutt, op. cit., Pl. 24.
25. Sotheby's, 22 February 1972, lots 51 and 54.
26. See Chapter 4, note 20.
27. Ivor Noel Hume, *All the Best Rubbish*, Victor Gollancz, London, 1974.
28. An example is illustrated by Frank Tilley in *Teapots and Tea*, 1957, Pl. XXI, No. 70; also Sotheby's 20 July 1971, lot 25 (same piece) and Sotheby's, catalogue of the Ainslie Collection, 7 March 1961, lot 150.

48. OCTAGONAL PLATE decorated in enamels and gilt with fretted scrolls in iron-red. Diameter 19.4 cm (7.6 in)
1752–8
See page 124

49. FLOWERPOT with applied rose sprigs and crabstock handles above face-mask terminals, enamelled with leaves and flowers around the rim and elsewhere, sometimes to hide firing cracks. On the base in brown enamel 'Thoˢ & Ann Target July 2th 1754' and a long green leaf to disguise the firing crack. Height 14.6 cm (5.75 in)
British Museum. See pages 110, 124, 176

50. THE 'ISLAND' PATTERN. On the right a Chinese export coffee cup and saucer decorated in enamels and on the left the Bow simplified version of the same design on a teabowl and saucer. 1753–8. *See pages 124, 126*

red and green, stylized to the point of a dab of colour with cross hatching. The palette used in this important stock design is distinctive, with brown and green predominant. Sometimes the island ground colour is yellow and there are numerous minor variations such as the substitution of a willow for the two trees on the left of the island. The treatment of the design is strongly reminiscent of the decoration on the Target bowl,[29] one of the most frequently illustrated pieces of Bow useful china. Sometimes a common useful shape, normally forming part of a service, is decorated in a distinctive way not recognizable as a stock pattern. In the absence of comparable pieces, it is difficult to know whether this represents a sole survivor of a single specially decorated service or whether it was indeed a solitary example distinctively decorated to special order. An example of the phenomenon is illustrated in Colour Plate E. The sparrow-beak jug is decorated in enamels with Chinese figures in a landscape in a way which is generally unfamiliar at Bow but which is unquestionably of that manufacture, dating from the early 1750s and of exceptional quality. A Chinese design with a lady holding a child by one hand with a fan in the other, with tables on each side, vases of flowers and other furniture seems to have been used exclusively for the decoration of mugs (Plate 51). There is a notable border design inside and out of leaves and flowers in the *famille rose* manner. Some of the mugs with that pattern have flared bases and are examples of the occasionally early use of the heart-shaped handle terminal.

The square-shaped dish with indented corners (Colour Plate F) is another example of Japanese influence and in this case we can be reasonably sure of the origin because exact Japanese originals are known. The Imari palette, commonly taken to be red, blue and gold alone, was never originally restricted to those colours and in this piece green, yellow and black are used as well. The cock and hen are frequently used in both Chinese and Japanese decoration but the dragons depicted here are three-clawed, which implies a Japanese origin. Square-shaped small dishes of the kind were also decorated in underglaze blue with the 'golfer and caddy' pattern (see page 162); on a powder blue ground with the usual river scene; with applied prunus and enamelled flower sprays, and also in a conventional *famille rose* manner.

Famille rose decoration (Colour Plate G) has been mentioned already and its importance in the range of Bow enamel designs was considerable. It was especially favoured for tewares and surprisingly large numbers of the characteristically small cups from these services survive. The stylized peonies, foliage and rockwork comprise a decorative resource which can, so to speak, be expanded to fill the space available, and in practice that is what seems to have

29. Bowl, diameter 18.3 cm (7.2 in), height 7.6 cm (3 in), with brown-edged rim, the sides decorated with Chinese figures in a landscape with rivers, islands, a bridge and buildings in green, brown, red, blue and maroon enamels and gilding. Under the base is the inscription 'Thos. Target 1754'. See also Frank Tilley, *Antique Collector*, April 1952, p. 66; G. Bernard Hughes, *Country Life*, 15 October 1959; Hugh Tait, *Bow Porcelain 1744–1776*, op. cit., Cat. No. 64, Figs. 25, 26, 27; Sotheby's, catalogue of the Ainslie Collection, 7 March 1961, lot 185 (illustrated).

51. BELL-SHAPED MUG painted in enamel colours with a Chinese lady and child standing beside tables with vases of flowers and a distinctive floral border. Height 9.5 cm (3.75 in) 1753-5
Courtesy of Christie's. See page 126

52. SPARROW-BEAK JUG painted in enamels with European flowers but in the stylized manner of *famille rose*. Height 8.7 cm (3.4 in) 1755-8
See page 127

happened. The palette varies a good deal from the full spectrum of emerald-green, turquoise-green, pink-red, rust-red, blue, yellow, lilac and black or brown for line work, to a combination of only four of these. The pink-red used for the flowerheads is reasonably consistent, as are the two greens. The blue varies from being totally opaque to being as translucent as the other enamels. The use of overglaze rust-red is rare. At worst the Bow *famille rose* is garish, mostly it is acceptable, and sometimes a 'pale' palette of deep pink, lilac, the two greens and translucent blue, with outlining in brown achieves a very pleasing effect. *Famille rose* decoration was rather less commonly used on flatwares, probably because the expansive qualities of the design consumed a good deal of pigment. It was sometimes used for miniatures. A common border design is a band of diaper divided up with single or double black lines with four black dots in each cell. Sometimes this is continuous, sometimes broken up by reserves with stylized flowerheads. The *famille rose* decoration seems to have been used throughout the fifties but gradually gave way to European-style flower painting. The transition was not easy for some of the painters, who occasionally managed to make the realistic roses and other flowers of the new tradition look like those of the *famille rose* (Plate 52).

The Bow concern seems to have made more shell salts and pickle stands than the other English factories and in a greater variety of shapes and decoration.[30] The origin of most shapes is probably in European silver but the forms seem to have been developed a good deal within the porcelain medium. Judging from surviving examples the style of decoration seems to be equally divided between enamels, underglaze blue and those left in the white. The enamel treatment parallels that on other wares. Following the restrained flower painting of the earliest examples (Colour Plate C) Kakiemon patterns were used. In Plate 53 a triple-shell sweetmeat surmounted by a dolphin, enamelled in the 'partridge' pattern, is shown adjacent to a biscuit waster of the same shape discovered in the 1969 excavations on the factory site. The method of simulating coral by pricking the clay repeatedly with a sharp-pointed tool is typical. In the middle and later fifties the amount of painting increases within the main shell and around the base to match the increased elaboration of the form (Plate 54). The edge of the shells may be feathered or otherwise picked out in puce. The flower painting is occasionally in *famille rose* style, but increasingly European flowers are used. The purpose of most of the shell centrepieces is a mystery except for the smallest 'salts'. Although these objects are often called sweetmeat dishes, it should be noted that Bowcock referred to a 'dolphin pickle stand' in his memorandum book (see Appendix IV).

Most Bow baskets are of circular shape, derived from metal originals. Handles, when present, are of rope-twist form sometimes reflected in the base surround. The 'partridge' pattern (Plate 55) was frequently used for basket decoration, lending itself admirably to the circular interior base and the trailing red leaf border to the inner rim. Moulded florets at the intersections on the outside are picked out in blue and yellow enamels. A rare large basket form[31] of oval shape after a Meissen original is illustrated in Plate 56. This example is enamelled in *famille rose* style but some are left in the white. The exterior is basket moulded and there are rope-twist handles with female-mask terminals. Inside the rim there is an elaborate border design of brown shagreen interrupted by reserves with flower sprays.

30. Single- and triple-shell dishes were made from the earliest times. There seems to have been a good deal of freedom as to how they were constructed, for no two are exactly alike. The base is formed to simulate rock or coral and incorporates a variety of realistic small marine shells. In some examples the main shell is supported by three whelk shells (Sotheby's, 12 March 1974, lot 153). Elaboration of the base increases with the addition of birds' nests with eggs, various coral forms and seaweed (Sotheby's, 3 April 1973, lot 142) and in one design a bird appears under the main shell (Sotheby's 12 March 1974, lot 133). The triple-shell dishes increase in size compared to the earlier versions and there are some rare large single-shell dishes (Sotheby's 3 April 1973, lot 148, diameter of shell 19 cm (7.5 in)). Triple-shell dishes sometimes have a central pillar surmounted by a single shell, or a dolphin or large conch or whelk shell to form a handle. In the largest versions there are three shells at the base, another three mounted above these, staggered so that no shell is immediately above another and finally a central pillar with a single shell at the top (Christie's, 19 April 1971, lot 27). The type with six detachable conical-handled cups has been mentioned in Chapter 7.
31. Sotheby's, 20 May 1969, lot 299; see also Michael Newman, 'English Adaptations of a Meissen Basket', *Antique Collector*, June 1956, p. 113. The Meissen original (Kaendler, 1732) is illustrated in the catalogue of the Fisher Collection, Cat. No. 950.

I. OCTAGONAL DISH with a transfer print of 'L'Amour' in purple with purple edge. Diameter 21.4 cm (8.4 in)
1756–8
See page 152

J. BARREL-SHAPED TEAPOT with an outline printed (brown) and enamelled Chinese scene with figures. Height 10.5 cm (4.1 in) 1758–65

See page 154

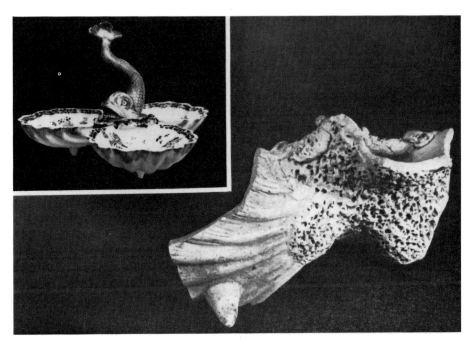

53. (*upper left, inset*) TRIPLE-SHELL SWEETMEAT DISH surmounted by a dolphin, the shells decorated with the 'partridge' pattern in enamels. *Right*, a biscuit waster of the same shape showing the underside with simulated coral. 1752–5. *Recovered during the 1969 excavations. See page 128*

54. SINGLE-SHELL SWEETMEAT decorated inside with European-style flowers and insects in underglaze blue with interspersed floral sprigs in enamel colours, the base of complicated form with naturalistic shells, coral and seaweed picked out in enamel colours and a crested bird peering out. Height 11.4 cm (4.5 in) 1755–8
Courtesy of Sotheby's. See page 128

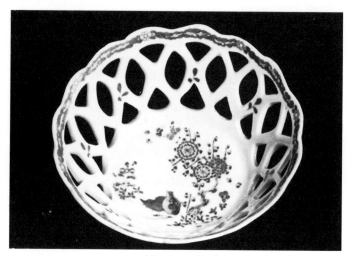

55. ROUND BASKET with pierced sides and wavy rim decorated in enamel with the 'partridge' pattern. Diameter 15.8 cm (6.25 in). 1756–8. *See page 128*

56. OVAL BASKET with rope-twist handles and rim after a Meissen original. The outside is basketwork moulded and has female face-mask handle terminals with applied flowers. Decorated in the *famille rose* style with an unusual shagreen ground border in brown interspersed with floral vignettes. Length 33.6 cm (13.25 in). 1754–8. *Courtesy of Sotheby's. See page 128*

Botanical-style painting on plates was done at Bow to a greater extent than is generally realized. Three plate shapes were used, circular with a ridged indented border and rim, after the metal shape (Plate 57), circular with lobed scalloped rim (Plate 58), the usual octagonal shape and also octagonal with rounded corners. The plate with lobed scalloped rim is decorated with hibiscus and insects including butterflies and a ladybird. The word 'Bisca' is painted, cryptically, on one of the leaves. The shape is unusual for Bow and this plate

57. PLATE with indented silver-shaped rim decorated with enamel in the 'botanical' style with a bunch of radishes, a cucumber, a head of celery and flying insects. Diameter 22.9 cm (9 in) 1754–8
Courtesy of Sotheby's.
See page 130

58. PLATE with boldly scalloped rim painted with enamels in the 'botanical' style with a hibiscus, butterflies and ladybirds. The word 'Bisca' is painted, cryptically, among the veins of a leaf. Diameter 20.9 cm (8.25 in) 1754–8
Courtesy of Sotheby's.
See page 130

59. OCTAGONAL PLATE painted in enamels with armorial
bearings and scattered floral sprays, the border a
trefoil repeat in gilt. Diameter 21.6 cm (8.5 in).
1754–8.
Moyses Hall Museum, Bury St. Edmunds. See page 132

may have been made as a replacement for a Chelsea one, but the number of
surviving Bow botanical plates makes it virtually certain that it was a standard
product. That type of decoration was done from the middle 1750s, but for how
long is uncertain. It is perhaps one of the earliest signs of a move away from the
oriental theme of decoration on Bow china. No dated examples are recorded.

Armorial decoration seems to have played a very minor role in the Bow
output. This contrasts with Worcester but the same can be said of Chelsea. It is
surprising on two grounds. Firstly, Bow was notably successful in the
production of flatwares, which are the chief vehicle for armorial bearings.
Secondly, the connection between the Bow concern and the East India
Company through Frye's acquaintance with Hillary Torriano would very
likely have made the former aware of the sizeable trade in armorial ware with
China. Perhaps there was an agreement not to encroach on this particular
preserve. An example of one of these rare pieces is illustrated in Plate 59. There
are some examples of octagonal plates and large dishes with the arms of
Murray, Earl of Dysart (Plate 60).[32]

32. Christie's, 16 October 1970, lot 137 (illustrated), also 28 June 1971, lot 175, and 19 February
1973, lot 145.

60. OCTAGONAL PLATE painted in enamels with the arms of Murray,
Earl of Dysart. Diameter 20.9 cm (8.25 in). 1754–8.
Antique Porcelain Company. See page 132

9

Bow Figures Before the Main Period of Meissen Influence

It is not generally appreciated that there is a period of about five years from the start of commercial operations at Bow which is almost entirely free from Meissen influence in style. That the same situation obtained at Chelsea is brought home by the well-known letter in 1751 from Sir Everard Fawkener to Sir Charles Hanbury Williams, British ambassador in Dresden, asking him to obtain Meissen porcelain as examples of good design for the Chelsea factory. From it we may deduce that Meissen porcelain, although known, was still rather uncommon in England in 1751. It is fortunate that this was so because it enabled the recently established Bow manufactory to find its feet, overcome basic problems and generally improve techniques before the arrival of large numbers of Meissen figure models. At Bow the period up to 1752 was one of modest figure production but of great interest to the student of English porcelain. The reputation of Meissen and its success preceded it but the material for copying and adaptation was not available. Native, classical and French sources were chosen instead. Three Bow figures bear the date 1750 in common with the six other useful wares similarly marked. The figure of the actress Kitty Clive in the part of the Fine Lady in David Garrick's farce *Lethe* is one of the best-known Bow figures and the date 1750 is inscribed on the base of the example in the Fitzwilliam Museum. She is modelled after an engraving by Charles Moseley which was published in London in 1750. The engraving is based on a water-colour by Thomas Worlidge. Like Thomas Frye, Kitty Clive was a native of Dublin who had come to London to seek, and indeed find, fame and fortune. The majority of Clive figures are left in the white but the example illustrated in Colour Plate H is a rare one with restrained contemporary fired colour in an easily identified Bow palette.[1] Three examples of this figure,[2] including one in the Schreiber Collection, are different from the majority being slightly smaller overall and having star-shaped flat bases instead of the usual rectangular pad or raised plinth with theatrical trophies. There are numerous

1. Some Clive and Woodward figures were evidently decorated by outside decorators such as William Duesbury through whose hands a pair passed in 1751–2. *William Duesbury's London Account Book*, published by Mrs Donald MacAlister, London, 1931, pp. 12 and 27.
2. Hugh Tait, 'Some Consequences of the Bow Porcelain Special Exhibition', Pt. I, *Apollo*, Vol. LXXI, February 1960, pp. 40–4.

minor differences in the moulding and some unusual applied flowers on the base. The general impression is that the workmanship is of a lower order than in the majority of Clives. Donald MacAlister[3] published an analysis of the body lead and phosphate content of the Schreiber example and found no phosphate but lead in excess of eight per cent. The absence of phosphate implies a non-bone-ash porcelain such as would be expected from the first Bow patent, but the high lead content virtually precludes a Bow attribution. It has also been pointed out[4] that no Clive figures could have been made before 1750 because the earliest known engraving of Kitty Clive in the role was published in London in 1750. Evidently she did not join the cast until some time in 1749 although the play was first put on some years before. The curious flowers with raised-edge petals on the base of these figures are found on some cream jugs[5] which have incised 'D', 'D 1750' and in one case 'Derby 1750'. Those jugs are not typical of early Derby porcelain and have a very low lead content (under two per cent). A complete quantitative analysis of the Schreiber Kitty Clive has not, to date, been published. A definitive attribution of these mysterious Kitty Clives is still awaited. Derby remains the likeliest possibility; a Bow attribution does not.

The figure of Henry Woodward (Colour Plate H) as the Fine Gentleman in *Lethe* is based on a mezzotint by James McArdell after a painting by Francis Hayman. The Woodward figure in the Untermyer Collection is inscribed with the date 1750. At least one example of the Woodward figure is in biscuit but is nevertheless in an otherwise finished state.[6]

There are two other figures in this early foray into the world of the contemporary London theatre. The figure of an actor in the part of Falstaff[7] in the Schreiber Collection was thought to be of James Quinn after a mezzotint by McArdell. Lane[8] suggests the source is an earlier engraving by Grignion after Francis Hayman. Toppin[9] discusses the possible origin of the model and favours an engraving by Truchy of a painting in Vauxhall Gardens by Hayman. If the latter is correct then the actor is unlikely to be Quinn. Another figure of an actor, possibly David Garrick, is in the Cecil Higgins Art Gallery, Bedford, and there are similar examples in the Brighton Museum and in the City of Leicester Museum.[10]

3. Donald A. MacAlister, 'The Material of the English Frit Porcelains, Part VI, Lead Oxide as a Factor in Classification', *Burlington Magazine*, Vol. LIV, 1929, pp. 192–9.
4. Hugh Tait, 'Some Consequences of the Bow Porcelain Special Exhibition', Pt. II, *Apollo*, Vol. LXXI, April 1960. Postscript to Pt I, p. 98.
5. Hugh Tait, op. cit. (note 2).
6. Collection Mrs S. J. Katz, formerly Mackenna Collection.
7. Schreiber Collection, Cat. I, no. 2.
8. Arthur Lane, *English Porcelain Figures of the Eighteenth Century*, Faber and Faber, 1961, pp. 85–95.
9. Aubrey Toppin, 'The Origin of some Ceramic Designs', *E.C.C. Transactions*, Vol. 2, No. 10, 1948, pp. 266–76.
10. The model is illustrated in *English Porcelain 1745–1850*, edited by R. J. Charleston, chapter on Bow by Hugh Tait, pp. 42–52, Pl. 10. The introduction by Charleston is an interesting and informative review of English eighteenth-century porcelain especially concerning the place of figures in the spectrum of ceramic products.

61. NEGRESS WITH
BASKET. Height 22.2 cm
(8.75 in)
1750. *See pages 136, 142*
Museum of London

There is an example of the Kitty Clive figure in biscuit[11] but the figure is in an unfinished state with the left arm missing and the base left open. That reveals the method of manufacture, for which Bow is well known, of press-moulding. The impression of the modeller's fingers is clearly visible. The thick section resulting from this practice is largely responsibe for most Bow figures being relatively heavy. Although these figures from the contemporary London stage were modelled from engravings they appear well in the round and careful attention to detail is evident even on the reverse. The figure of Woodward, though very familiar, is a particularly good example of sculptural modelling in miniature.

An important exception to the proposition that Meissen influence on Bow figure models was not evident before 1752 is the third figure to carry the incised date 1750, the so-called 'negress with basket' (Plate 61),[12] comprising a covered basket with a female blackamoor standing by it in turbanned headdress and loose skirt. It is a direct copy of a Meissen original. All known examples are undecorated and there is considerable variation in the final colour, from cold grey-white to creamy white. The covered basket by which the negress stands is of moulded wickerwork with a twig handle and applied flowers around the base. The same basket occurs,[13] without the negress figure, on a more elaborate

11. British Museum.
12. Hugh Tait, *Bow Porcelain 1744–1776*, op. cit., Cat. No. 44 and Fig. 6. Katz Collection. An undated example is in the Museum of London. See also A. J. Toppin 'Bow Porcelain. Some recent excavations on the site of the factory', *Burlington Magazine*, May 1922, pages 224–33.
13. Sotheby's, 19 May 1970 (Toppin Collection), lot 11 (illustrated).

62. URANIA or possibly
THE SCIENCE OF ASTRONOMY.
Height 15.5 cm (6.1 in)
1747–50
Castle Howard.
See pages 137–44

rustic base with two putti supporting it. These baskets were undoubtedly
tableware for dessert but what they were to contain is a matter of conjecture.

In 1929 Aubrey Toppin drew attention to a group of early Bow figures of
Muses.[14] Seven figures were described (Plates 62–7 illustrate six similar
examples), some standing and some seated, four being coloured and three left
in the white. That suggests that the figures formed a series but were not sold as

14. Aubrey J. Toppin, 'Early Bow Muses', *Burlington Magazine*, Vol. LIV, 1929, pp. 188–92.

63. (*left*) TERPSICHORE, the
name incised on the back.
Height 17 cm (6.7 in)
1747–50
*Salisbury and South Wiltshire
Museum. See pages 137–44*

64. (*right*) POLYMNIE, the
name 'polimnie' incised on the
back. Height 17.8 cm (7 in)
1747–50
*Courtesy of Sotheby's. See pages
137–44*

65. CLIO, the name 'clion'
incised on the left page of the
book. Height 15.9 cm (6.25 in)
1747–50
*Castle Howard.
See pages 137–44*

66. (*left*) EUTERPE, incised on the back 'euterpe for the musical instruments'. Height 15.5 cm (6.1 in). 1747–50. *Victoria and Albert Museum. See pages 137–44*

67. (*right*) ERATO, incised on the back 'Eraton for the Love'. Height 16.5 cm (6.5 in). 1747–50. *Victoria and Albert Museum. See pages 137–44*

a set; and indeed there are no reports of complete sets.[15] All the figures proved to be phosphatic by qualitative test. It was suggested that the figures were probably made two or three years prior to 1750 on the grounds of their primitive character when compared to the more competent figures already mentioned, some of which are dated 1750. This seems highly probable and is supported by evidence of inadequate technique in similar early figures such as

15. Of the nine Muses of classical mythology only seven Bow Muse figures have come to light, the missing ones being Calliope and Thalia. The attributes given to the Bow Muse figures are not always in accord with classical tradition although this was itself subject to some variation. No figure of Apollo contemporary with this series has been reported although there are later Bow versions. The Victoria and Albert Museum has most Muse figures but no complete set. Castle Howard in Yorkshire has three Muse figures as well as Juno, Jupiter and Mercury in similar style.

Hope (Plate 68) where the body is heavily stained through underfiring, the glaze much pooled and crazed. Some parts of the figure, the left hand and the anchor stock are missing although glazed over. A chinoiserie group[16] representing Air is similarly afflicted with staining and inadequate kiln support technique, whereby some parts have become displaced, probably at the glost firing stage. Yet both these figures and other examples of very imperfect pieces were (presumably) sold out of the factory. Both Air and the companion figure group of Fire derive from engravings by P. Aveline after Boucher originals.

All except one of the Muse figures described by Toppin have their names inscribed on the back or side in such a way as to suggest that the workman responsible was attempting to translate the titles of illustrations, evidently French in origin, upon which the figure models were based. For example, the Muse Erato is inscribed 'Eraton for the love', Euterpe as 'Euterpe for the musical instruments', Clio as 'Clion'. With the possible exception of the Muse Clio[17] the source of these engravings has not been identified.

Some of the figures have the mark 'T' or 'To' impressed on the base and the mark occurs on many later Bow figures. It is believed to be that of the 'repairer', that is the workman responsible for assembling the separate sections which comprise a figure model, and he has been identified with the 'Mr Tebo' referred to by Josiah Wedgwood in a letter[18] to Bentley in 1775. The mark occurs on Bow porcelain up to about 1765, on Worcester porcelain (including figures) up to about 1770 and thereafter on Bristol porcelain. Geoffrey Godden[19] discusses the 'To' mark on some Worcester or possibly Caughley oval baskets. He mentions a china modeller whose name was John Toulouse and suggests the 'To' mark is his. Further evidence has accumulated which tends to confirm this suggestion. Firstly the name Charles Toullous occurs in the Bow parish registers in October 1750 (see Appendix VI), and secondly Henry Sandon[20] has evidence that the Toulouses were a family of modellers probably originally from France. John Toulouse died in 1809. The raised intials 'IT' occur on some of the oval baskets mentioned. The possibility that the 'To' mark was applied by more than one workman would help to explain its wide distribution. However, there are many unsatisfactory aspects to the story. Why, for example, did only one 'repairer' (or a relative) make a practice of applying a mark, since, with the possible exception of the very rare 'ladder' mark, impressed marks on Bow figures are not seen, although painters' marks

16. Hugh Tait, 'The Bow Factory under Alderman Arnold and Thomas Frye', E.C.C. Transactions, Vol. 5, Pt. 4, 1963, pp. 195–216, Pl. 193. British Museum. A coloured version is illustrated in the catalogue of the Untermyer Collection, Fig. 239.
17. Aubrey J. Toppin, 'The Origin of some Ceramic Designs', E.C.C. Transactions, Vol. 2, No. 10, 1948, p. 273 and Pl. C1, a and b.
18. Wedgwood letter to Bentley, 3 July 1775.
19. Geoffrey A. Godden, Caughley and Worcester Porcelains 1775–1800, Herbert Jenkins, London, 1969, p. 10.
20. Henry Sandon, Flight and Barr Worcester Porcelain 1783–1840, Antique Collectors Club, 1978, p. 208.

68. HOPE. The usual anchor is missing although its indentation, glazed over, can be seen. Similarly the left hand. Height 20.5 cm (8 in) 1747–50
See page 140

are quite common? Is it possible that the mark is that of the modeller rather than the repairer? If so, it was applied with remarkable inconsistency. In any case the modeller would not normally be concerned with figure production at a stage when placing an impressed mark would be possible unless the mark was incorporated in relief in the mould. Only a small proportion of the Muse figures have the 'T' or 'To' mark, and a large number of other figure models in the distinctive 'Muses modeller' style are not marked.

Toppin first drew attention to the distinctive style of the modeller of the Muses figures, which might be described as spirited but generally unsophisticated. The treatment of the head is characteristic with heavy-lidded eyes, wide brow and receding chin. The lips are often parted. The head is disproportionately small for the body, arms are excessively long, draperies show deep folds. Arthur Lane[21] suggested that all the early Bow figures are the work of a single modeller. Reginald Haggar[22] thinks there are at least two distinctive modelling styles in the early figures. Without doubt there is great variation in style and modelling quality within the group and that is perhaps what might be expected when a master modeller was working with a number of

21. Arthur Lane, op. cit., p. 87.
22. Reginald Haggar, *Northern Ceramic Society Newsletter*, No. 29, p. 22.

journeymen. But there are certainly examples in this early group where the characteristics of the 'Muses modeller' are difficult or impossible to discern, an example being the figure of the 'negress with basket', where the head and limbs are well proportioned, the mouth closed, the chin does not recede and the eyes and eyebrows are as they should be. Much the same applies to the figures of Woodward, Kitty Clive and Falstaff, though Lane considered them all to be the work of the 'Muses modeller'. Coloured examples however are not painted in a typical manner (Colour Plate H). Toppin[14] pointed out that the model of Melpomene which, despite being uniform with the rest of the group in size, base and in having the name incised, had distinctively different modelling, especially of the head (which does not appear to have been replaced), and did not appear to him to be the work of the same hand. The face of Melpomene is immediately recognizable as familiar in Bow and appears, with a lion and cornucopia, as Earth in the Bow Elements and is also seen on later Derby figures and later still on Staffordshire pottery figures. The well-known early but very rare 'Mongolian heads',[23] formerly known as the 'Roumanian Minister and his wife' are further examples of excellent modelling which has nothing in common with the Muses figures (Plate 69). The Thames Waterman figure[24] (Plate 127) is obviously native inspired and although slightly later is not in 'Muses modeller' style. Another example of an early figure in a style different from that of the Muses modeller is the Boy with the vase for flowers on his head (Plate 119).[25] The general treatment of this figure is very much in keeping with that of the Muse Melpomene except that the base is an early attempt at rococo style, similar to the base treatment of an early version of the Liberty and Matrimony pair. The bases on the majority of these early figures were of the simplest kind, mostly in the form of a square flat pad.

Much of the distinctive appearance of the Muses models derives from the face painting, which was untidy with poorly shaped lips and eyebrows, aptly described by Lane as 'looking like over-emphatic maquillage'. Typical examples are the figures of Polymnie (Plate 64) and of the early version of Minerva.[26] Tait[27] has drawn attention to the distinctive painting as opposed to modelling

23. Dr Bellamy Gardner. *E.P.C. Transactions*, No. 2, 1929, Pl. VII, illustrates the pair and a possible source for the models in a pair of carved rococo wall brackets. See also Sotheby's, 6 May 1969, lot 89 and 10 December 1973, lot 156. An example of the female head is in the Passmore Edwards Museum, Stratford. The Bowcock memorandum book has an entry for April 1756: 'Think of the Chinese head for Mr. Weatherby.'
24. Illustrated by Arthur Lane, op. cit., Pl. 41, p. 88. In this case the badge he wears is that of the fouled anchor proper to the Admiralty barge. See also Sotheby's, 28 October 1969, lot 101 (illustrated), where he wears Doggett's badge (and coat). In 1715 Thomas Doggett the comedian founded the coat and badge as a prize to be rowed for by Thames watermen annually on 1 August, between London Bridge and the Old Swan at Chelsea, in commemoration of the accession of George I.
25. Arthur Lane, op. cit., Pl. 43, p. 89. Victoria and Albert Museum.
26. Arthur Lane, op. cit., Pl. 41B. Victoria and Albert Museum.
27. Hugh Tait, 'Some consequences of the Bow Special Exhibition', Pts. II and III, *Apollo*, LXXI, April 1960 and June 1960, and Pt. IV, *Apollo*, LXXII, October 1960.

69. Pair of busts known as THE MONGOLIAN HEADS, formerly called 'the Roumanian Minister and his wife' and referred to in the Bowcock memorandum as the 'Chinese heads'. Height 26.6 cm (10.5 in). 1749–56. *Antique Porcelain Company. See page 142*

in this group, referring to the 'Muse painter's style and palette' in relation to some female sphinx figures, to early versions of the Liberty and Matrimony pair and to a unique seated figure of a woman playing a lyre. The figure is modelled and painted in the Muses style but has a prototype four-footed rococo scroll base with large applied flower sprays. The woman is in unusual dress and wears ear-rings and a prominent bead necklace very similar to the Bow sphinx figures.[28] The figures of Erato and Euterpe also wear ear-rings. The sphinx figures are without doubt French in origin but whether from an engraved source, a bronze, or garden statuary is not known. There are at least two versions of the Bow sphinx figure pairs, in white and enamelled. The popular contemporary actresses Peg Woffington and Kitty Clive are said to be represented but facial likeness to portraits of either[29] is difficult to perceive. The quality of modelling improved very rapidly over two or three years and soon the factory was producing highly competent figure groups such as the 'Fortune Teller' group (Plate 70) after Boucher's *La Bonne Aventure*.[30] That painting was known mainly from the engraving of it by P. Aveline, in which as is usual with the copper plate technique the image is reversed. The Bow group has the same disposition as in the Boucher original, implying that the model was either taken from the original or a drawn or painted copy of it.[31] The group occurs both in the white and with enamel colouring and the latter is a good example of the distinctive body colour treatment of this early period. Rather uneven colour washes of yellow, lilac, pale green, brown-red and chocolate brown were used. Gilding was applied over chocolate brown. The rare figure group of the Chinese goddess Ki-Mao-Sao (Plate 71) is another example of a French source used at Bow. Aubrey Toppin[32] discovered the engraving of the Watteau original on which it is based and also found engraved French sources for two important Italian Comedy groups after Watteau, 'Mezzetin and Isabella' and 'Harlequin and Columbine', both groups in typical 'Muses modeller' style. The seated group of 'Lovers with a Bird Cage'[33] also derives from a French source, an engraving by Nicholas Lancret, and the very rare 'Fisher Girl and Gallant'[34] is probably similarly derived, although no source has been found.

It is evident that there was a heavy reliance on French sources in the early years of figure production at Bow. Taken together with the imperfect translations from the French of the incised names on the Muses and assuming that the Charles Toullous (a French name) in the Bow parish registers is one of the family of modellers at Worcester years later then perhaps a tentative

28. Hugh Tait, ibid., Pt. III.
29. Janet Dunbar, *Peg Woffington and her World*, Heinemann, London, 1968.
30. William King, *Eighteenth Century English Porcelain Figures*, London, 1925, Fig. 2.
31. Hugh Tait, op. cit., Pt. II, pp. 95, 96.
32. Aubrey J. Toppin, *E.C.C. Transactions*, Vol. 2, Pt. 10, p. 274, Pl. CII a and b.
33. Arthur Lane, op. cit., Pl. 38, p. 87.
34. Hugh Tait, *Bow Porcelain 1744–1776*, op. cit., Cat. No. 48(a), Fig. 15.

K. TEAPOT with recessed lid decorated in underglaze blue with a
fence, rocks and stylized flowers. Knop replaced.
Height 10.2 cm (4 in)
1754-6
See page 160

L. SPITTOON with heart-shaped handle terminal decorated in underglaze blue with a flowering peony and bamboo, the trellis border interrupted with stylized flowers on blue ground.
Height 10.8 cm (4.25 in)
1759–65
See page 160

70. THE FORTUNE TELLER, after Boucher. Height 17.8 cm (7 in). 1748–52
Puttick & Simpson. See page 144

71. THE GODDESS KI-MAO-SAO, after Watteau. Height 17 cm (6.75 in). 1750
Hampshire County Museum Service. See page 144

speculation is permitted. There seems to be a possibility that the 'T' or 'To' mark on Bow porcelain was applied by one of the Toulouse family functioning as a 'repairer' and that a relative was the 'Muses modeller', the family having recently arrived to work at Bow bringing with them French illustrations for figure models including the Muses.[35] The distinctive painting of nearly all the typical figures may be an indication that one of the family was involved in this as well.

We cannot be certain whether some of the early Bow versions of the Italian Comedy groups derive directly from prints or from Meissen porcelain. The latter seems more likely in the case of the 'Indiscreet Harlequin' group, of which there is a well-known Meissen version. The 'Muses modeller' style extends well into the period of dominant Meissen influence and will be considered in the appropriate section. The figure of a Sailor[36] dressed in authentic mid-eighteenth-century English lower-deck rating attire (there was no uniform as such) is known in white and coloured versions (Plate 124) and has a female companion figure. Classical figures of the early period in overt 'Muses modeller' style include Juno, Jupiter and Mercury. Both the modelling and painting of these figures is at a very early stage of development. The rare 'Charity' group[37] is rather better done only a little later.

35. A further speculation, entirely unsupported, would be that the discontented French potters who wrote anonymously to the English nobleman proposing the establishment of a porcelain manufacture were the Toulouses. The period of the letter is uncertain but dates from *c.* 1746–9. See Chapter 5, note 27.

36. Arthur Lane, op. cit., Pl. 40, p. 88.

37. Arthur Lane, op. cit., Pl. 42, pp. 48, 87.

10
Transfer-Printed Decoration

Transfer printing is one of the few entirely English contributions to the art of porcelain decoration. That certainty stands in stark contrast to the mysteries which surround its actual introduction as a decorating medium by potters. But it should be easy for us to understand that in an industry where technology was, and is, intimately bound up with profitability, there would be much secrecy surrounding innovations. Research into patents and petitions for patents[1] has yielded important information and focused our attention on John Brooks, the Irish engraver who had come to England from Dublin early in 1746, as the first person to petition for a patent for 'a method of printing, impressing and reversing upon enamel and china from engraved etched and mezzotinto plates, and from cuttings on wood and mettle (sic), impressions of History, Portraits, Landskips etc'. The date of the petition was 10 September 1751, and it was addressed from 'Birmingham in the county of Warwick'. John Brooks was subsequently associated with the Battersea enamelling factory and two subsequent petitions dated 25 January 1754 and April 1755 were addressed from York Place, Battersea. These petitions broadened the scope of the first to include printing on glass and 'Delft'. Until Brooks' first petition came to light it was thought that the invention of transfer printing on enamels and porcelain was made by him at Battersea in 1753 (the Battersea Enamel factory functioned only from 1753–6). Now it appears that the preliminary work was done at Birmingham but how long this was going on prior to the petition is not known. In the event none of the petitions was granted. It is in the nature of things that technical developments often proceed at different places along parallel lines quite independently. The first person who lodges a petition may or may not be the true inventor. In the case of transfer printing on ceramics it is certain that the process was under development in the early 1750s at Liverpool and may have been going on elsewhere. The most likely reason for the rejection of the petition was that the process was already known and possibly in use. John Brooks plays no further part in the story as far as Bow is concerned but earlier

1. Bernard Watney and R. J. Charleston, 'Petitions for Patents concerning Porcelain, Glass and Enamels with Special Reference to Birmingham, "The Great Toyshop of Europe"', *E.C.C. Transactions*, Vol. 6, Pt. 2, 1966, pp. 57–123.

authorities[2,3] surmise that the famous engraver Robert Hancock worked at the factory for a short time after leaving Battersea, where he was supposed to have gone in 1753. He went to work at the Worcester concern in 1756 and stayed there for the next eighteen years. Hancock served his apprenticeship, which ended in 1753, at Birmingham under a little-known engraver called Anderton. The reason for these assumptions regarding Hancock's movements was the existence of two Bow pieces carrying transfer prints signed by him, and of numerous unsigned prints on Bow porcelain judged to have been derived from his engravings. There were also a number of prints, believed to be Hancock's, on Battersea enamels. The theory was first put forward by R. W. Binns[4] and A. R. Ballantyne[5] in the latter half of the nineteenth century and not seriously challenged until Bernard Rackham[6] pointed out that there was no satisfactory evidence that Hancock ever worked at Battersea or indeed in London. This view was further challenged[7] but despite much research effort, especially by Aubrey J. Toppin, no evidence was forthcoming. The situation was changed by the discovery[8] of John Brooks' petition from Birmingham, which had the effect of re-orienting thinking on early transfer printing on porcelain and enamels towards the Midlands. The 'supposed peregrinations'[9] of Hancock from Birmingham to Battersea, Bow and then Worcester have conditioned thinking to the effect that transfer printing must have begun at Bow before it was introduced at Worcester. The existence of the so-called 'smoky primitives' on Worcester porcelain and Birmingham enamels, associated with the names of Boitard and Hancock, has always been difficult to reconcile with the assumption that Bow was first in the field. It now seems probable that these early prints on Worcester porcelain emanated from Hancock at Birmingham or possibly were even applied at Birmingham perhaps a year before transfer printing was practised at Bow. There is a rather belated realization that copper plates were objects of trade and that the prints from them could be used for various media including paper if reverse was acceptable. Plates used for transfer printing at Bow, Worcester and Bristol were found, years later, at Coalport. There was no need, therefore, for the physical presence of Hancock at either Bow or Battersea for his work to appear on the wares. In the event, a high proportion of the overglaze prints used at Bow originated from engravers of the French school such as Cochin, Gravelot, Aveline and Chardin, even though Hancock and no doubt others were involved in adapting their designs for use as transfer prints.

2. Cyril Cook, *The Life and Work of Robert Hancock*, Chapman and Hall, London, 1948.
3. W. B. Honey, *English Pottery and Porcelain*, London, 1933.
4. R. W. Binns, *A Century of Potting in the City of Worcester*, London and Worcester, 1865 and 1877.
5. A. R. Ballantyne, *Robert Hancock and his Works*, London, 1885.
6. Bernard Rackham, *E.P.C. Transactions*, 4, 1932, p. 56.
7. H. W. Hughes, 'Authorship of Some Designs on Porcelain and Enamel and Robert Hancock's Connection with Battersea and Bow', *E.C.C. Transactions*, No. 3, 1935, p. 85.
8. Bernard Watney and R. J. Charleston, op. cit.
9. Bernard Watney, 'Notes on Bow Transfer Printing', *E.C.C. Transactions*, Vol. 8, Pt. 2, 1972.

It is of course quite certain from the Bowcock papers that Bow was marketing transfer-printed ware in 1756: 'a sett compleat of the second printed teas', '1 pint printed mug, 5s; 1 half-pint do., 3s 6d' are mentioned in May and June respectively. It would also be reasonable to assume that transfer printing was carried out at Bow some time prior to 1756, but it is not possible to say for how long.

During the first years of transfer printing at Bow, covering the period up to about 1760, the products are all printed overglaze in brick-red, purple, pink-magenta or purplish-black (rare). The number of surviving pieces is fairly small, suggesting that production was limited. That is surprising, for the process was introduced as an economical method of decoration. This would not have been the case if the ware had to be transported elsewhere for printing, but there is no evidence that this was done. A few fragments of Bow transfer-printed ware were discovered on the site by Aubrey Toppin in the 1921 excavations.[10] It is not certain whether these were wasters or not, but it has been taken to mean that transfer printing was carried out at the factory. The role of Thomas Frye in the matter is an enigmatic one. As an accomplished mezzotint engraver he must have been well acquainted with both the problems and the possibilities of large scale production. Innovation in an industrial context is not always readily acceptable to the work force and at Bow, with the large number of painters employed, the method may have been unpopular.

In 1971 Bernard Watney[11] proposed a definitive classification of Bow transfer-printed ware and this will be adhered to in the descriptions that follow.

The first group includes the earliest known printed wares from the factory and the typical feature is the painted polychrome floral border which is identical to the floral border on early enamelled wares including the cachepot inscribed 'Thos & Ann Target July 2th 1754'[12] in the British Museum. The border is also seen on Bow mugs.[13] A plate and a dish with the polychrome floral border in the British Museum are printed in brick-red with a combined print of 'The Tea Party No. 1'[14] and 'The Wheeling Chair', and are signed 'R. Hancock fecit'. The combination of the two designs is seen only at Bow. The scene of the tea party is regarded as very much in the French style and is probably adapted by Hancock from an unknown source. These two pieces form the basis of Hancock's putative association with Bow. A plate with similar

10. Aubrey J. Toppin, 'Bow Porcelain: Some Recent Excavations on the Site of the Factory', *Burlington Magazine*, May 1922.
11. Bernard Watney, op. cit. (see note 9).
12. Tait, *Bow Porcelain 1744–1776*, op. cit., Cat. No. 62, Fig. 23 (illustrated). Also illustrated by Bernard Watney, op. cit., Pl. 159d (see note 9).
13. Sotheby's, 6 June 1972, lot 60 (illustrated). Flared base, heart-shaped terminal. Painted in enamels with a Chinese domestic scene. Similar example, bell-shaped mug, Christie's, 19 March 1973, lot 212. Another example is in the National Museum of Ireland, Dublin.
14. Cyril Cook, op. cit., items 104 and 116. The three versions of 'The Tea Party' are illustrated by Cook, items 104–6.

floral border has a pink-magenta print of the arms of the Anti-Gallican Society,[15] which is also found on Battersea enamels and on salt-glazed stoneware. The well-known 'L'Amour'[16] print (Plate 72) is copied from a design by C. N. Cochin *fils*. The print, in brick-red, is sometimes reversed and the standing figure behind the seat is sometimes omitted.

The second category is characterized by a printed trefoil-loop border in brick-red, and on mugs there is a painted looped border design round the footrim. Prints noted in this class include 'The Hurdy-Gurdy Player' in brick-red on a plate; 'Aeneas and Anchises' in brick-red on a plate,[17] after a print by H. Gravelot; 'The Young Archers', after H. Gravelot,[18] on a plate; 'The Letter' in brick-red on a mug[19] (source unknown); 'The Tea Party No. 1' in brick-red on tewares; 'Marbles' ('Le Jeu de la Gobille') after H. Gravelot in brick-red on mugs;[20] 'Shuttlecock and Battledore'[21] after Gravelot, in brick-red on mugs; 'The Singing Lesson' (Plate 73)[22] on tewares and a mug, from an engraving signed 'Boitard delin., Hancock Sc.'; and 'Mezzetin and Columbine'[23] adapted by Hancock from an engraving by C. N. Cochin after Watteau, in brick-red on a coffee can (Plate 73).

The third group covers the period *c.* 1757–60 and includes the largest number of prints which are in purple, red or lilac and often have brown, purple or black painted rims. A combined print of 'The Tea Party No. 1' and 'The Wheeling Chair' in purple, occurs on a bowl with a variety of subsidiary prints. 'Le Feu'[24] and 'La Terre'[25] from the four Elements by Boucher, engraved by P. Aveline, are known only on mugs, and enamel colours are used over the print. The same designs are found on Worcester and hard-paste Bristol mugs, without enamel colours, and evidently these prints are from different engravings. Two transfer-printed fragments (finished state) from 'Le Feu' were found on the Bow factory site in 1921 by Aubrey Toppin, but there is some doubt as to whether these are Bow, and conclusive analytical evidence is not yet available. One of the best-known but very rare Bow prints is 'Le Négligé ou La Toilette du Matin'[26] copied from an engraving by Jacques

15. Cyril Cook, op. cit., item 125 (supplement). Also illustrated by Bernard Watney, op. cit. (note 9), Pl. 159a and b. It appears that prints from the same worn plate were used at Battersea and subsequently, after the closing down sale in 1756, at Bow.
16. Cyril Cook, op. cit., item 2. See also Aubrey J. Toppin, *E.C.C. Transactions*, Vol. 2, No. 10, Pl. XCVIIa.
17. Cyril Cook, op. cit., item 1.
18. Cyril Cook, op. cit., item 5.
19. Cyril Cook, op. cit., item 140 (supplement).
20. Cyril Cook, op. cit., item 65.
21. Cyril Cook, op. cit., item 9.
22. Cyril Cook, op. cit., item 101.
23. Cyril Cook, op. cit., item 24 (*comédie Italienne*).
24. Cyril Cook, op. cit., item 35.
25. Cyril Cook, op. cit., item 108.
26. Cyril Cook, op. cit., item 109.

72. PLATE with transfer print of 'L'Amour' in lilac
with painted polychrome floral border. Diameter
20.3 cm (8 in). 1754–8. *See page 150*

73. COFFEE CAN with transfer print of 'Mezzetin and Columbine' in
brick-red. Height 6.1 cm (2.4 in). COFFEE CUP with transfer print of
'The Singing Lesson' in brick-red. Height 6.2 cm (2.4 in). 1754–8.
See page 150

Philipe le Bas after a picture by Jean Baptiste Chardin. The prints are
unsigned, as are many of the prints on Bow porcelain, and the identity of the
engraver is therefore a matter of opinion. It is inevitable that when artists copy
the work of others unsigned, a loss of identity must ensue. The engraving used
for 'Le Négligé' prints has been attributed to Ravenet but Cyril Cook argues,
rather unconvincingly, in favour of Hancock. 'The Toys',[27] a rare but
charming design in purple on teawares, is illustrated in Plate 74. A seated lady
is engaged in conversation with two standing children. A model horse on
wheels and other toys stand on a small table. The accompanying coffee cup has
a print of the commoner version of 'L'Amour'. The print on the saucer serves
to remind us of the engraver's problem of fitting a print to the small round
shape and, in this instance, of how to solve it! 'L'Amour', in purple, in the
commoner version, found on plates and teawares, with the lover kneeling on
the right, is illustrated in Colour Plate I. The third figure is omitted. Some
variants omit the garden roller and dog.[28] The vignettes round the rim play a
role in the overall composition of many of the designs on flatwares. Their origin
is often obscure. There are no known two-figure versions of this print signed
by Hancock. Ballantyne[5] did not think 'L'Amour' was an original Hancock
design[16] and he possessed a print of it by 'a French engraver' which had verses
in French, appropriate to the scene, beneath it. It is now lost. The two-figure
version of 'L'Amour' also occurs on some mid-eighteenth-century wall-
paper.[29] The arms of the Anti-Gallican Society (in red-brown) also occur in
this category where the painted floral border is replaced by rural vignettes
printed in black. 'The Stag Hunt' (Plate 75)[30] in purple on plates is an
uncommon print and no source has been found. The vignettes appear to be
Italian scenes. 'The Game of Trictrac' (backgammon)[31] in purple is rare and
derives from an engraving by Charles Eisen. 'The Piper and Woman on
Horseback'[32] in purple, is known only on one teapot formerly in the Toppin
Collection. The design is adapted from J. Aliamet's engraving of a picture by
N. Berghem. 'Le Bosquet de Bacchus'[33] in purple on an oval dish with wavy
rim shows two figures sitting on the ground and two standing in a rural
landscape. The engraving is by C. M. Cochin *père* after Watteau. Two sheep
printed in black on a plate in the Victoria and Albert Museum (Schreiber I
No. 113) are from a print by H. Stevens after N. Berghem. The Chinese
landscape (Plate 76) is copied from part of a larger design engraved by J.
Pillement and illustrated in *The Ladies Amusement* (2nd edition, 1762, p. 172).

27. Cyril Cook, op. cit., item 171.
28. Cyril Cook, op. cit., item 2, Fig. 2.
29. Victoria and Albert Museum, *Catalogue of Wallpapers*, 1929, item 38.
30. 'The Stag Hunt', Bernard Watney, op. cit. (note 9), Pl. 166.
31. 'The Game of Trictrac', Bernard Watney, op. cit. (note 9), Pl. 167.
32. Illustrated in *E.C.C. Transactions*, Vol. 2, No. 9, 1946, p. 232, Pl. LXXVIc; also Sotheby's,
19 May 1970, lot 17; also Bernard Watney, op. cit. (note 9), Pl. 168, which also illustrates the
source engraving.
33. Victoria and Albert Museum, Schreiber I, No. 112.

74. SAUCER with a transfer print of 'The Toys' in purple with brown rim. Diameter 11.2 cm (4.4 in). COFFEE CUP with a transfer print of 'L'Amour' in purple with brown rim. Height 5.7 cm (2.2 in). 1756–8. *See page 152*

75. (*left*) OCTAGONAL DISH with a transfer print of 'The Stag Hunt' in purple with brown edge. Diameter 22.5 cm (8.8 in). 1754–8. *See page 152*

76. (*right*) NAPPY PLATE with a transfer print in lilac of a Chinese landscape. Diameter 19.8 cm (7.8 in). 1754–8. *See page 152*

'The King of Prussia'[34] in purple on a rare teapot in the Victoria and Albert Museum (Schreiber I No. 110) is derived from an engraving by J. G. Wille after a portrait by Antoine Pesne. The print is also used on mugs. Two examples[35] only are known of a bowl transfer printed in purple with designs after Sebastian Le Clerc depicting two beggar-women and children and various other figures, including a man and woman standing by a fence, which appears in *The Ladies Amusement* (3rd edition, p. 231) signed by J. June and taken from a song sheet. On one bowl the accompanying prints are 'L'Amour', 'The Tea Party No. 1' and 'The Wheeling Chair' (Schreiber I No. 115). A number of prints depict birds including 'Pheasants' (Plate 77), 'Partridges',[36] 'Cocks and Hens' in two versions and 'Ducks and Pigeons'. Some of these prints derive from engravings by P. Tempest after Francis Barlow's *Various Birds and Beasts drawn from Life*.[37] All are in purple on plates, mugs, bowls or vases.

The fourth group dates from the 1760s and consists of outline prints coloured in with enamels. A Bow beaker-cup[38] outline-printed with the 'Red Cow' pattern and in-filled with enamels is a curiosity and closely resembles the same print and enamelling on a Chelsea beaker-cup and a Worcester teabowl. Watney suggests that they are trial pieces enamelled at the same place, possibly Worcester. The remaining items in the group are chinoiserie designs such as the 'Ladies Choosing Accessories' on an oval dish[39] which is taken from *A New Book of Chinese Designs* by Edwards and Darley (London, 1754, p. 32).[40] The Mating Chickens',[41] sometimes referred to as 'The Peeping Tom' pattern (Plate 78), appears to derive from a Chinese original. The general effect of this type of decoration is not very pleasing and there is an impression of messiness, but occasionally the execution is more careful and the results satisfactory, as on the teapot illustrated (Colour Plate J).

The fifth group comprises a number of examples of underglaze-blue transfer-printed decoration which are thought to date from the late 1750s and continue for an unknown period through the 1760s. The technique never replaced underglaze-blue painting at Bow, which was continued to the end of trading. One of the more interesting examples of this type of decoration is the Coronation mug[42] with a portrait bust of Queen Charlotte similar, but not

34. Bernard Watney, op. cit. (note 9), Pl. 169c. The companion print on a mug shows 'The King of Prussia on Horseback', inscribed 'The Prussian Hero' together with war trophies and Fame, and is illustrated by Hurlbutt, *Bow Porcelain*, London, 1926, Pl. 11b and p. 91; also Cyril Cook, op. cit., items 89 and 90.
35. 'The Beggars'. Victoria and Albert Museum, Schreiber I, No. 115. Cyril Cook, op. cit., items 10 and 72. Sotheby's, 11 May 1970, lot 19.
36. Sotheby's, 19 May 1970, lot 20. The prints have been clobbered in green and red enamels.
37. Bernard Watney, op. cit. (note 9), Pl. 170, 171 a, b and c.
38. Bernard Watney, op. cit. (note 9), p. 216 and Pl. 172a, b and c.
39. Victoria and Albert Museum, Schreiber I, No. 116. Bernard Watney, op. cit. (note 9), Pl. 173.
40. Bernard Watney, op. cit. (note 9), Pl. 173b.
41. Bernard Watney, op. cit. (note 9), Pl. 174b.
42. Cheltenham Museum. Illustrated by Bernard Watney, *English Blue and White Porcelain of the Eighteenth Century*, 2nd ed., 1973, p. 22, Pl. 14B.

77. OCTAGONAL PLATE with a transfer print of 'Pheasants' in purple with brown edge. Diameter 19.4 cm (7.6 in). 1754–8. *See page 154*

78. BOWL with an outline printed (brown) and enamelled Chinese scene, 'The Mating Chickens'. Diameter 15.6 cm (6.1 in). 1758–65. *See page 154*

79. PLATE with
indented faceted rim
transfer printed in
underglaze blue with
flowers and a moth
1758–65
See page 156

identical, to the copper plate in the Dyson Perrins Museum at Worcester believed to be engraved by Hancock.[43] The accompanying prints are full-length standing figures of 'Britannia' and 'Fortune'. Individual prints of flower sprays and insects are used on a number of shapes including large meat dishes,[44] plates (Plate 79), cups, vases and bowls. The same prints are found on Lowestoft, Worcester, Caughley and Liverpool porcelain. Occasionally the quality of underglaze-blue printing with flower sprays was of a remarkably high order as shown on the rare finger bowl and stand in Plate 81.[45] The piece is unusual in having the Meissen mark as well as the numeral 2. A pleasing design on octagonal plates, with a Chinese lady accompanied by two children, one of whom holds a parasol over her, is known as 'La Dame Chinoise'.[46] The same print was used at Derby, Worcester and Bristol. The border pattern was subject to some variation. A prototype 'Willow Pattern' is seen on teawares (Plate 80). A Chinese scene[47] with three figures standing by an ox has delicate flower sprays round the rim. The central print is a version of the so-called 'Herdsman and the Spinning Maiden' design.[46]

It seems likely that there are a number of underglaze-blue designs that have not yet come to light. It is a matter of regret that the Bow proprietors did not exploit the possibilities of underglaze-blue transfer printing on a large scale and for longer than they did. If they had done so, as happened at Worcester and Caughley, it is possible that the factory's failure might have been averted or at least postponed.

43. Cyril Cook, op. cit., item 91.
44. Bernard Watney, op. cit. (note 42), Pl. 15c.
45. Sotheby's, 21 December 1971, lot 106.
46. Dr John Ainslie, 'Underglaze-blue printing on Bow porcelain', *The Antique Collector*, April 1957. Also Bernard Watney, op. cit. (note 9), Pl. 175c. Also Victoria and Albert Museum.
47. Sotheby's, 22 February 1977 (Mullens sale), lot 124 (illustrated).

80. SAUCER with a transfer print of a Chinese river scene in underglaze blue with a painted diaper border. Diameter 11.8 cm (4.6 in). 1760–5
See page 156

81. FINGER BOWL AND STAND with transfer prints of flowers and insects in underglaze blue. Mark: crossed swords and numeral 2 in underglaze blue. Height 8.9 cm (3.5 in). 1758–62. *See page 156*

11
Underglaze-Blue Decorated Wares of the Middle and Later Periods

It has been customary to divide the manufacture of Bow blue and white wares into three periods, 1750–4, 1755–63 and 1764–76. The reader will not be slow to realize that divisions of this kind may exist chiefly or solely in the minds of those who attempt to write the history of such industries. They might have little meaning to the people who worked there at the time. The most important dates in the history of an industry are when it began and when it ended. What happens in between is a continuum of problems and their solutions, the overriding need being to achieve and maintain profitability. These simple truths are mentioned for the good reason that they are mostly neglected by connoisseurs, collectors and investors, who for their diverse reasons take an interest in what remains of the output of a long-dead manufacturing industry. It is quite exceptional for a ceramic historian of the mid–eighteenth–century period to be aware of management decisions concerning the introduction of new products or the phasing out of old, though such changes must have occurred frequently.

The traditional approach to the problem of applying a time scale to a factory's products is to use dated pieces[1] as a framework. Although for the present that is virtually the only possible approach, it is subject to three limitations worth mentioning. Firstly there may not be enough dated specimens to throw light on any evolutionary process that was afoot. This is true of Bow where, after the four blue-and-white pieces dated 1750 or 1752 there are only two pieces dated 1754[2] until we come to the 'E.P.E.C.' mug dated 1757.[3] Thus the period of great expansion to a peak of prosperity in 1755 is covered by only four dated specimens. The second limitation is that the dated specimens may not be typical of the general run of products at the time. This factor could operate in two ways. The piece might be atypical because it is dated and therefore picked out or even produced specially for the purpose.

1. Bernard Watney, *English Blue and White Porcelain of the Eighteenth Century*, 2nd edition, 1973, p. 14.
2. The cream jug inscribed 'W. Pether May 10 1754' and small bowl with the date 1754 on the base (Plate 83).
3. Tait, *Bow Porcelain 1744–1776*, op. cit., Figs. 28, 29, 30, Cat. No. 91.

82. (*left*) SAUCEBOAT with fluted sides decorated in underglaze blue with 'desirable residence' pattern. Length 10.8 cm (4.3 in). 1755–60. *See Plate 22 and page 159*

83. (*right*) BOWL decorated in underglaze blue with unusual scroll design and solid cell border with the date 1754 inscribed on the base. Diameter 12.7 cm (5 in). *Phillips. See page 159*

That limitation might affect the decoration rather than anything else and applies to the Pether jug[2], the decoration of which harks back to an earlier time. Secondly, the specimen may be ante- or post-dated in relation to when it was made. Such considerations are mentioned as cautions to the unwary and not because we have any new or better scheme to offer. In practice, dated specimens are not much used for placing a particular piece into its period because, if for no other reason, access to dated pieces is limited.

The mind of the experienced connoisseur works out these problems in a way which is difficult for him or anyone else to rationalize but obviously relates to a sum total of experience, helped by a retentive memory. It is pertinent to mention that if the pace of technological development is maintained, applied science may provide us with a ceramic dating capability more than sufficient for our needs.[4]

The expansion period after 1750 is notable for the continuation of a few successful designs of the 'early blue' period. That includes the 'desirable residence' pattern, the early version of which is shown in Chapter 6, Plate 22; a later version from the period 1755–8 is shown in Plate 82. A slightly earlier version of this sauceboat shape is known in which the footrim is indented to form four short feet. One of these was found in the 1969 excavations and a drawing of it is shown (see Appendix XIV). The pattern has undergone some evolution in that the 'telegraph poles' have frayed somewhat but all the essential elements of the pattern are still present. Another continued pattern is the 'two-storied hut' (Chapter 6, Plate 24) used on teawares. The small bowl dated 1754 is shown in Plate 83. The decoration of this bowl is rather unusual and no reason for the dating is apparent. In the period we see considerable variation in style and quality of painting and an example of particularly fine

4. The time-scale resolution of the technique of thermoluminescence looks particularly promising in this respect.

84. MUG decorated in underglaze blue with finely drawn Chinese landscape. Height 12.8 cm (5.1 in). 1753–5
See page 160

quality underglaze-blue painting is seen on the mug in Plate 84, possibly the same hand as seen on a basket with pierced sides illustrated by Watney.[5] The design of this basket is based on a silver original. The practice of copying silver shapes in porcelain increased greatly during the period, particularly as regards sauceboats, tureens and shell-based shapes, although there are comparatively few of the latter decorated in underglaze blue, most being left in the white or enamelled. The practice of using a European metal form but decorating in oriental style began about the middle fifties and persisted for some years. Two examples are illustrated in Colour Plates K and L. The spittoon is an exceptionally rare shape for Bow although the florid peony and border pattern was commonly used on flatwares. Apart from the increasing adoption of European silver shapes during the early fifties other more subtle shape changes were evolving. The small globular severely Chinese teapots were getting a little larger and a little taller. The earlier squat fat-bellied cream jugs were giving way to taller, more slender types. Footrims on plates and saucers became better defined. Coffee cans acquire footrims instead of the flat base. Many of the patterns which have come to be identified with Bow particularly, made their appearance during the period 1750–5. The majority are taken directly from the Chinese without any attempt to transform, distort or modify the original in any way. It will be recalled that from 1750 and earlier part of the marketing effort of the company took the form of projecting a close identity with imported oriental porcelain by the use of the name 'New Canton'. The idea was quietly dropped after three or four years. A possible reason was the growth of the coloured product-range, particularly figure models, as we shall see in the appropriate

5. Bernard Watney, op. cit., Pl. 7B.

M. OCTAGONAL PLATE decorated in underglaze blue with a powder
ground, the central reserve painted with a Chinese scene with two
figures in conversation, one pointing to a covered vase which stands
on a plinth. Around the base of the vase the word 'BOW' is written
cryptically. Eight surrounding reserves are painted with precious
objects and leafy twigs. Diameter 21.6 cm (8.5 in)
1759–62
See page 167

N. CHAMBER CANDLESTICK of fluted leaf form with a tulip-shaped candle nozzle decorated in underglaze blue with naturalistic flowers and feathered border. Length 15 cm (5.9 in)
1758–64
See page 167

85. CUP of tall shape and SAUCER decorated in underglaze blue with 'the koto player'. Height 7.5 cm (2.9 in) 1754–8 *See page 161*

86A. (*left*) Small CHINESE PLATE decorated in underglaze blue with the 'jumping boy' pattern. Diameter 10.7 cm (4.2 in). *c.* 1720. *See page 161*

86B. (*right*) BOW PLATE decorated in underglaze blue with the 'jumping boy' pattern. Diameter 17.8 cm (7 in). 1754–8. *Courtesy of Sotheby's. See page 161*

section. The 'New Canton' image of cheap blue and white oriental useful wares was not quite compatible with that of the supplier of sophisticated ornamental china based on European artistic inspiration. Nevertheless, they continued to make large quantities of it. A typical pattern was 'the koto (or zither) player' (Plate 85) shown here on an unusually tall coffee cup and saucer. Another typical pattern is the so-called 'jumping boy' (Plate 86) shown here with a

Chinese original. This design was also used very effectively at Liverpool (Chaffers). The 'dragon' pattern is unknown in the early blue class but becomes very popular during the middle fifties and is painted on a variety of shapes including bowls (especially), teapots and stands, and on some ambitious shapes like the enormous helmet-shaped jug in the Museum of London (Plate 87), which is probably based (loosely) on an oriental original of the monk's-cap jug type.[6] Since it was first pointed out by Watney[7], it is now widely appreciated that the 'Bow' dragon has an 'arrow' for a tongue and that this is a useful distinguishing feature among dragons as well as being mnemonic. Worcester and Lowestoft also used dragon decoration and the authors are aware of at least one Worcester dragon on a large mug with an arrow tongue. Plate 88 shows the rather crowded application of a dragon to a chamber candlestick. Spero[8] has recently reviewed the use of the 'dragon' pattern by the principal English factories. Another important design for tewares and all but the largest tablewares was the 'image' or 'bordered image' pattern (Plate 89). The pattern was a popular one judging from the references to it in the Bowcock memorandum book, and that accounts for its relative frequency today. It has never been apparent why the 'image' pattern was so-called and contemporary collectors have solved the problem by renaming the pattern the 'golfer and caddy'. The wavy border is unusual and otherwise occurs (Plate 90) only on Bow plates and dishes decorated with Meissen harbour scenes, which probably derive from Chinese copies, as evidenced by the pagoda often found on the right of the scene and the type of small boat in the foreground. No vases painted in the early vivid underglaze blue have been reported, but this ornamental form was not long neglected. Watney[9] illustrates an early small vase of a somewhat corrupt Yen Yen shape, decorated with trailing branches and large flowerheads. The base is scratch 'R' marked. A pair of magnificent vases of about 1755, much illustrated,[10] of Chinese form decorated in underglaze blue with exotic birds are a notable achievement. A variety of vase shapes were introduced during the middle and late fifties, all based on classical oriental forms, including an early Ch'ing (1644–1912) simple bottle form, a bottle form with expanded section of neck, and in one case the latter shape with applied flower decoration.[11] The baluster-shape vase illustrated in Plate 91 is a strict copy of the Chinese in form and decoration

6. Anthony du Boulay, *Chinese Porcelain*, Weidenfeld and Nicolson, London, 1963, Pl. 48, p. 59.
7. Bernard Watney, op. cit., 1st edition 1963, p. 24.
8. Simon Spero, *Collector's Guide*, June 1978.
9. Bernard Watney, op. cit., 2nd edition, Pl. 4A.
10. Bernard Watney, op. cit., 2nd edition, Pl. 9B. Hugh Tait in *English Porcelain 1745–1850*, edited by R. J. Charleston, Ernest Benn, London, 1965, Pl. 8A. *English Ceramics 1580–1830*, R. J. Charleston and Donald Towner, E.C.C. 50th Anniversary Catalogue, Sotheby Parke Bernet, London, 1977, Pl. 131.
11. Bernard Watney, op. cit., 2nd edition, Pl. 17A. Now in the Victoria and Albert Museum.

87. Unusually large HELMET-SHAPED JUG with moulded
face mask decorated in underglaze blue with the 'dragon'
pattern. Height 29.8 cm (11.75 in). 1775–8. *Museum of
London. See page 162*

which is of the powder-blue ground type with reserves. This important type of
decoration is generally reckoned to have been introduced about 1759 because
of the famous Bowcock bowl,[12] inscribed 'JOHN & ANN BOWCOCK 1759' on the
base, and with the initials 'I.B.' on the outside. It is decorated on the exterior in
underglaze powder-blue having four reserves elaborately framed with rococo
scrolls and painted with Chinese riverscapes. The interior scene shows three
sailors dancing by the shore with their hats and staves in their hands. A central
figure wearing a tricorn hat is holding a punch bowl. John Bowcock was clerk to

12. Bernard Watney, op. cit., 2nd edition, Pl. 12B and p. 21.

88. CHAMBER
CANDLESTICK decorated in
underglaze blue with the
'dragon' pattern. Mark:
numeral 12. Length 17 cm
(6.7 in)
1755–8
See page 162

89. NAPPY PLATE decorated
in underglaze blue with the
'image' pattern. Diameter
17.8 cm (7 in)
1755–60
See page 162

the Bow China works for ten years and there has been some speculation[13] as to the significance of the date and the scene on the bowl. The difficulty is that 1759 does not coincide with any known anniversary or any event in Bowcock's career though he may have been appointed manager on Thomas Frye's retirement in 1759. In the foreground of the scene in the bowl are trophies of war, and it is known that Bowcock had been involved in sea fights against the French during his youth at sea. Assuming the central figure represents Bowcock, he is shown in authentic sailor's attire holding a punch bowl. A rowing boat by the shore has its oars stowed. These facts lend most support to the theory that the scene symbolizes a new permanent appointment at the factory and Bowcock's final break with the seafaring life. The bowl had been with the Bowcock family in the north west of England for many years classified by local experts as Liverpool delft. In 1955 the late Ernest Allman recognized the bowl, then in a private collection, as Bow porcelain.

The date 1759 on the Bowcock bowl does not seem to be a very good reason

13. Hugh Tait, *Bow Porcelain 1744–1776*, op. cit., Cat. No. 125 and Fig. 33. The bowl is now in the British Museum.

90. OVAL DISH decorated in underglaze blue with a view derived from a Chinese copy of a Meissen harbour scene. Width 23.5 cm (9.25 in)
1755–60
Courtesy of Sotheby's. See page 162

91. BALUSTER VASE AND COVER decorated in underglaze blue with a powder-blue ground and reserves painted with oriental-style flowers. Height 30.5 cm (12 in)
1758–62
Courtesy of Sotheby's. See page 162

92. LOBED OVAL DESSERT DISH decorated in underglaze blue with a powder ground and reserves with Chinese river scenes and stylized flowers. Mark: six imitation Chinese characters in blue. Occasionally one of these characters is replaced by the Meissen crossed swords mark. Length 26.2 cm (10.3 in). 1758–62. *See page 166*

for assuming that powder-blue ground decoration was first used in that year. It was probably used earlier and judging from the large number of surviving pieces it must have been a most important product line. The technique of powder-ground decoration involved sprinkling pigment evenly on to the biscuit body with the reserves masked in some way. The key to success was even distribution of pigment and close masking to prevent staining the reserves, since the stark contrast between the dark ground colour and the white reserve was an important feature of this decoration. Alas, all the English factories using powder ground encountered difficulties in meeting the last requirement. The Chinese appeared to have had no difficulty, judging by the appearance of K'ang-hsi vases decorated in this way. The solution to the problem at Bow (and also at Lowestoft) was to paint a thin line in blue along the margin of the blue ground. It had the effect of emphasizing the line of division. It was not necessarily done to all the reserves and is sometimes omitted round the central reserve. That feature can be seen on the dish in Plate 92. The central scene is a typical one and was reproduced with great exactitude. The boatman was sometimes omitted from the scene. The decoration is seen on all shapes of tea and dinner ware, on vases, mugs, pomade pots, shell centrepieces,

93. COFFEE CUP AND SAUCER decorated in underglaze blue with a powder ground and reserves with Chinese river scenes and stylized flowers. Mark: crossed swords in blue. Height 6.5 cm (2.6 in). 1758–62. *See page 167*

baskets and jardinières. A coffee cup and saucer (Plate 93) are unusual in that both pieces are marked with crossed swords in underglaze blue. An octagonal plate (Colour Plate M) with unusual shaped reserves shows two Chinese looking quizzically at a large covered vase standing on a plinth. Facing us, but out of sight of the two Chinese, the word 'BOW' is written, rather cryptically, around the base of the vase. The subtle humour of this delightful scene is rare in porcelain decoration. There were twelve such plates originally, and eleven went through the salerooms in October 1969.[14]

An important change in decorating style occurred in the later 1750s and early 1760s with the gradual introduction of European-style naturalistic flower painting. The Bow concern was rather slow to introduce it, especially in underglaze-blue decoration, and it never displaced the dominant oriental influence in this medium. It is closely related to similar developments in enamel flower painting and makes a striking contrast with the free flowing stylized flower painting of oriental inspiration. The style is illustrated here (Colour Plate N) on a leaf-moulded chamber candlestick, on a covered bowl

14. Sotheby's Caldwell sale, 7 October 1969, lots 52–7. Eleven plates were listed.

94. BOWL AND COVER decorated in underglaze blue with naturalistic flowers and insects. Diameter 13.5 cm (5.3 in), height 10.3 cm (4 in). 1760–5. *See page 168*

(Plate 94), on a lobed-edge basket-moulded dish (Plate 95), on a coffee cup and saucer (Plate 96) and on a bell-shaped mug (Plate 97). The same hand is at work in a good deal of such flower painting. The basket-moulded dish has the unusual mark of a crescent moon with a face outline in it. The painter did not use the mark consistently but the painting style is very reminiscent of the decoration on some underglaze-blue decorated wares from the Bonnin and Morris undertaking in Philadelphia. The mug is of oriental shape and at the base of the handle the heart-shaped terminal, for which Bow is well known, can be seen. That feature is common on mugs of the period 1755–70. There are a few examples on earlier pieces.[15] In the form used at Bow the device is a mere vestige of the bold, projecting heart-shaped terminal on oriental mugs. Its presence is a fairly reliable guide to Bow as the factory of origin although it does occur, very rarely, on Liverpool, Lowestoft and Plymouth porcelain. The chamber candlestick, cup and saucer and basket-moulded dish all show Meissen influence in shape. The saucer is unusual in having a central indentation for the cup.

The porcelain body at Bow deteriorates towards the middle fifties. It becomes more porous and less translucent and lighter in weight. The usual

15. Bernard Watney, op. cit., 2nd edition, p. 23, footnote referring to Sotheby's 28 January 1964, lot 221.

95. LOBED OVAL DISH with basket-moulded surface and reserves painted in underglaze blue with naturalistic flowers and insects. Mark: a crescent moon with face outline inside. Length 23.5 cm (9.25 in). 1760–5. *Norfolk Museums Service (Norwich Castle Museum).*
See page 168

reason given for the change is underfiring, as analysis does not reveal any dramatic change in the body composition; but this possibility is not completely ruled out by the available data (see Appendix XV). Underfiring may not imply a lower peak kiln-temperature but a shorter firing time (less heat-work) which would of course be economically advantageous. The quality of the body thenceforward is reasonably consistent until some time after 1770, when there is a further deterioration. The late Bow body has been and still is occasionally mistaken for pottery.

The theme of moulded decoration was a strong one at Bow and continued in the 1760s. Pineapples first reached England in the late seventeenth century and their shape and surface texture seem to have fascinated designers of the time, for architectural as well as ceramic purposes. A pineapple-moulded caudle cup, cover and stand is shown in Plate 98. Pleated moulding with shaped reserves for painted scenes is shown in Plate 99 applied to a decidedly European-shaped

96. CUP AND SAUCER decorated in underglaze blue with naturalistic
flowers and insects and a cell border. The saucer has a central cup well.
Height 5.7 cm (2.2 in). 1760–5. *See page 168*

97. BELL-SHAPED MUG decorated in underglaze blue with
naturalistic flowers and insects and a cell border. Heart-
shaped handle terminal. Height 12 cm (4.75 in). *Norfolk
Museums Service (Norwich Castle Museum). See page 168*

98. Pineapple-moulded CAUDLE CUP, COVER AND STAND decorated in underglaze blue with cell borders. Height 15 cm (5.9 in). 1760–5. *See page 169*

99. BREAKFAST CUP AND SAUCER with pleated moulding and reserves decorated in underglaze blue with a cell border and Chinese scenes on the saucer and a floral border and flower sprays on the cup. (Unmatched decoration.) Mark: 'B' on the base of the cup. Saucer diameter 16.5 cm (6.5 in); cup height 6 cm (2.4 in), diameter 12 cm (4.7 in). 1762–8. *See page 169*

cup and saucer, and the rose-moulded sauceboat with scrolls, illustrated in Plate 100, is an example of a silver shape adapted to porcelain. The identical shape occurs in Staffordshire saltglazed stoneware and in Worcester porcelain, where it is sometimes decorated in underglaze blue and sometimes in enamels. There are some surviving blocks of this sauceboat shape for mould production. A curious and perhaps unique vase (Plate 101 and Appendix X) is of a shape that was nearly always used for enamel decoration but in that case is decorated in underglaze blue. The vase is somewhat simplified, compared to the enamelled versions, and is without applied flowers.

Miniature teawares were produced over a long period at Bow and the commonest decoration was the 'trailing vine' pattern in underglaze blue (Plate 102). It is sometimes said that these miniature pieces were travellers' samples but this is not plausible on various grounds, chiefly because the range of shapes and decoration is severely limited, and because complete miniature teasets, a few of which have survived, would hardly have been necessary for sales promotion.

Products of the period 1765–76 are rather uncommon (or uncommonly attributed to that period), but we obtain some help from the dated specimens of which there are two decorated in underglaze blue with the date 1770. The Pennyfeather mug (Plate 103)[16] carries the inscription 'Joseph and Margret Pennyfeath^{er} April 1770' on the base. The elaborate oriental landscape painting is well done if somewhat overcrowded. The handle has a heart-shaped terminal. If the mug was not dated it is most unlikely that anyone, even an English porcelain expert, would say that it was as late as 1770. Presumably that is one of the reasons for the apparent paucity of pieces after 1765. Much the same thing can be said of the 1770-dated octagonal plates[17] which are inscribed on the back, 'Mr Robert Crowther Stockport Cheshire January 1770.' The script is by the same hand as the Pennyfeather mug. The plates are painted with an over-fussy border and have the script initials 'R.C.' in a cartouche of flowers and scrolls. These plates evidently came from a set. The large octagon dish (31.2 cm, 12.3 in) diameter) shown in Plate 104 is undoubtedly very late, probably 1772–4. The body is totally opaque and the glaze a dull muddy grey, but structurally it is a sound product, quite unwarped. It serves to remind us of how successful were the Bow proprietors in producing large flatwares—something that other manufacturers such as Worcester and Lowestoft found very difficult. The decoration is unusual in that it is an underglaze-blue version of the 'botanical' enamel flower-painting style, complete with insects.

The marks on underglaze-blue decorated wares do not present a coherent picture in relation to pattern or painters' identity. The commonest mark is a numeral, and values up to 60 are recorded but are uncommon before 1754. The

16. Victoria and Albert Museum. Illustrated by Tait, *Bow Porcelain 1744–1776*, op. cit., Cat. No. 140, Figs 50–2.
17. Victoria and Albert Museum. British Museum. Sotheby's, 6 May 1969, lot 115. Illustrated by Tait, *Bow Porcelain 1744–1776*, op. cit., Cat. No. 139, Figs. 53 and 54.

100. SAUCEBOAT with rose moulding on the sides decorated in underglaze blue with a cell border and painted scrolls and flower heads. Heart-shaped handle terminal. Length 18.3 cm (7.2 in). 1762–8. *See page 172*

101. FRILL VASE with pierced top and circle of leaves around the lower part, spirally fluted with face masks beneath moulded leaves, decorated in underglaze blue with floral garlands and a cell border. Height 20 cm (7.9 in). 1762–8. *See page 172*

102. MINIATURE TEAWARES decorated in underglaze blue with the 'trailing vine' pattern. Saucers diameter 5 cm (1.9 in); coffee cup height 3.5 cm (1.4 in), teapot height 8 cm (3.2 in); jug height 5 cm (1.9 in). 1758–64. *See page 172*

103. BELL-SHAPED MUG with heart-shaped handle terminal decorated in underglaze blue with a Chinese river scene. The floral border interrupted by a shaped cartouche with the initials 'I^{P}M', the base inscribed 'JOSEPH & MARGRET PENNYFEATH^{ER} April 1770'. Height 14.3 cm (5.6 in)
Victoria and Albert Museum. Crown Copyright. See page 172

104. Large OCTAGONAL PLATE decorated in underglaze blue with flower painting in 'botanical' style
Diameter 31.2 cm (12.3 in). 1770–4. *See page 172*

'dragon' pattern seems to be associated with the number 21 more often than chance alone would suggest. Various letters of the alphabet, including 'B', 'G', 'J,' 'I', 'W', 'C', a cross and an arrow occur. On plates and dishes decorated with powder ground, imitation Chinese characters are common. The significance of the Meissen mark is obscure unless the pieces were replacements. One rare, notable painter's mark is a crescent with a face in it, already referred to.

12

Later Enamelled Wares

1759–1776

There is a gap of five years between the 1754 dated enamelled 'Target' flowerpot (Plate 49) and the 1759 dated enamelled 'William Taylor' mug (Plate 105) in which we have little evidence of the evolution of enamel painting style. The decorative style of the former (though not its shape) is decidedly oriental, with applied flower sprigs and *famille rose* enamel flower painting, whereas the latter is enamelled in the naturalistic flower-painting style which originated (on ceramics) at Meissen about 1740 and became popular throughout Europe. There is a world of difference in the decorative styles of the two pieces, but it is difficult to know exactly when the European flower-painting style began to displace the oriental at Bow. The evidence from the painting on figures would suggest a knowledge of the style from about 1753. The dated 1757 figure of a shepherd[1] shows European-style flower painting but there is no earlier dated figure of Meissen origin with it. In any case, the painting on useful wares need not necessarily have been in step with the figure painting, which may have been done by different artists. The lack of dated pieces that might illustrate the transition is matched by a similar dearth of pieces with the later flower-painting style that can with reasonable certainty be attributed to the years between 1754 and 1759. Obviously that does not apply to the 'botanical' plates described in Chapter 8 but this type of decoration was rather unusual and was not destined to play a very important part in the Bow output. The difficulty is apparent in the selection of enamelled pieces to cover the period 1754–8 for the British Museum Bow Porcelain Special Exhibition, held in 1959/60. Of eleven pieces selected, only one appears to be in the European flower-painting tradition. None of this is surprising if one is thinking solely in terms of the Bow factory, but it is an indication that Bow, compared to Chelsea and even Longton Hall, was late in coming to grips with the fashionable new style. The most telling evidence for such an assertion is contained in the Bowcock memorandum book (Appendix IV) which covers the period January to November 1756. As we have seen, it was the personal memorandum book of John Bowcock and lists wares required at the Bow

---

1. Tait, *Bow Porcelain 1744–1776*, op. cit., Cat. No. 101, Fig. 31. The initials 'I.B.' and '1757' are painted on the upper end of the chanter of the bagpipes held by the shepherd.

O. BELL-SHAPED MUG with grooved loop handle and heart-shaped
terminal decorated in enamels with a flower spray. Unusual border
design in red with stylized flower heads in scrolled arches.
Height 14.6 cm (5.7 in)
1765–70
See page 180

P. **BUTTER DISH, COVER AND STAND** with flower-moulded handles and a cherry knop with applied leaf, decorated in enamels with flower sprays and scattered flowers, all edges with brown line.
Length of dish 11.7 cm (4.6 in), height 8.5 cm (3.3 in)
1760–5
See page 183

105. BELL-SHAPED MUG with ribbed handle and heart-shaped terminal decorated in enamels with sprays of naturalistic flowers and insects and flower garlands pendent from the rim, the base inscribed in puce enamel 'Wm Taylor 1759'. Height 14 cm (5.5 in) *Victoria and Albert Museum. Crown Copyright. See pages 176, 178*

warehouse for china dealers and for individual customers, with many interesting notes relating to the business. Many useful wares are clearly specified together with figures, including animal figures and other ornamental wares. It would appear that the memorandum book, although obviously far from complete, contains a reasonably representative sample of the factory's products over the period. The year 1756 is of particular interest because although we know from surviving account books that the peak sales occurred in 1755, there was a steady decline thereafter; but neither Bowcock nor indeed any of the managers would have been aware of this trend. The products listed must therefore be representative of an output that had captured a remarkable share of the market in the nine years or so that the manufactory had been in existence. By the same token, to some extent they were the products that would see the factory into a slow but steady decline over the next two decades. What were these products and, more important, how did they appear to the buying public?

In this context it seems likely that decoration was of greater importance than shape, particularly for the useful wares, where the evolution of form would have been a slow process with many stock shapes remaining unchanged over long periods. A careful analysis of the decorative themes of all the useful wares (excluding figures) mentioned in the memorandum book shows that of sixty different items thirty-one (51.7%) were decorated with essentially oriental designs, e.g. 'sprig'd upright teapot', 'oval tureen, image pattern', 'an enamelled partridge coffee-pot' etc. In sixteen (26.7%) the decoration was not specified and in thirteen (21.6%) the decoration was definitely of European origin, e.g. 'the knife handles, how many sold of the Dresden flowers?', 'a sett complete of the second printed teas' etc. Assuming only half of the wares with unspecified decoration were treated in the oriental way, that would imply that in 1756 at least sixty-five per cent of the useful and ornamental wares coming from the factory were decorated in oriental style.

We have seen that the Bow concern entered the market with a range of products predominantly in oriental style and called the factory 'New Canton' to emphasize the point. Nine years later, although a significant proportion of the products are now decorated in European style, the oriental is still the dominant influence even more in the blue-decorated than in the enamelled wares; and so it must have appeared to the customers. That is entirely understandable in view of the prosperity achieved, but this very success seems to have induced a reluctance to change when there must have been powerful commercial reasons for doing so. It stands in contrast to the rapid and almost exclusive adoption at Bow of Meissen figure models from the early fifties onwards. Chelsea particularly seems to have adopted the European style for useful wares to a greater extent and earlier than Bow. It would appear that the long period of dominant oriental influence in style was a factor in the slow decline of the factory, although almost certainly not the main one. The illness and deaths of three of the principals by 1765 were undoubtedly of greater importance in this respect. The bell-shaped mug (Plate 105) inscribed on the base in puce enamel 'Wm. Taylor 1759' is a key piece in the evolution of a flower-painting style fully committed to the European taste. Even so, the pendent floral swags round the rim owe more to English inspiration than do the insects and flower sprays round the sides. The mug is one of a small group of enamelled wares all decorated in the European style which, collectively, show that about this time the factory was making a determined if somewhat belated attempt to keep up with fashion. These pieces are all dated or otherwise documented to the years 1759–61 and include several clock cases[2] and vases,[3] some of which carry inscriptions commemorating the death of George Frederick Handel, the Craft bowl,[4] the Roberts bowl[5] and the 'ICG' teapot.[6]

The clock or watch cases (Plate 106) are amongst the most ambitious

2. Hugh Tait, 'Handel and Bow', *Apollo*, June 1962.
3. Tait, *Bow Porcelain 1744–1776*, op. cit., Cat. No. 104, Fig. 36. The 'Handel' vase.
4. See Chapter 3. The bowl is illustrated by Hurlbutt, op. cit., Pl. 26, p. 103. Both the bowl and the lid of its cardboard box with its famous statement are illustrated by William Chaffers in *The Keramic Gallery*, Gibbings, London, 1907, Figs. 487 and 488. The statement mentions the bowl 'was made about the year 1760'. Also illustrated in Hugh Tait, *Bow Porcelain 1744–1776*, op. cit., Cat. No. 111, Fig. 37. British Museum.
5. A bowl decorated on the inside with a floral band round the rim and fruit and foliage in 'botanical' style. The outside is decorated with European-style flower painting. The base carried the inscription 'John & Elizab^h Roberts 1761'. Untermyer Collection. Illustrated in Tait, *Bow Porcelain 1744–1776*, op. cit., Cat. No. 105, Figs. 41 and 42, diameter 22.1 cm (8.7 in).
6. Globular teapot with scroll-moulded handle and spout decorated with a blue scale ground with panel reserves on each side framed with rococo scrolls in gilt. An exotic bird is painted in

106. CLOCK CASE surmounted by a figure of Father Time with the inscription 'TEMPVS FVGIT' beneath his feet. On the lower part of the back is the inscription 'To great handle the god of musick' and surrounding this on painted sheets of paper are the initials 'GFH', 'GH' and the date '1759'. Musical scores are painted on the front and sides and these are identified from contemporary sources. None are by Handel. Height 35 cm (13.5 in) *Antique Porcelain Company.* See page 178

products of the factory. They stand about 35 cm (13.5 in) high and are based on a Meissen original. The exterior is moulded with elaborate rococo scrollwork and the top is surmounted by a figure of Father Time holding a scythe, with *putti* on each side, sometimes holding musical instruments, while there is a small figure of an owl or cock on the base. The scrollwork is picked out in blue and puce, there are scattered flower sprays and butterflies and painted sheet-music sometimes with titles. Some of the music is identifiable from contemporary sources and is accurately transcribed. Four of these clock cases have been described: one[7] carries the inscription 'To great handle the god of musick' (sic), the initials 'GFH' and 'GH' and the date 1759. Another,[8] generally similar but without the *putti*, in the Cecil Higgins Art Gallery at Bedford, has the date 1759 and the initials 'GH' appear four times on music sheets. Another,[9] generally similar to the preceding, was exhibited at

one panel and a flower spray in the other. On the base in underglaze blue is the inscription 'I^CG 1761', height 16 cm (6.25 in). The Glynn Vivian Art Gallery, Swansea. Illustrated in Tait, *Bow Porcelain 1744–1776*, op. cit., Cat. No. 106, Figs. 38, 39, 40.
7. Formerly the property of the Antique Porcelain Company.
8. Cecil Higgins Art Gallery, Bedford.
9. Formerly the property of D.M. and P. Mannheim and loaned by them for the Detroit Exhibition in 1954.

the Detroit Institute of Arts Exhibition of English Pottery and Porcelain in 1954. This example is not recorded as having a date or any inscription referring to Handel. It has the 'To' mark impressed. The only other recorded clock case,[10] was exhibited at the E.C.C. 50th Anniversary Exhibition in 1977 and illustrated in the catalogue (Sotheby Parke Bernet Publications, London 1977), No. 132. It has 'Nov. 5 1759' painted at the head of a letter and one of the music sheets is headed 'Handle'. The figure of Father Time on it is different from that on the other three. The 'To' mark is impressed on the base. The significance of the date is not known. None of the music inscribed on these clock cases can be attributed to George Frederick Handel, who died on 14 April 1759.

The 'Handel' vase is of double-ogee shape with rustic handles and rococo scroll moulding picked out in puce, and has scattered applied flowers picked out in enamel colours. Three putti stand round the vase on an enlarged base, and from their attributes we know that they symbolize Music, Drama and the Dance. Round the sides are four reserves and one of these is painted with music sheets entitled 'Minuette', 'Song' and 'Waltz'. The first of these is identical to the music sheet painted on the clock case inscribed 'To great handle . . .' etc.,[7] but the vase is not dated and carries no inscription referring to Handel. One of the music sheets is headed by the initials 'T.F.' It is a matter of conjecture whether the initials refer to Thomas Frye, who retired from the factory in ill-health in 1759. Other examples of this vase are known[11] though none has painted music sheets as decoration. The attributes of the putti are varied in these other examples. The 'I^CG' 1761 teapot represents a leap forward into sophisticated form and decoration, but before that matter is discussed some of the more modest stock patterns of the period will be considered.

An important pattern is the somewhat formalized flower-spray arrangement shown in Plate 107 on a sparrow-beak jug. The central chrysanthemum is surrounded by a 'daisy', a rose and a poppy. The border design of a line in red with arches and dots beneath was applied to the outside of jugs (and bowls) but to the inside of coffee cups. The design was used extensively for tewares and was reproduced with remarkable consistency. A more elaborate version of the same design was used on large mugs (Colour Plate O). The border design, although basically similar, is also elaborated. The unpractical small handles on some late Bow mugs such as this one suggest they may have been intended for ornament rather than use. Another important stock pattern for tewares during the period 1759-76 continued the oriental theme (Plate 108). A Chinese lady is seated on a rock from which issue long trailing branches. She is offering a flower to a young boy. Another female figure points towards two large jars or garden seats. Variations include omission of the third figure and a version where the seated lady holds a fan instead of a flower. As usual when European

10. Formerly in the collection of Mrs Donald J. Morrison of Nova Scotia, sold at Sotheby's, 3 April 1973, lot 194.
11. Sotheby's, 3 December 1968, lot 37 and 10 December 1973, lot 204. Another example is in the Northampton Museum (reserve collection).

107. SPARROW-BEAK JUG
decorated in enamels with a flower
spray including a central
chrysanthemum, a 'daisy', a rose
and a poppy. Loop and dot border
in red. One of the commonest
patterns for teawares over the
period 1758–70. Height 7.8 cm
(3 in)
See page 180

108. SPARROW-BEAK JUG
decorated in enamels with Chinese
figures including a lady offering a
flower to a boy. Height 7.6 cm (3 in)
1758–70
See page 180

painters attempt to depict orientals, the faces tend to be 'Europeanized'. The
converse was true of the Chinese portrayal of Europeans.

The design and decoration of vases underwent a notable change from about
1759 onwards with the virtual abandonment of the classic oriental shapes and
the introduction from the Continent of complicated designs with elaborate
decoration. A typical example is the pot-pourri vase illustrated in Appendix X,
No. 17. It was the most popular vase during the early sixties and there are
many surviving examples. The Derby factory made an exactly similar one. A
very rare example decorated in underglaze blue is mentioned in Chapter 11
(Plate 101). A trumpet-shaped vase pierced at the top, with a domed cover and
bird knop, is in similar vein (Appendix X, No. 18). There were probably more
baskets, tubs (Plate 109) and sheaves of flowers produced at Bow than
elsewhere. Sheaves of flowers were produced in at least two sizes and were
sometimes made in a 'flatback' way as if to adorn a mantlepiece. A remarkably
large one is in the Museum of London (reserve collection). A striking pattern of
this period (Plate 110) was the decoration of octagonal and shaped oval dishes
with large fruiting vines, sometimes in relief. The turquoise and green leaves

109. TUB of realistically modelled flowers decorated in bright enamel colours. Height 18.4 cm (7.25 in). 1760–5. *Albert Amor Ltd. See page 181*

110. OCTAGONAL DISH decorated in enamels with fruiting vine branches, the turquoise and green leaves edged in pink and yellow, with a central flower spray. Length 33 cm (13 in). 1759–65. *Courtesy of Sotheby's. See page 181*

111. LEAF-SHAPED MOULDED DISH with a peg handle surmounted by a moulded flowerhead, decorated in enamels with flower sprays and edged in brown. One of six from a table centrepiece. Various incised marks including numerals 2 and 7. Length 10.6 cm (4.2 in). 1760–5. *See page 183*

are edged with pink and yellow and at the centre there is a large bouquet of natural flowers. A similar bouquet with scattered flowers is the decorative theme of the rare shape of butter tub, cover and stand shown in Colour Plate P. The knop is in the form of a cherry among applied leaves and the handles are in the form of flattened half-flowerheads. The same hand can be seen in the flower decoration of the unusual small dish (Plate 111) which, with at least five similar ones, was attached to a centrepiece (missing) by the cylindrical stem. As usual with specialized dishes of this kind the exact purpose is unknown to us. The 'I^{C}G' 1761 teapot[6] in the Glynn Vivial Art Gallery, Swansea, is notable in two respects. It is an example of scale-blue ground decoration at least as early as any on Worcester porcelain, and the bird and flower painting and gilding are of high quality. There are also two bands of roses and leaves painted in a way which is familiar on other unmarked Bow porcelain. On the other hand, there are examples of bird and flower painting of less good quality on later Bow porcelain of a kind which can also be identified on English mid-eighteenth-century porcelain from a number of factories including Worcester, Chelsea, Chelsea-Derby, Plymouth, Longton Hall and on some English-decorated Chinese porcelain as well. An example of this is illustrated in Plate 112, which is a lobed-rim plate[12] in the Worcester style with 'exotic' birds and insects painted in the

12. Christie's, 20 October 1969, lot 326 (illustrated). A Bow plate, diameter 21 cm (8.25 in), with gilt lobed rim, painted with exotic birds and insects in shaped reserves on a scale blue ground. Blue square seal and red anchor and dagger marks. A similar pair of plates is in the Museum of London (reserve collection) but the blue ground colour is not of the 'scale' kind.

reserves in bright enamels on a mazarin[13] ground of rather uneven texture. The reserves are framed in gilding and there is a gilt dentil-edge border. The plate is marked with an anchor and dagger in overglaze red. The device was for many years considered to be the factory mark of Bow porcelain but it occurs on only a small proportion of enamelled useful wares after about 1760 and on a larger proportion of figures after that date. Its exact significance is still a mystery but it is now considered to be the mark of an outside enameller on Bow porcelain. W. B. Honey[14] was the first to suggest that the anchor and dagger mark might have been applied to Bow porcelain enamelled in the workshop of James Giles of Kentish Town and Soho.[15] Honey made a very carefully argued case for identifying the painter of the 'dishevelled birds' which occur on a variety of English porcelain as an artist working in the atelier of James Giles, if not Giles himself. He thought the same hand occurred on some, but certainly not all, anchor and dagger marked Bow. Fruit painting in which some pieces are cut through is well known on Worcester porcelain but also occurs on anchor and dagger marked Bow (Plate 113).[16] Honey thought this also revealed the hand of the 'dishevelled bird' painter and likewise the remarkable cabbage-leaf moulded tureen in the Victoria and Albert Museum (C. 307–1927) which has a landscape with figures and flower sprays painted inside and also on the stand. Another example of fruit painting on anchor and dagger marked Bow porcelain is shown on the sauceboat illustrated in Plate 114.

There has never been any question that some Bow enamelled porcelain was outside-decorated from fairly early in the factory's history, as it is mentioned in Duesbury's London account book 1751–3[17]. Furthermore, among the surviving Bowcock papers (British Museum) and evidently addressed to John Bowcock are a number of invoices[18] from Richard Dyer 'at Mr Bolton's, Enameler, near the Church, Lambeth'.[19] The invoices list a number of easily

13. Named after Cardinal Mazarin for an unknown reason. Term used by the French to describe a deep purple-blue ground and more generally to describe any deep-blue even textured ground colour.
14. W. B. Honey, 'The Work of James Giles', E.C.C. Transactions, Vol. 1, No. 5, 1937, pp. 7–23, from a paper read on 19 November 1935.
15. For biographical information and evidence on the identification of enamel painting from the workshop of James Giles see Aubrey J. Toppin, 'Contributions to the History of Porcelain-making in London', E.C.C. Transactions, Vol. 1, No. 1, 1933, pp. 30–43. W. B. Honey, op. cit. H. R. Marshall, 'James Giles, Enameller', E.C.C. Transactions, Vol. 3, No. 1, 1951, pp. 1–9. R. J. Charleston, 'A decorator of porcelain and glass—James Giles in a new light', E.C.C. Transactions, Vol. 6, Pt. 3, 1967, pp. 292–316. Anne M. George, James Giles, China and Enamel Painter 1718–1780, Catalogue of an exhibition of porcelain and glass decorated in the atelier of James Giles, Albert Amor Ltd., 3–18 March 1977.
16. Hurlbutt, op. cit., Pl. 27a, p. 103. A similar plate is in the Museum of London (reserve collection).
17. Mrs Donald MacAlister, William Duesbury's London Account Book, London, 1931.
18. Hurlbutt, op. cit., pp. 69–72, reproduces six of these invoices.
19. This may be the John Bolton who, in association with William Kempson and Michael Alcock, started a porcelain factory in Kentish Town in 1755. Bolton had been induced by Kempson to 'quit the service of Messrs Crisp and Sanders, by whom he was then employed in their China Manufactory at Vauxhall' in order to work at or possibly to manage the Kentish

112. (*left*) PLATE with lobed rim decorated with mazarin blue ground with vase and urn-shaped reserves painted in enamels with 'exotic' birds and insects, gilt around reserves and gilt dentil rim. Marks: square seal in underglaze blue and anchor and dagger in overglaze red. Diameter 21 cm (8.25 in). 1765–70. *Museum of London. See page 183*

113. (*right*) PLATE with indented rim moulded with vine leaves and grapes decorated in enamels with fruit including cut fruit, gilt rim. Mark: an anchor and dagger in red enamel. Diameter 23.8 cm (9.4 in). 1765–70. *Museum of London. See page 184*

114. SAUCEBOAT decorated in enamels with a mazarin blue ground and fruit in a reserved edged with gilt scrolls. Anchor and dagger mark in red. Length 19 cm (7.5 in). 1765–70. *Museum of London. See page 184*

identified Bow figures such as 'slave candlesticks', 'Boys on Lyon and Leopard', 'Nuns and fryers' and a few useful wares, with prices against them. The scale of these charges makes it quite clear that the cost relates to a finishing operation such as enamelling and perhaps gilding rather than the cost of the object itself, as they amount to only about one quarter or less of the sums entered against similar items in the Bowcock memorandum of 1756. Invoices to the Bow concern imply contracted-out work, which is a totally different practice from that of Giles in purchasing parcels of porcelain from the manufacturer, decorating and then selling it direct from his own showroom. We know virtually nothing of Mr Bolton's establishment at Lambeth and it would be particularly interesting to know if it was related in any way to Nicholas Crisp's 'Manufactory of China at Lambeth'[20] whence Bolton came to Kentish Town in 1755 to establish the short-lived porcelain factory there. Crisp's establishment was sometimes described as being 'at Vauxhall', which is in the parish of Lambeth. Several potteries were located in this area. In a biographical sketch of the famous sculptor John Bacon, who was apprenticed to Crisp (1755–64), published in the *Gentleman's Magazine* in 1794 and again in 1799, the Revd Richard Cecil referred to the factory as 'the Lambeth hand of the Bow factory'. Nicholas Crisp was primarily a jeweller with premises at Bow Churchyard, Cheapside, over a long period (1752–64), though there is some suggestion that he may have had a porcelain-decorating business there as well.[21] With regard to the anchor and dagger mark and the Giles atelier, much depends on whether any of the painting on Bow with this mark can be linked with the Grubbe plates[22] which are the only examples of decoration known, with virtual certainty, to have been done in the Giles workshop. One of these is decorated with 'cut fruit' and flowers, which is a design commonly found on Worcester porcelain decorated in the Giles workshop but very rarely on Bow. Comparison of the Bow and Grubbe 'cut fruit' leaves one doubtful that they are by the same hand. Charleston[23] thought that more than one hand was involved in the 'cut fruit' painting on whatever porcelain it occurred. Another possibility to be considered is that the anchor and dagger mark was applied to all outside

Town enterprise. This soon failed and Kempson and Alcock were declared bankrupt in January 1756, the petitioner being John Bolton, who was owed money by Kempson for the payment of wages to the Kentish Town workers. It is clear from the petition that the 'buildings, sheds, mills and kilns' were erected at Kentish Town and that porcelain was actually produced but there is no evidence as to what type of ware was made. Bolton was evidently a potter of some repute in London and he was summoned (from the debtors' prison unfortunately) before both the Commons and the Lords in 1775 in connection with the Bill to extend Cookworthy's patent. See Aubrey J. Toppin, op. cit. (note 15 above).

20. *The British Magazine and Review or Universal Miscellany*, Vol. 1, p. 256, October 1782, in an article on the sculptor John Bacon. Quoted by Toppin, op. cit.

21. Aubrey J. Toppin, op. cit.

22. W. B. Honey, op. cit. These four plates are all undoubted Worcester porcelain all decorated in enamels with different patterns. They are in the Victoria and Albert Museum.

23. R. J. Charleston, op. cit. (note 15 above).

decorated Bow wherever and whenever it was done simply as a means of differentiating it at the warehouse from the factory enamelled wares, for accounting purposes. That would accord with the 'contracted-out' decoration mentioned above.

An important stock pattern[24] with the anchor and dagger mark which was used for the decoration of tablewares consists of a central eight-pointed star of dark blue (underglaze) edged with gold with a central 'sunburst' design in gold. Around the star there are exotic birds on leafy branches with scattered insects. The border is often of gilt dentil-edge type. A point of interest with regard to outside decoration is that where underglaze blue was involved this was always done at the factory with appropriate reserves left white. Bow sometimes marked wares of the kind with a dot or cross in underglaze blue and in some instances with a dagger or a capital letter ('A' is recorded), so this mark occurs in addition to the overglaze-red or occasionally gilt anchor and dagger. Examples of contemporary similar wares with and without anchor and dagger marks are illustrated in Plate 115 (without) and Plate 116 (with). Although the design of neither vase can be regarded as an unqualified artistic triumph, the quality of painting and gilding on the former (unmarked) one is notably better than on the latter.

Selection on the grounds of quality is not a reliable guide, however, and the ambitious design of the plate (anchor and dagger mark in red) in the French manner (Plate 117) with *gros bleu* border, elaborate goldwork and Watteauesque scene, is a rather better example of what the outside decorator could achieve. The great variation in quality of outside decoration on all English porcelain is probably an indication that a number of establishments were involved in this work and that the preoccupation with Giles is unwarranted.

The remarkable punch bowl in Plate 12B[25] (see page 76) was made to special order for the Masonic Royal White Hart Lodge, Number Two, at Halifax, North Carolina. The Lodge minutes for the meeting of 28 December 1767 are preserved and the order was worded: '4 bowls Bow China to hold 1 gallon each with the words Enameled upon them Halifax Lodge Nº Carolina.' The latter instruction covered twelve dozen glasses and nine decanters ordered along with the bowl. It is the only known reference to an order for Bow porcelain decorated specially for the American market. Underglaze blue is used for the cartouche, the name and eight fringed swags with diaper on the inside rim, and overglaze red for the masonic symbols (rubbed), tassels and cord and the four interior flowering branches. The calligraphy is typical for Bow. The exterior has a turquoise ground of uneven texture with reserved panels edged with gilt

24. Illustrated in colour by Egan Mew, *Old Bow China*, published in the Masterpieces of Handicraft series, Jack, London, 1909, Pl. IX.
25. B. L. Rauschenberg, 'A Documented Bow Bowl made for Halifax Lodge North Carolina', *Journal of Early Southern Decorative Arts*, Vol. 1, No. 1, May 1975.

115. OVOID VASE with applied scrollwork, 'frill' and flowers, decorated in enamels and gilding and painted in the centre with exotic birds in a landscape. Height inc. cover 30 cm (11.75 in). 1768–75. *Museum of London.*
See page 187 and Appendix X, No. 22

116. BALUSTER VASE on a
high pierced foot with shaped
pierced handles and applied
flowers, the neck and lid
pierced, decorated in enamels
and gilding and painted in
the centre with an exotic bird
and foliage. Mark: an
anchor and dagger in red.
Height inc. cover 29 cm
(11.5 in)
1768–75
*Museum of London. See page
187 and Appendix X, No. 21*

117. PLATE with *gros bleu*
rim and feathered edge in gilt
the centre painted in enamels
with Watteauesque figures in
a landscape. Mark: an anchor
and dagger in red. Diameter
23.5 cm (9.25 in)
1768–70
*Albert Amor Ltd. See page
187*

118. BELL-SHAPED MUG decorated in enamels and
lavishly gilt with the figures of a shepherd and shepherdess
in a fantastic landscape. Heart-shaped handle terminal and
gilt dentil border. Height 11.4 cm (4.5 in). 1770–5. *Luton
Hoo. See page 190*

rococo scrollwork enclosing exotic birds amongst palms. On the reverse there is
a large bouquet of natural flowers. The gilt footrim pattern is similar to a
border pattern used on earlier underglaze-blue wares. The lack of a mark
supports the theory of factory decoration. The bowl was probably made in
1768 and was recovered, broken, from a rubbish pile in recent times.

The only example of dated enamelled Bow of the late period is the
remarkable Bromley mug[26] in the British Museum which is enamelled with a
reclining shepherd boy talking to a standing milkmaid in a fantastic landscape
of rococo scrolls and foliage. On the reverse is a man in Eastern costume and
turban smoking a very long-stemmed pipe. On the base in enamel is inscribed,
'This Pint was Painted for Mrs Mary Bromley of Campden Gloc[shire] by her
Loving Son John D[e] Lanauze January 1770.' The only known counterpart is a
mug (Plate 118) in the Wernher Collection, Luton Hoo, with different subjects.
The gilt dentil edge and unfamiliar enamelling on the Luton Hoo mug suggest
outside decoration, but the absence of any mark is perhaps against this.

26. Tait, *Bow Porcelain 1744–1776*, op. cit., Cat No. 120, Figs. 47–49.

13
Bow Figures 1753–1775
including Animal Models

We have seen that Meissen influence on figure models produced at Bow was not apparent, with only one exception,[1] in the four years or so between the factory's foundation and 1752. When Meissen figures became available thereafter—and we have no idea how this occurred at Bow[2]—it seems that most of the models were of a considerably earlier period. That is evident from the figure bases, which were severely baroque at Meissen up to about 1740, often in the form of a plinth as used for full-sized statuary. There is a brief manifestation of this at Bow with a few of the Kitty Clive figures being mounted on a high formal plinth, but that was more or less the end of it. The Meissen modellers had, by about 1745, changed to a rounded pad base[3] with scattered applied flowers giving the impression that the figures were disporting themselves in a flowery meadow in the open air.[4] The majority of Bow copies of the period 1753–6 have bases of the kind, ten years after they were first introduced at Meissen. The earliest evidence of rococo at Meissen occurs on chinoiserie figure groups[5] of about 1745 and the style is being more widely applied by 1749. Apart from the Ki-Mao-Sao group,[6] which has a suggestion of rococo scrollwork, the earliest rococo at Bow is the Liberty and Matrimony pair (Plate 4)[7] of about 1753 by the 'Muses modeller'. It shows definite if rather

1. 'Negress with basket'. See Chapter 9, note 12.
2. It is possible that Meissen figures or at least the designs were brought to Bow by workmen from the German factory. An advertisement in the *Public Advertiser* gave notice of two sales by public auction to be held in 1758, by order of the Bow proprietors, of the entire stock of their warehouse on the 'Terrace in St. James' Street', which was given up at that time. The second of these sales commenced 10 April 1758 and in the introduction by Mr Lambe, the auctioneer mentions 'Service of Dishes and Plates, Sauceboats, Bowls, Compleat Tea and Coffee Equipages, a large Assortment of fine Enamel and fine Partridge Sets, which are most beautifully painted by several of the finest Masters from Dresden etc.' No evidence in support of this statement has been forthcoming. J. E. Nightingale, *Contributions toward the History of Early English Porcelain*, Salisbury, 1881, p. xlix.
3. Sometimes referred to as a 'mound' base.
4. Arthur Lane, *English Porcelain Figures of the Eighteenth Century*, Faber and Faber, 1961, p. 45.
5. Figure of 'Chinese lovers in an arbour'. Eberlein, *c.* 1745. British Museum.
6. See Chapter 9, Plate 71, note 32.
7. Arthur Lane, op. cit, Pls. 44 and 45, and p. 89.

half-hearted rococo scrolls on the base. This implies that they were copied within a short time, perhaps a mere two or three years, after their production at Meissen. The large figure of a Boy with a flower vase on his head (Plate 119) of about 1753 also has rudimentary rococo scrolls on the base but he is not known to derive from a Meissen original. Up to a point, Bow seems to have suffered from the same problem as Chelsea, which had to rely on Sir Charles Hanbury Williams' collection for models to copy. Although conveniently located in London at Holland House, the collection was representative of an earlier period. The exception to the rule noted at Bow—the figure of a negress with a basket—implies access to another source of Meissen figures. Indeed, it would be surprising if the enterprising and resourceful proprietors at Bow, two of them for long engaged in the china trade, had not found a way round the problem.[2] It was pure coincidence that the English factories were getting started just at the time when the most profound change in artistic style in eighteenth-century Europe occurred. A consequence of the late start at Bow and other English porcelain factories was that the change from baroque to rococo was compressed into a relatively short time-span compared to the more 'natural' evolution that occurred on the Continent.

Evidence for the evolution of style by a study of the bases of porcelain figures is rewarding because it is 'internal' factory evidence, often completely independent of the source used for a figure model. But much was subordinated to the requirements of support and stabilization during the firing. Lane, in an excellent review[8] of the techniques involved in the manufacture of porcelain figures, suggests that there is no evidence for the use of stilts or supports for the projecting parts of figures. That view must be modified in the light of finds on the factory site during the 1969 excavations, when numerous such supports were found. They took the form of slender rods tapering to a fine point at one end, to minimize the area of contact, and were made of porcelain indistinguishable from the body of the figures themselves. The purpose of this was to ensure that shrinkage was similar for both figure and support. Such support would only be required during the biscuit firing, when the different parts of the assembled figure would become fused. The great problem for the porcelain figure modeller was the fact that erect man is supported by two rather insubstantial pillars—his legs. It works well enough in life because of the active participation of opposing muscle groups combined with a sense of balance. The static inanimate figure must be finely balanced and well supported, or otherwise it will distort or sag when in a semi-plastic state at the peak of firing. Alas, many figures did distort in this way and no doubt there was a proportion of complete failures. Curiously, none of the three excavations on the Bow site or nearby has produced much waster material from figures. Some examples of finished figures with obvious defects acquired during manufacture have been mentioned (Chapter 9) and that may indicate a reluctance by the proprietors to

8. Arthur Lane, op. cit, ch. 2.

119. STANDING BOY with a flower vase on his head. Height 37.7 cm (14.8 in).
1752–4. *Victoria and Albert Museum. See pages 142, 192*

120. LOVER BLOWING A KISS in the early free-standing version. Height 17.8 cm
(7 in). 1753–5. *Victoria and Albert Museum. See page 193*

accept a total loss on a product so time-consuming and troublesome to
manufacture.

There are some rare Meissen figures of the 1730s which are free-standing,
that is, without a base, standing on their feet. It was a very remarkable technical
achievement but it was not continued, probably because of the difficulties of
support during firing, and the finished figures must have been very vulnerable
to accidental damage. However, to those accustomed to eighteenth-century
porcelain figures with their conventional bases the appearance of these free-
standing models is very striking, the life-like quality enhanced by their very
vulnerability. This must have represented an experimental phase because
some of the very earliest Meissen figures in red stoneware, *c.* 1715, were on
plain square bases similar to those used later. Surprisingly, there is an echo of
these free-standing figures in the faithful Bow copy of the 'Lover blowing a
kiss' (Plate 120), where he has one foot firmly on the ground while the other is
concealed in part of his long dressing-gown, which forms a larger area for

121. STANDING COW AND BULL after Meissen originals. Height 15.2 cm (6 in). 1755–8. *Courtesy of Sotheby's. See page 194*

contact.[9] It is the only known Bow example of anything of the kind. The companion figure[10] of a 'Lady striking a pose' (the pair derive from a German play) is notable for her unusual tiered skirt. It is the skirt which was used to disguise the supporting pillar rising from the base which secured her stability during firing. This figure pair first appear about 1755 at Bow and there are two later versions with different bases and in these her attire is changed as well.

Many ingenious devices were invented at Meissen to overcome the problem of support during firing which we so often take for granted in the finished figure. The skirt, especially the pannier skirt, was a great boon to the modeller and repairer as it was a ready-made solution to the problem of concealing the means of support. Likewise long clothes in the male figures. Seating the figure was useful and with a group the figures could sometimes be arranged to give mutual support. The 'Muses modeller' 'Charity' group[11] is a modest example of this and there is a notable Meissen chinoiserie group[12] of a standing Lady with two children, one crouched on the ground, the other standing, where, by contact at different levels, a chain of support is established. The final admission of defeat was represented by the ubiquitous 'stump' with a few applied leaves placed a little to the back of a figure. It seems that four legs were little better than two for support and both the Meissen figure of a cow by Reinicke[13] and the Bow copies (Plate 121)[14] were given massive and conspicuous stumps

9. Egan Mew, *Old Bow China*, Jack, London, 1909, Pl. XV. Hurlbutt, op. cit., illustrates a later model, Pl. 57.
10. There is a late version in the Lady Ludlow Collection at Luton Hoo.
11. Arthur Lane, op. cit., Pl. 42, pp. 48, 87.
12. Antique Porcelain Company.
13. The Earl of Shrewsbury and Waterford Collection.
14. Sotheby's, 24 November 1970, lot 73.

122. RECUMBENT LION AND LIONESS pair. Length 27.3 cm (10.75 in).
1750–5. *Courtesy of Christie's. See page 195*

123. LION AND LIONESS pair in white seated with one front paw raised on a
stump. Height 10.2 cm (4 in).
1753–8. *Courtesy of Sotheby's. See page 195*

under their bellies. Equestrian figures all suffered the same fate.[15] Lions seem
to have gripped the imagination of the Bow modellers and there are at least four
basic models all derived from Meissen originals. In two the lions are recumbent
(Plate 122),[16] in another pair, the most popular, the lion and lioness are
sitting on their haunches, with one paw raised on a small pillar and the other
extended, on the ground, forming a triangular support (Plate 123).[17] In the

15. Bow figure of a 'Polish hussar on horseback', Schreiber Collection, Victoria and Albert
Museum, also Meissen figure of a mounted peasant, Cecil Higgins Art Gallery, Bedford.
16. Christie's, 22 March 1965, lot 27. There is a similar pair in the Museum of London (reserve
collection).
17. Sotheby's, 7 November 1967, lot 45.

only Bow standing lion pair[18] support is given to each animal by a flowering tree placed immediately behind but in contact with the lion's flank. That stands in contrast to at least one successful attempt at Meissen to manufacture free-standing quadrupeds without bases or support 'stumps'.[19]

The figure of a Sailor (Plate 124), mentioned in Chapter 9, reappears on a rudimentary rococo base but with arms outstretched and feet in a barely discernible dancing position.[20] He is sometimes catalogued as the figure of Tom Bowling. He reappears again[21] after 1760 on the full-blown four-footed rococo scroll base which became something of a hallmark for Bow porcelain. The reappearance of figures on these later bases is a constant theme at Bow from the middle 1750s to the end. It is difficult to avoid the conclusion that the constant reuse of earlier figure models was necessitated in part by the lack of new material from Meissen over the period of the Seven Years War 1757-63, and the subsequent decline in artistic innovation there. The development of the figure model itself must be closely observed in relation to the base. Sometimes, as with the Sailor, the figure itself is virtually unchanged despite changes in the base. We must, however, remain aware that a different base does not always imply a different time of manufacture. The evidence for this is contained in the invoices (Chapter 12, note 18) to the company from Richard Dyer the enameller where '12 Boys not with plints' and '6 Boys with plints' are listed in one invoice dated 19 July 1760. Another invoice for 5 May 1760 lists '2 sets of Small Seasons, no plints'. The charges made were for colouring and the 'Boys not with plints' cost a penny less than the boys with. That implies that for some figures there was a choice of a more elaborate or simpler base at the time of sale. Evidence from dated contemporary documents is often useful in confirming the existence of figure models at the time. Duesbury's account book (Chapter 12, note 17) for January 1753 refers to 'Bogh Seasons'. This is likely to refer to the busts after Meissen originals on shaped plinths (Plate 125) marbled in manganese, the attributes of the seasons being displayed in the head-dresses of the figures.[22] The figure of Winter is a rare survivor of these sets. The invoice made out to the 'Hon. Gen. Clayton' (Chapter 5, page 85) includes '1 pr. Enameld Ballad Singers'. It is probable that that refers to the squat figures (Plate 126) of a man playing a hurdy-gurdy and his companion carrying a cradle with a sleeping baby,[23] after Meissen originals. Lane warns us that from 1753 the influence of Meissen on figure models at the English factories was so all-pervading that it is unsafe to say that any figure might not be either a direct copy or derived from a Meissen original. We have already

---

18. Sotheby's, 19 July 1966, lot 131, coloured.
19. A free-standing lion and lioness, coloured, Collection Nelson A. Rockefeller.
20. Sotheby's, 23 February 1971, lot 183.
21. Arthur Lane, op. cit., Pl. 55, p. 92.
22. Hurlbutt, op. cit., Pl. 47A, p. 121, also Sotheby's, 22 October 1968, lot 58.
23. Sotheby's, 20 July 1971, lot 2 in white. There is a coloured version of the pair in the Victoria and Albert Museum with a garbled inscription.

124. SAILOR with
outstretched arms,
standing on an early
rococo base. Height
17.8 cm (7 in)
1753–8
*Courtesy of Sotheby's. See
pages 146, 196*

125. BUSTS on shaped marbled plinths representing Spring, Summer and Autumn.
Height 15.2 cm (6 in).1753–7. *Courtesy of Sotheby's. See page 196*

126. HURDY-GURDY PLAYER AND HIS WIFE in white, carrying a cradle with sleeping baby. Coloured versions are known. Height 15.9 cm (6.25 in). 1753–6. *Courtesy of Sotheby's. See page 196*

come to one, however, the figure of the Thames Waterman (Plate 127: see Chapter 9) and we shall undoubtedly find others, but there are not many. Another pair listed in the Clayton bill is '1 pr. ditto fluter and companion with Tabor'. Male and female figures playing the flute are numerous and the men are apt to be called 'piping shepherds' whether sheep are present or not. There are in fact a large number of figure models, male and female, playing musical instruments and they derive from an important Meissen series of street musicians. The instruments featured include the flute, zither, bagpipes, hurdy-gurdy, tambour, drum, violin, lute, mandolin, cello and salt-box. A dog is often present, sometimes in a begging attitude. After 1759 the musician figures become rather less the street-musician beggar type and are generally more sophisticated and better dressed, and appear more at home in the music room or even with the orchestra. No pair as early as those listed in the Clayton bill have come to light but their descendants are illustrated by Egan Mew in his book *Old Bow China*, published in 1909, where they are called 'idyllic musicians'.[24] Figures mentioned in the Bowcock memorandum of 1756 are listed in Chapter 5 and are a useful reference to some of the models available in that year. Without exception they derive from Meissen. The standing Huntsman with his distinctive cap and long muzzle-loading flintlock and his companion, known as 'sporters', were a popular pair. A slightly less familiar pair are illustrated in Plate 128. A Lady Falconer with a dog at her feet is

24. Egan Mew, op. cit., Pl. XVI.

127. THAMES WATERMAN
wearing Doggett's coat with
its special badge and a cap.
Height 22.2 cm (8.75 in)
1753–5
*Courtesy of Sotheby's. See
page 142, 198*

128A, B. SPORTSMAN (*a*) AND COMPANION (*b*). Height 13.3 cm (5.25 in).
1754–7. *Courtesy of Sotheby's. See page 198*

129. PAIR OF HOUNDS, often referred to as 'dismal hounds'. The figure of a recumbent puppy is also known. Height 8.9 cm (3.5 in). 1755–9. *See page 200*

sometimes shown as the companion although this is not a sport compatible with the gun. The dog at the feet of the Huntsman is a close relative of the famous Bow 'dismal hounds' (Plate 129), which are examples of highly sympathetic modelling after the Meissen originals. The Bow animal models are a rather neglected group and have not been systematically considered by earlier writers. They are frequently of great merit and their number is considerable. What Lane said about figures after 1753 applies with equal force to the animal and bird models—it would be unsafe to say that any were not derived from Meissen. They are more difficult to date than the human figures, but the following are listed in the Bowcock memorandum of 1756: swans, swans with wings spread, white boars, bucks, birds on pedestals, squirrels, coloured squirrels and goats. Bow swans seem to be exceedingly rare, also white boars. Pugs must have been popular, to judge from the number surviving. There were three basic models, one with the dog scratching and the others with it sitting, alert, sometimes with its head turned to the tail (Plate 130). The base was often formed as a cushion with tassels at the corners, otherwise as a simple pad mound with a ring inset to attach a lead. There are white and coloured versions. The 'birds on pedestals' could refer to a number of different models. The commonest support for a single bird was a simple stump with a few applied flowers. The variety of birds is surprising and includes cocks and hens (Plate 131), ducks, pheasants and partridges as tureens (Plate 132), herons,[25]

25. Hurlbutt, op. cit., Pl. 21.

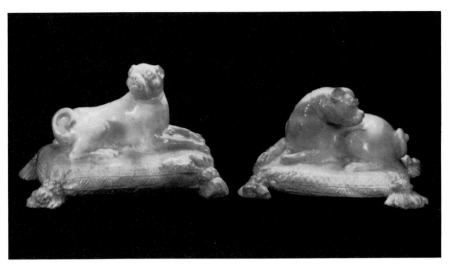

130. PAIR OF PUG DOGS in white, recumbent on tasselled cushions. Height (head erect) 8.3 cm (3.25 in). 1756–60. *Courtesy of Sotheby's. See page 200*

131. COCK AND HEN on a simple mound base with applied leaves and flowers. Height 10.8 cm (4.25 in). 1754–8. *Albert Amor Ltd. See page 200*

132. NESTING PARTRIDGE in the form of a soup tureen.
Height 12 cm (4.75 in). 1758–63. *Albert Amor Ltd. See page 200*

133. PEACOCK AND PEAHEN perched on flowering tree-stumps.
Height 18.25 cm (7.25 in). 1754–8. *Courtesy of Sotheby's. See page 203*

134. GOLDFINCH perched on a
flowering branch on a
raised four-pillar base.
Height 12.7 cm (5 in). 1756–60
Courtesy of Sotheby's. See page 203

135. SEATED CAT with an alert expression.
Height 7.4 cm (2.9 in). 1753–8
Albert Amor Ltd. See page 203

peacocks and peahens (Plate 133), kestrels,[26] owls,[27] parrots, sometimes on
raised four-footed bases,[28] pigeons (as tureens and as figure models),
bullfinches, goldfinches (Plate 134), buntings, wagtails and canaries.[29] Other
animals seen include deer, sheep in various attitudes, goats and kids,[30] monkeys,
sometimes with their young, squirrels, hares and cats (Plate 135), sometimes
with a doomed mouse.

26. Sotheby's, 17 March 1970, lot 158.
27. A pair of tawny owls is in the Victoria and Albert Museum.
28. A pair of parrots on raised four-pillar bases, Sotheby's, 11 May 1971, lot 187.
29. A pair of canaries in white. Christie's, 22 March 1965, lot 26.
30. A goat and kid standing in front of a flowering shrub on an oval mound base with applied
flowers.

Appendix I

Royal Exchange Assurance Fire Policies, concerning the Green Yard Glasshouse, East Smithfield

Vol. I 9 July 1754 29777 Surveyed & approved July ye 8 1754 Thos. Mutter	Geo. Harrison, John Weatherby, Jnº Crowther & Thos. Quinton, On their New Glasshouse and two Warehouses adjoining timber built situate on the left hand side of their Yard in the Green Yard at East Smithfield £300 Utensils & Goods in Trade in the same 200 On Goods in Trade in their Old Glasshouse & in 10 Warehouses adjoining in the Rooms over them timber built situate on the Right Hand Side of the Yard aforesaid 1000 Agreed the above £1200 on Glass @ 5p. Cent ———— £1500

```
300 @ 3p.c.        –  9 –
1200 @ 5p.c.     3  – –
                 _____

                 3  9 –
                    7 6
                 _____

              £3 16 6
```

Vol. IV 1756 16 Aug. 32268 Survey'd ye New Warehouse Augᵗ 14 1756 & approved Thos. Mutter	Jnº Weatherby, Jnº Crowther, Thos. Quinton, (Richard) Windle of the Green Yard East Smithfield On Household Furniture in the Dwelling House of the said Thomas Quinton brick built situate on the West Side of their Yard in the Green Yard aforesaid being his own Property £200 On their New Glass House & 2 Warehouses adjoining timber built situate on the South Side of the said Yard 300 Utensils & Goods in Trade in the same 200 On the New Warehouse & Sheds adjoining part timber built situate on the North Side of the Yard aforesaid 70 On the Fitments of the said Warehouse 30 Trade in the same, in 4 Warehouses adjoining, in the Rooms over them & in ye Old Glasshouse adjoing timber built 900 ———— £1700

(Premium £3 16 0) Return £3 2 9 for 10 months 3 weeks & 4 days unexpired time on this Policy. Agreed the above £1100 on Glass @ 5p. Cent.

Vol. VI	Thos. Quinton & Richard Windle of the Green Yard	
5 Oct. 1758	Eastsmithfield (sic)	
34583	On Household Furniture in ye Dwelling House of the said	
	Thos. Quinton brick built situate on the West side of their	
	Yard in the Green Yard aforesaid being his own Property	£200
	On their New Glass House & 2 Warehouses adjoining	
	timber built situate on ye South Side of the said Yard	300
	Utensils & Goods in Trade in the same	200
	On the New Warehouse & Sheds adjoining part timber	
	built situate on the North Side of ye said Yard	70
	On the fitments of the said Warehouse	30
	Trade in the same & in 4 Warehouses adjoining & in ye	
	Rooms over them & in ye Old Glass House adjoining	
	timber built	900
		————
		£1700

Agreed ye above £1100 on Glass @ 5/– p. Cent (Premium £3 17 0.)

Appendix II

List of Ships mentioned in the Schedule of Debtors to the Benjamin Weatherby Executors of John Higgons Co-Partnership, July 1775

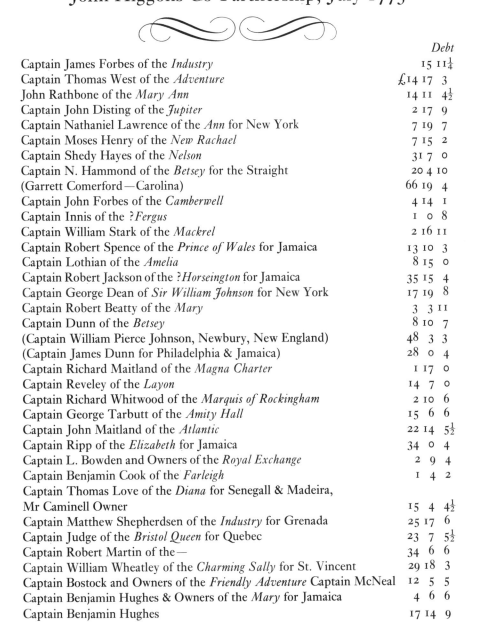

	Debt
Captain James Forbes of the *Industry*	15 11¼
Captain Thomas West of the *Adventure*	£14 17 3
John Rathbone of the *Mary Ann*	14 11 4½
Captain John Disting of the *Jupiter*	2 17 9
Captain Nathaniel Lawrence of the *Ann* for New York	7 19 7
Captain Moses Henry of the *New Rachael*	7 15 2
Captain Shedy Hayes of the *Nelson*	31 7 0
Captain N. Hammond of the *Betsey* for the Straight	20 4 10
(Garrett Comerford — Carolina)	66 19 4
Captain John Forbes of the *Camberwell*	4 14 1
Captain Innis of the *?Fergus*	1 0 8
Captain William Stark of the *Mackrel*	2 16 11
Captain Robert Spence of the *Prince of Wales* for Jamaica	13 10 3
Captain Lothian of the *Amelia*	8 15 0
Captain Robert Jackson of the *?Horseington* for Jamaica	35 15 4
Captain George Dean of *Sir William Johnson* for New York	17 19 8
Captain Robert Beatty of the *Mary*	3 3 11
Captain Dunn of the *Betsey*	8 10 7
(Captain William Pierce Johnson, Newbury, New England)	48 3 3
(Captain James Dunn for Philadelphia & Jamaica)	28 0 4
Captain Richard Maitland of the *Magna Charter*	1 17 0
Captain Reveley of the *Layon*	14 7 0
Captain Richard Whitwood of the *Marquis of Rockingham*	2 10 6
Captain George Tarbutt of the *Amity Hall*	15 6 6
Captain John Maitland of the *Atlantic*	22 14 5½
Captain Ripp of the *Elizabeth* for Jamaica	34 0 4
Captain L. Bowden and Owners of the *Royal Exchange*	2 9 4
Captain Benjamin Cook of the *Farleigh*	1 4 2
Captain Thomas Love of the *Diana* for Senegall & Madeira, Mr Caminell Owner	15 4 4½
Captain Matthew Shepherdsen of the *Industry* for Grenada	25 17 6
Captain Judge of the *Bristol Queen* for Quebec	23 7 5½
Captain Robert Martin of the —	34 6 6
Captain William Wheatley of the *Charming Sally* for St. Vincent	29 18 3
Captain Bostock and Owners of the *Friendly Adventure* Captain McNeal	12 5 5
Captain Benjamin Hughes & Owners of the *Mary* for Jamaica	4 6 6
Captain Benjamin Hughes	17 14 9

	Debt		
Captain Evers & Owners of the *Susannah* for Jamaica	4	0	0
Thomas Ewen, Doctor of the *Charming Sally*	11	1	6
Captain Malaghlin of the *Isabella* for Carthagena	49	6	6

The names of many other Captains are included in the list, but without the name of the ship also it is not possible to prove their title naval rather than military.

Appendix III
Thomas Frye's Epitaph

An Epitaph
To the Memory of THOMAS FRYE, a PAINTER.
Ireland gave him his birth, & Nature his Profession.
To London he very early resorted,
Where his great talents could not long lie undiscovered.
About the age of twenty-eight he had the honour of painting his R.H. Frederick Pr. of Wales.
His Genius was not confined to that Art,
For he was the Inventor and first Manufacturer of PORCELAIN in England:
To bring which to Perfection
He spent fifteen years among Furnaces,
Till his Constitution was near destroyed:
He therefore quitted these works, and retired into Wales
(Expecting with Resignation the Fate common to ALL)
Change of Country soon restored him to Health:
In twelve months he returned to London,
And resumed his original Profession.
At once he broke out upon the World
As the Sun from behind a Cloud,
And sunk as suddenly as that sinks in the Deep.
To his beloved Art he fell a Martyr;
For his intense Application
Brought on his Dissolution with the Haste of the most precipitate Consumption:
He waved his hand, as if painting,
Till the final Gasp put an End to his Labours.
This happened on the second day of April, 1762;
When he was arrived at his fifty-second year.
No one was more happy in delineating the human Countenance:
He had the correctness of Van-Dyke, & the Colouring of Rubens.
In miniature painting he equalled, if not excelled, the famous Cooper;
And left some fine Specimens of his Abilities for that sort of engraving called Mezzo-Tinto.
To say he was an honest Man, is but barely to do him Justice,
For he inherited every social Virtue.
And you who are no Strangers to the heart-breaking Pang
When the ghastly Tyrant severs the strongest knot of Amity,
Can only know what his Friends felt on the Loss of him.

1764, published in the *Gentleman's Magazine*

Appendix IV
John Bowcock's Memorandum Book

1756

Insure £450 on board the Antilope: John Cowling. Mr Crowther paid Thos. Osborne for an anchor for the ship Antilope £12: 1: 0.

2 doz. crimson buttons for Mr Frye.

Jany. 29. Mr Fogg: a sprig'd sallad vessel, 12s.; 1 pair sprig'd boats, 6s; 16 cooks, 2s each, abated; a swan; two harlequins (returned), 7s.

March. Mr Fahy: 9 gentlemen and ladies at 9s, £4: 1s;

Mr White; 1 small fluter, white; 3 pair of boys and girls; 1 pair small fiddler and companion; 1 pair tambourines; 1 cook.

Mr Fogg: 2 doz. odd cups and 2 doz. imag'd small; 2 pair imag'd ewers; 6 swans; 6 white boars; 6 sprig'd handled cups and 6 cans; 1 pair sauce boats, Mr Vere's pattern, 4s; 1 pair large ribbed boats 4s; 1 large dragon milk-pot; 12 dragon breakfast cups and saucers with a good deep colour; 1 sprig'd upright teapot 3s; 1 sprig'd cream ewer; 24 octagon nappy plates, partridge pattern; 1 vine leaf milk-pot.

March 27. Mrs Ann Howard, the Lamb, in Broad Mead, Bristol: 10 round dishes; 2 of each size from the smallest to the largest, both included; 1 largest octagon dish. 1 next less size dish; 36 table plates; 12 soup plates; 2 pair ribbed boats; 3 pair flat salts without feet; they must all be the bordered image, blue and pale, as you please. She has it greatly in her power to serve the factory. I hope they will be very neat and charged reasonable; I have not told her any price. Add one soup dish, 13 or not above 14 inches oval; 12 table plates. Imag'd pale blue.

Quy. What's to be done with white bud sprigs; what quy. of Cupids and B. is wanted white; what floras etc.

Apl. 22. Colol. Griffin. Brook Street, 4 small upright pint mugs to be painted to the very finest landskip pattern, as soon as possible.

Apl. 22. 4 doz. blue plates, Newark pattern; 8 doz. mosaic do.

Apl. 28. Lord Southwell. Mr Heylin has promised him to make an oval tureen, the image pattern, and to be done in 6 weeks without fail. Think of the chinese head for Mr Weatherby.

May 4. Mr Vanderkist: an enamelled partridge coffee-pot, 9s.

Mr White: 1 imag'd cup and 7 sprig'd chocolates. What is meant by 36 white men with salt-boxes? Mr Hunter desires to have some mustard ladles as the cream ladles, only small boles and long handles; 6 enamelled roses; 2 pr. green leaf candlesticks; 4 white leaf candlesticks.

Mr Kentish: Mandrill coffee-pot.

Mr Fogg: 2 swans, wings open.

Mrs Whitfield to have 1 pr. white branch candlesticks. Mr Williams, 1 pr. sporters; 1 enamelled pero, 6s. 1 shepherd, imperial, 7s; Q shepherdess, 9s.

May 7. Quy. whether any Windsor bricks were received at the glass house, which is charged to the porcelain company.

Paid Mr Heylin, Minshull's draft, £10, 10s 0d. J.B. paid Sir Joseph Hankey for Messrs. Weatherby and Crowther, £348, 18s. 0d.

Mr Fahy: 1 pr. of the new shepherd and compn.; 1 pr. Dutch dancers, 9s; 1 gentleman and lady, 18s; 1 cook, 7s; 1 boy and girl, 12s; 1 Paris cries, 6s; 1 woman with chicken, 7s.

Whether any bucks is wanted? There was 5 pair sent down, and only 1 pair came back.

Send down what does there is in town, and send down the Bow books.

May 28. Patterns received from Lady Cavendish: a Japan octagon cup & saucer lady pattern; a rib'd and scollop'd cup & saucer, image pattern; a basket bordered dysart plate; a Japan bread and buttered plate.

Mr Williams: 12 setts blue teas, at 2s 10d; a sett compleat of the second printed teas.

May 15. Rec'd a pair of birds on pedestals, to be painted for Mr Legg, corner of Birchen Lane.

Lady Stairs: a compleat sett Dresden sprig, the canister top; partridge octagon plates. Mrs Whitfield to have 1 pr. white biscuit candlesticks.

May 20. Duchess of Leeds: 2 square enamel and sprig'd desst. 15s; 1 blue dolphin pickle stand, 5s; one white basin & cover, 3s; the Duke of Argyle's acct.; £207 5s. The Duchess of Portland's acct. to be made out, and wait on the steward, Mr Guidon, in Privy Gardens, Whitehall, and will be paid when her ladyship returns.

June 18. Mr Fogg: 1 pint printed mug, 5s; 1 half-pint do. 3s 6d; 1 fine plate, 4s; 1 partridge handd. cup and saucer, 3s 6d. Allowed Mr Fogg. In a Pero's broken hat, 1s; in 2 Turks, 3s; octagon dysart partridge plate, 3s 6d. Mr Fogg to know the price of the best cock plates; 4 pair rib'd boats at 4s good; 2 pr. small imag'd boats and plates; 6 squirrels; butter tubs; 2 small dragon milk-pots; 2 do., a little larger; 1 dragon sugar-dish. Mr Morgan lent me a leaf for the roses; 4 vauses; 1 pair Minervas of each size. 2 double dozn. dysart rose pattern knife handles; to be mounted and sent in Baxter's parcel.

July 24. Mr Fogg to have one pair of coloured squirrels. The knife handles: how many sold of Dresden flowers? and to have a double dozn. mounted. Has Mrs Bernardeau had what she ordered of the wheatsheaf? To buy a partridge either alive or dead. To bring down the Chelsea cabbage leaves and bason. Recd. and gave Mr Beswick receipt for £107 12s in full to Sept. 1755, for Weatherby and Crowther. J.B. Mr Coleman: harliquin, columbine and pero. 1 small sprig'd round tea-pot. Goats, swans and every other sort of toys to be sent in Baxter's order, flat drawers to be made on purpose, and each kept separate. A plate of the Princess (of) Wales' pattern, good.

Aug. 30. Paid Mr Heylin's draft on Mr Crowther for £13, and charged Mr Crowther's cash account with it: quy. how is Mr Heylin made Dr. and J. C. Creditor?

Nov. 29. J. Bowcocke borrowed of Mr Crowther for Bow £30. Mr Fogg caudle cups white sprig'd and saucers; 3 pr. image cream ewers full blue; 4 white leaf candlesticks 2s 3d; 1 set large sprig'd teas handled; 2 pr. rib'd boats, at 4s 6d; 1 sprig'd tea-pot, 4s good. Patterns received from Lady Cavendish; a Japan octagon cup and saucer, lady pattern; a rib'd and scollop'd cup and saucer; a basket bordered dysart plate; a Japan bread & butter plate. To be returned in a month, May 28th 1756.

Appendix V
Workshops and Buildings listed in Insurance Policies

	BOW						CHELSEA			
	1749	1750	1755	1763	1766	1767	1760	1761	1765	1771
Dwelling House	✓	✓	✓	✓	✓	✓	✓	✓	✓	✓
Elaboratory	✓									
Warehouse(s)*	✓	✓	✓*	✓*	✓	✓				
Workhouse(s)	✓	✓	✓*	✓*					✓	✓
Millhouse(s)	✓	✓		✓*	✓*	✓*			✓	✓
Mill(s)		✓		✓*	✓*	✓*	✓	✓		
Kilnhouse(s)	✓	✓	✓*	✓*	✓*	✓*	✓	✓	✓	✓
Kiln(s)				✓*	✓	✓*				
Drying House(s)		✓	✓*	✓						
Stables		✓	✓	✓		✓			✓	✓
Shed			✓				✓	✓		
Compting House			✓							
Painters Room Gallery							✓	✓	✓	✓
Woodhouse									✓	✓
Sliphouse				✓	✓	✓				
Engine House					✓	✓				
Dip, Dipping House				✓	✓	✓				

Total Valuation for Insurance

Year		BOW	CHELSEA	WORCESTER	LOWESTOFT
1749		£4000			
1750		£6500			
1752			£2000		
1754			£3000		
			£5000		
1755		£8650			
1756					£370
1757				£1000	
1760			£2000		
1761			£3000		
1763		£4900		£1000	
1765			£3000		£300
1766		£3400			
1767		£4200			
1768					
1771			£1500		£1000
1772				£1500	
1773					

Factory	Year	Buildings	Stock and Utensils
BOW	1749 July	£2500	£1500 (Factory)
	1750 Nov.	£3450	£3050 (Factory)
	1755 Dec.	£2750	£5900 (inc. goods at Cornhill).
	1763 July	£1850	£3050 (inc. goods at Cornhill).
	1766 Jan.	£950	£2450 (inc. Stock at St. Mildred's Court).
	1767 Jan.	£1290	£2910 (inc. Stock at St. Mildred's Court).
CHELSEA	1752 April		£2000 (Pall Mall)
	1754 May		£3000 (Pall Mall)
	1754 Oct.		£5000 (Pall Mall)
	1755 Oct.		£2000 (Piccadilly)
	1760 June	£500	£1000 (Lawrence St.)
	1765 June	£500	£2000 (Lawrence St.)
	1771 Oct.	£200	£1300
WORCESTER	1757 Feb.	£1000	£2000 (Factory and London)
LIVERPOOL Wm. Reid	1755 Dec.	£600 (£200 for windmill)	
	1760 Oct.	£800 (£400 for windmill)	£200 (Factory)
Sam¹. Gilbody, Jʳ.	1761 Feb.	£200	
LOWESTOFT	1756 Jan.	£170	£200 (Factory)
	1765 June	£300	
	1771 April	£400	£600

Appendix VI

List of Known or presumed Bow Workers

Name	Occupation	Date of first mention
Angel, John Philip	Painter	July 1751
Astbury, John	Painter	(Simeon Shaw)
Astbury, Joshua	China Man	August 1760
Bacon, John	Modeller	
Ball, Richard	Potter	March 1751
Ball, William	Potter	December 1746
Barber, Lewis	Painter	
Barrs, Francis	Painter	August 1752
Bonner, John	Painter	June 1750
Bullock, William	Modeller	June 1749
Craft, Thomas John	Painter	March 1756
Gadd, William	Painter	May 1760
Gazeley, John	Painter	November 1749
Harrison, Robert	Potter	November 1760
Harrison, Thomas	Potter	August 1755
de Lanauze, John	Painter	*c.* 1770
Lawton, Thomas	Slipmaker	(Simeon Shaw)
Meir, Richard	Fireman	(Simeon Shaw)
Moser, George Michael	Modeller	
Mottershead, Samuel		March 1760
Parr, Samuel	Potter	February 1751
Pavett, Henry		August 1754
Phenix, Robert	Potter	January 1749/50
Redgrave, James		1748–52
Sherwood, Christopher	Labourer	January 1747/48
Smith, John	Potter	April 1748
Smith, Joseph	Potter	February 1747/48
Stevenson, John	Potter	June 1750
Toullous, Charles		October 1750
Tunstall, Aaron		*c.* 1750
Warburton, Joseph	?Potter	?early 1750s
Ward, Gilbert	Potter	August 1752
Welch, James	Painter	August 1754
Weyman, Charles	China Painter	(Pre-1772)[1]

---

[1] *Norwich Mercury*, 4 July 1772: 'Charles Weyman, China Painter at the Bow Manufactory in the County of Middlesex (sic) had for several years suffered under a Scorbutic Disorder of a malignant and complicated Nature . . . found relief by using Velmo's Vegetable Syrup.' (Notice pointed out by Sheenah Smith, lately Assistant Keeper of Art, Norwich Castle Museum.)

Travellers, and at Cornhill Warehouse
John Bowcock 1753–64
William Brown 1753–76
—Burnett
Mr Sandys
—Stephenson
Joseph Thorp 1758
Hugh Williams

Packers (mostly from registers of St. Michael Bassishaw; probably worked at Cornhill Warehouse)
Jonathan Biggs 1758
William Chamberlin 1751
Charles Gibbon 1756
Richard Goodday 1760–62
Edward Heylyn Jr. 1757
Charles Heylyn
Edmund Hutton 1755
Robert Long 1761
John Saunders 1751
Thomas Watts 1750

Appendix VII
Ceramic Costing in the Eighteenth Century

Reginald Haggar was kind enough to provide us with the following most interesting note on ceramic costing in the eighteenth century:

'The figures which are provided in the Bowcock papers and described for us in Chaffers, and Jewitt, fascinating though they are, raise many more questions than they answer. We are given no information how they were arrived at or who provided them, nor have we comparable figures for other contemporary factories. We are almost at a total loss concerning cost accounting procedures in the ceramic industry in the eighteenth century. The prices of wares offered for sale must have been arrived at in a very rough-and-ready fashion. We know from the letter which Sir Everard Fawkener wrote to Sir Charles Hanbury Williams, already quoted, that Chelsea had great difficulty in determining the prices of their articles. Bow must have experienced similar problems. No doubt some attempts were made to cost out labour, materials, decoration, fuel and firing, but this is not apparent in the figures that survive. We are left guessing.

In this matter of costing again Josiah Wedgwood stands apart, although it must be stated that we have no knowledge of the methods of his competitors. But even he had to admit, as late as 1772, his inability 'to find the proper data and methods of calculating the expense of Manufacturing . . . to be laid upon each article of manufacture.[1]

Indeed it was the misconduct of employees and the effects of the disastrous economic crisis of 1772, which in the space of two years produced a thousand bankruptcies in English commerce, that compelled him to attempt a more thorough and detailed study of his methods of costing. As a result he costed out thirty-one items of trade through every stage of production—preparation of raw materials, throwing, turning, finishing to the oven, biscuit firing, glost firing, mould-making and modelling, heating, wages to all departments, rent, wear and tear, gilding, carriage to London and packing, loss from breakages, accidents and imperfect ware, interest on capital in trade. He was meticulous in detail down to the $\frac{1}{2}$d he allowed for fuel for the workshops, excluding slip-kilns and ovens. If Josiah Wedgwood had difficulty in establishing satisfactory criteria for estimating his costs and prices, how much more difficult must it have been for other pottery and porcelain manufacturers less given to such difficult and mentally exhausting labours.

The 1770s were uneasy years for English trade particularly in the recessions of 1772 and 1778. It was in the mid-1770s that the bold ventures of Sprimont at Chelsea and Frye at Bow came to an end, leaving behind a memory of great endeavour and a legacy of fine porcelain.'

[1]Letter of Josiah Wedgwood to Thomas Bentley, 23 August 1772, cited by Neil McKendrick, 'Josiah Wedgwood and Cost Accounting in the Industrial Revolution', *Economic History Review* (2nd series), Volume 23, 1970, p. 49.

Appendix VIII

List of Wares of Bow Manufacture,
taken from the Bowcock Papers, Bills, Accounts, etc.
and compiled by Reginald Haggar

Apples
'Artichoak' cup

Basin and cover
Basins
Baskets
Beakers
Boats, and plates, imag'd
Boats, ribbed
Boats, sauce
Boats, sprigged
Bottles
Bowls
Branches, decorated with flowers
and figures
Bread and butter plate
Butter tubs

Candlesticks, leaf
Cans
Chandeliers
'China for desarts' (apples, baskets,
    leaves, melons, shells)
Coffee cups and saucers, honeycomb
Coffee equipages
Coffee pots
Cream ewer, sprig'd
Cups, 'artichoak'
Cups, breakfast, large, with saucers
Cups, caudle, with saucers
Cups, chocolate, with saucers
Cups, coffee, honeycomb, with
    saucers
Cups, imag'd, small
Cups, handled, with saucers
Cups, ribbed and scolloped, with
    saucers

Cups, sprigged, handled
Cups, tea
Cups, tea, honeycomb, handled (the
    mention of handled cups implies
    the existence of teabowls or
    unhandled cups)
Cups, water, and saucers

Desserts, square
Dishes, oblong
Dishes, octagon, various sizes
Dishes, round, various sizes
Dishes, soup, 13 or 14 inches, oval
Dolphin pickle stand
'Dysart' plates

Heads for canes

Inkwells

Knife handles

Ladles, cream
Ladles, mustard
Leaf candlesticks
Leaves

Mandril coffee pot
Mellons
Milk jugs
Milk pots (2 sizes indicated)
Milk pots, barrel shape
Mugs, half pint, pint
Mustards

Partridges ('parteridges')
Partridge sets

Passavant board plates
Pickle stands
Plates
Plates, basket bordered dysart
Plates, bread and butter
Plates, dysart
Plates, octagon dysart
Plates, octagon nappy
Plates, soup
Plates, table

Roses

Sallad bowl, scolloped edge
Sallad vessel
Salts, flat
Salts, flat, with feet
Sauce boats

Shells
Sugar dishes
Sugar dishes with covers

Tea cups, handled
Tea cups, handled, honeycomb
Tea cups, imag'd
Tea cups, ribbed and scolloped
Tea cups, sprigged
Tea equipages
Teapots, barrel shape
Teapots, round, sprig'd
Teapots, upright, sprig'd
Tureen, oval

Vauses

Water cup, and saucer (finger bowl)

Appendix IX
Bow Teapot Shapes

1. SMALL GLOBULAR SHAPE with simple loop handle, slightly curved spout and conical knop. Decorated in Japanese style in underglaze blue, overglaze red and gilding. Total height 12 cm (4.75 in), height to rim 8.9 cm (3.5 in). *c.* 1752–4
    This plain globular shape in three sizes was used from the earliest times over a long period. Main variation was applied decoration to the body left in the white. All Bow miniature teapots are basically globular shape with plain loop handles and slightly curved or straight spouts.

2. PEAR SHAPE with scroll handle and twig knop. Decorated in underglaze blue. Height 11.4 cm (4.5 in). 1747–54
    Some examples have applied decoration and there are handle and knop variations. Lids are either flat or slightly domed.

3. BALUSTER SHAPE with plain loop handle, slightly curved spout and conical knop. Decoration in *famille rose* enamels. Borders in alternating panels of lozenge-cell lattice and florets. Total height 12 cm (4.75 in), height to rim 9.5 cm (3.75 in). *c.* 1746–54
    Variations include ribbed body, spout and handle, double scroll handle with bridge attachment to body, bent-twig knop. Some examples (after 1759) have powder-blue ground with fan-shaped reserves.

4. DEPRESSED GLOBULAR SHAPE. Applied prunus decoration. Conical knop. Three-scroll handle with lower bridge attachment similar to the handle used with the pear shape (2 above). Height 11.4 cm (4.5 in). *c.* 1747–53

5. GLOBULAR with flush cover, plain loop handle, bun knop. Decorated in underglaze blue with peony, rocks and fence design. Border of trellis diaper alternating with florets. Height 10.8 cm (4.25 in). *c.* 1755–60
    Some examples have overglaze printed decoration.

6. BARREL SHAPE with plain loop handle and hexagonal section, slightly curved spout, flower knop. Rows of raised dots around upper and lower body. Decorated with Chinese figures, outline transfer printed in brown with enamel in-painting. Height 12 cm (4.75 in). *c.* 1759–65
    Variation includes moulded and applied decoration.

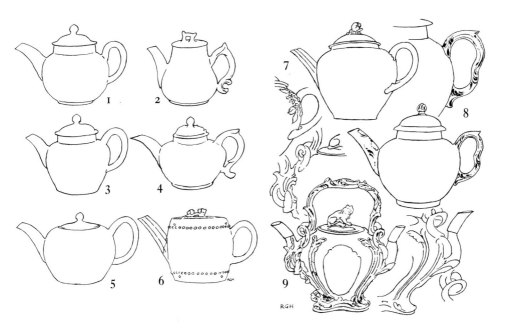

7. INVERTED PEAR SHAPE with applied leaf decoration around the upper handle attachment. Plain loop handle dividing into two branches at the lower attachment. Flower knop. Ribbed spout. Decorated with overglaze transfer print in brown showing Frederick the Great and painted lettering with 'The Prussian Hero'. Height 15.8 cm (6.25 in). *c.* 1756–60.

8. GLOBULAR SHAPE with indented scroll handle, thumb rest and divided lower attachment. Moulded spout and conical knop. Decorated with underglaze-blue scale ground, reserved panels with rococo frames, gilded, containing exotic birds and flower sprays. Borders with yellow and puce roses. Height 15.8 cm (6.25 in). Inscription in underglaze blue on base

'C

I.G

1761'

Similar examples are moulded with rose sprays (left in white) or rib-moulded with entwined branches and reserves painted with oriental scenes in underglaze blue.

9. DOUBLE TEAPOT with internal division into two compartments for Indian and China tea. Moulded base, spouts and handle. Lion knop. Decorated with powder-blue ground and exotic birds in large reserves, the moulded scrolls picked out in puce. Height 21 cm (8.25 in). *c.* 1760–5
Only one example known.

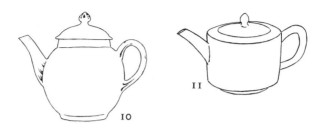

10.   LATE OVOID GLOBULAR SHAPE with simple loop handle, spout with slight
        double curve and conical knop. Decorated with naturalistic flower painting, the
        borders with red line of arches and dots. Total height 13.3 cm (5.25 in), height
        to rim 10.1 cm (4 in). *c.* 1765–70
        Some examples have 'open mouth' spout.

11.   CYLINDER SHAPE with flat recessed cover, conical knop, plain loop handle and
        slightly curved spout. Decorated in enamels with a European landscape
        including a castle, ruins, trees and distant mountains. Border in red and gilt
        fleur-de-lis design. Height 10.1 cm (4 in). *c.* 1760
        Only one known example. Possibly painted by J. H. O'Neale.

Appendix X
Some Bow Vase Shapes

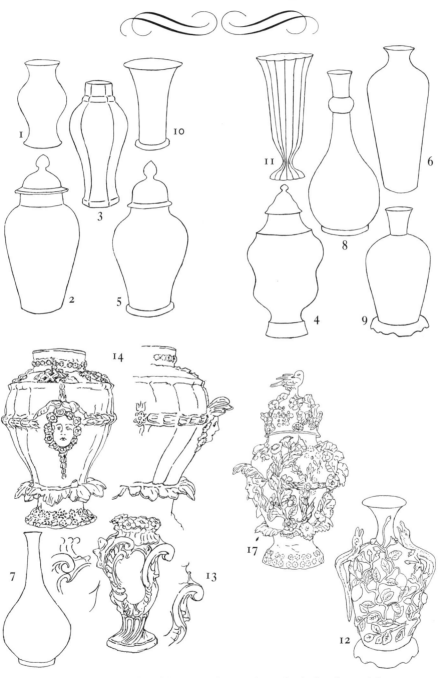

(The vase shapes are numbered in approximate chronological order and for
reference in the text)

(The vase shapes are numbered in approximate chronological order and for
reference in the text)

Appendix XI
Marks on Bow Porcelain

No factory mark as such was used at the Bow China Manufactory throughout its history. The marks found on Bow china therefore represent workmen's marks used for tally purposes or as personal signatures. The application of marks was remarkably inconsistent and a very large proportion of Bow wares are completely unmarked. However this should not be interpreted as meaning that tally marking was not done in a regular way as fugitive media may have been used for this purpose. A biscuit waster found in the 1867 excavation was marked in pencil script with the name 'Norman'. Some incised or occasionally impressed potters' marks occur, of which the best known are the scratch 'R' and the linear scratch. These marks are found on early wares of white or underglaze-blue decorated porcelain often of less conventional shapes. A biscuit waster fragment from the base of a tankard and marked with a typical scratch 'R' was found on the site during the 1969 excavation. Most of the early blue group (Chapter 6) is unmarked. The commonest marks on underglaze-blue decorated wares are numerals up to 60 and imitation Chinese characters, the latter being used extensively on powder-ground decorated wares. Occasionally one of the characters from a six character mark is replaced by the Meissen crossed swords. The latter are occasionally used alone. The impressed 'T' or 'To' mark which also occurs on later Worcester, Plymouth and Bristol porcelain has for long been considered as representing a figure repairer called Tebo. An alternative suggestion, first advanced by Geoffrey Godden, that the mark is the signature of a member of the Toulouse family of potters is discussed in Chapter 9. Overglaze-enamel marks in colour are rare. The exact significance of the anchor and dagger mark is still not known. It is mostly done in red enamel, occasionally in gilt. It is sometimes accompanied by a dagger (the dagger possibly derives from the arms of the City of London) in underglaze blue. The anchor and dagger mark is seen over the period 1760–75 on only a proportion of the wares. It seems likely that it is the mark of an outside (i.e. London) decorator working under contract to the factory. See Chapter 12 for further discussion on the possible significance of the anchor and dagger mark.

Incised

Incised

Impressed

In Blue

In Blue
except '32'
which is
In Red

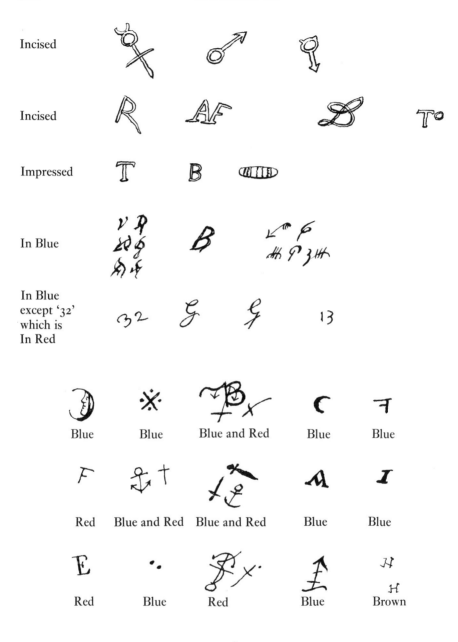

Blue   Blue   Blue and Red   Blue   Blue

Red   Blue and Red   Blue and Red   Blue   Blue

Red   Blue   Red   Blue   Brown

Blue

Appendix XII
The Bow Factory and its Environs

The map is drawn from a number of sources over the period 1744 to 1867 including Rocque's map of 1746, John Noble's map of 1747, Chapman and André's map of 1777, Pennington's map of 1787, James Clayton's map of 1821, Ordnance Survey map of 1869, Aubrey Toppin's map (drawn *c*. 1921 and published by Tait in *Apollo*, April 1960) and a Lea Conservancy Board map of 1935. The last-mentioned map defines an important alteration made in the course of Bow Back River during river improvements made over the period 1933–5. Although the area occupied by the factory buildings is known with reasonable certainty, the sites of particular buildings are not known, with three exceptions. The first is the main two-storied factory building defined in several insurance policies as 173 feet long, brick built and 'fronting the High Street'. This is the building later converted into tenements (probably 12 or 14) and known at some time as 'China Row' and not finally demolished until 1919, thus narrowly missing inspection by Aubrey Toppin, who visited the site in 1921. It is known the factory had a main entrance with an arch and this was most likely in the centre of the long building and was certainly still in use in 1869 and probably later. The second is the site of the stables, which were known to be located on the west of the site, and a building defined as stables is in the position indicated on the Clayton map of 1821. A residential property with garden and driveways is shown immediately south of the stables in the Clayton and Ordnance Survey maps so there is a possibility that this was the house occupied by Frye and later by Crowther over the period 1749–75. A 'genteel dwelling house, offices and gardens' form part of Lot V in the property sale at auction held on 22 June 1787 (see Plate 10, Chapter 3 and Appendix XIII). It is said to have been called 'Essex House'.

Waster finds have occurred on or near the site either by accident or design since 1867, when John Higgins, temporarily employed by Bell and Black's Match Company, collected numerous fragments from a drain-laying trench adjacent to the factory in Hunts Lane on the south side of the High Street. These finds were reported in the *Art Journal* of 1869 (Vol. 31, p. 239) by William Chaffers, came into Lady Charlotte Schreiber's possession and are now in the Victoria and Albert Museum together with a sketch book of the fragments (without text). Aubrey Toppin visited the site in 1921 during excavations for factory foundations and recovered a large quantity of fragments. These finds were reported in the *Burlington Magazine*, May 1922, p. 224. Most of the recovered material is in the Victoria and Albert Museum. In 1969 an excavation took place on recently vacated property in the south-west corner of the site and much waster material was recovered and recorded with notes of location and stratigraphy accompanied by photographs. These finds were published in a preliminary report in the *St. Mary's Gazette* (University of London), Vol. LXXV, no. 4, June 1969, p. 120, and further reports and some of the waster material were deposited at the Passmore Edwards Museum, Stratford, London E15 and were exhibited in 1970.

An opportunity to excavate was missed in 1962 when the entire site was cleared (Aerofilms, Hunting Surveys Ltd. Albemarle Street, London W1, vertical view ref. HSL/UK/62/232, first no. 0354) for the building of a large office block—Central House. No structures which might relate to kilns or other factory buildings have been reported from any of the excavations on the site.

J. H. O'Neale's probable viewpoint when he drew the scene 'from behind ye China House at Bow' is also indicated on the map. It provides unusual confirmatory evidence of the factory's location by alignment of three particular windmills to the north of Stratford High Street (see Plate 9, Chapter 3).

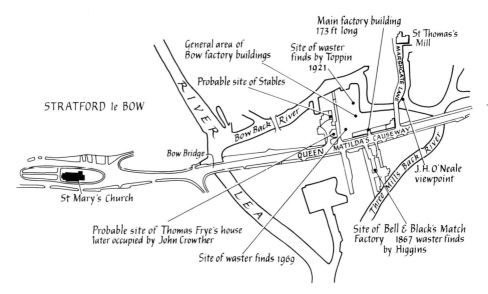

Appendix XIII

Particulars of Properties offered for Sale at Auction by Mr Skinner and Co. on Friday 22 June 1787 at Garraway's Coffee House, Change Alley, Cornhill

The title page is reproduced in full as Plate 10, Chapter 3. The document provides useful confirmatory evidence as to the exact location of the factory on the following grounds. The various properties were situated on the north side of the High Street because Lots I to VIII are listed in a sequence which begins in the 'High Road', i.e. Stratford High Street, anciently Queen Matilda's Causeway, and ends in Marsh Lane, presumably Marshgate Lane, which is situated on the north side of the High Road. The particulars of Lot VI confirm that a public house, then called the Red Lion, adjoined the factory site to the east at the corner of the High Road and Marshgate Lane. This accords with tradition and the corner site is marked 'PH' in the first Ordance Survey map of the area published in 1869. The particulars of Lot V include a 'dwelling house, offices and gardens'. Both the Clayton map of 1821 and the Ordnance Survey of 1869 show a house and garden on the west side of the factory site where it would be to windward of the kilns. Lots I–IV are all adjoining with frontages of 12–19 metres (40–63 feet) on the High Road, depths of 67 metres (220 feet) and river frontages of 12–18 (40–60 feet). The site depths of 67 metres make it certain that Lots I–IV adjoin Lot V because this is the only part of the High Road with that order of depth to the river. Further west the distance from the High Road to the river diminishes markedly. It is necessary to assume that the reference to the river Lea in the particulars refers to the branch later known as Bow Back River. The mention of 'six messuages in Front of Road' would seem to imply that by 1787 only one half of the 52.7 metre- (173 foot-) long factory building had been converted to 'tenements'. These tenements were at one time known as China Row and were not demolished until about 1919. The Ordnance Survey of 1869 shows a long building on the site divided up into twelve dwellings, six on each side of a central covered passage which probably formed the main factory entrance. The Clayton map of 1821 shows only six dwellings to the left of the central passage so the rest of the factory building was probably not converted until later. The mention of a 'distil-house' as part of Lot V is of interest because 'Stratford Distil-House' is shown as on or near the site in Rocque's map of 1746 (see Plate 8) and the site was certainly used for the distillation of tar and turpentine later (see Chapter 3, note 33 and also Tait in *Apollo*, LXXI, April 1960, pp. 93–8). It is of interest that the site was still in use for the distillation of crude oil by the Wiggins Oil Company up till 1968. See also Appendix XII.

The Particulars, Etc.

	Present Yearly Rents £ s d	Supposed Yearly Value £ s d
LOT I A Very eligible FREEHOLD ESTATE, most advantageously situate adjoining the River Lea, at Stratford, near Bow Bridge, within Three Miles of London; comprising a desirable Wharf, 40 Feet next the River, 220 Feet deep, and 45 Feet fronting the High Road; with a Dwelling House and Offices, Stable, and a large Shed; in the Occupation of Mr William Wight, but let to Mr Brooks, with the Two following Lots, for an unexpired Term of 3 Years from Michaelmas 1787, at an annual nett Rent of 46l. The apportioned Part of present Rent for Lot I per Annum	22 0 0	40 0 0
LOT II A Very eligible FREEHOLD ESTATE, situate adjoining the preceding Lot; comprising a desirable Wharf, 60 Feet next the River Lea, 220 Feet deep, and 65 Feet fronting the High Road; with a Stable and sundry Sheds, in the Occupation of Mr Dyche, Stone Mason, but let to Mr Brooks, with Lots I and III for an unexpired Term of 3 Years from Michaelmas 1787, at an annual nett Rent of 46l. The apportioned Part of present Rent for Lot II per Annum	6 0 0	12 10 0
LOT III A Very eligible FREEHOLD ESTATE, situate adjoining the preceding Lot; comprising a desirable Wharf, 54 Feet next the River Lea, 220 Feet deep, and 40 Feet fronting the Road; with a Dwelling House, Offices, Stabling, and a spacious Malting; in the Occupation of Messrs Betts and Son, but let to Mr Brooks, with Lots I and III for an unexpired Term of 3 Years from Michaelmas 1787, at an annual nett Rent of 46l. The apportioned Part of present Rent for Lot III per Annum	18 0 0	45 0 0

	Present Yearly Rents £ s d	Supposed Yearly Value £ s d

Lot IV

A FREEHOLD ESTATE, desirably situate adjoining the preceding Lots; comprising the Fox and Hounds Public House; in the Occupation of Mr Bailes, but let to Mr John Brooks, Brewer, for an unexpired Term of 7 Years from Michaelmas 1787, at per Annum

	12 12 0	15 0 0

Lot V

A Valuable extensive FREEHOLD ESTATE, advantageously situate adjoining the River Lea, at Stratford, and formerly

THE BOW CHINA MANUFACTORY
COMPRISING

A genteel convenient Dwelling House, Offices, and Gardens, capital Warehouses and Store-houses, Distil-house, Cooperage, and numerous other Buildings; capacious Wharf and Yard, and Six Messuages in Front of Road; let to Joseph Flight, Esq. for an unexpired Term of 15 Years from Michaelmas 1787, at a very low Rent of only 63l per Annum, with a Covenant for an additional Term of 7 Years, if the present Freeholder should so long live, at 68l per Annum.

	Present yearly Rent 63 0 0	100 0 0

Lot V is subject to a Quit Rent of 1l 5s per Annum.

Lot VI

A FREEHOLD ESTATE, desirably situate adjoining the preceding Lot; comprising the Red Lion Public House, and large Yard; in the Occupation of Mr Edward Staines, Tenant at Will, at per Annum

	16 10 0	21 0 0

Lot VII

A FREEHOLD ESTATE, situate in Marsh Lane, Stratford, adjoining to Lot V and bounded by the River Lea; comprising a Dwelling House, Offices, Garden, and numerous spacious Workshops, Stabling, and Sheds, and a large Yard; in the Occupation of Mr Thomas Pilgrim, for an unexpired Term of 10 Years from Lady-day 1787 at a very low nett Rent of per Annum

	24 0 0	31 10 0

	Present Yearly Rents £ s d	*Supposed Yearly Value* £ s d

Lot VIII

A FREEHOLD OZIER GROUND, containing upwards of One Acre, situate about Half a Mile down Marsh Lane, Stratford; in the Occupation of Mr Thomas Thresher, Tenant at Will, at per Annum

| | 3 0 0 | 4 0 0 |

Lot IX

A desirable FREEHOLD ESTATE, situate at West Ham, near Stratford; consisting of a Brick Dwelling House, Offices, and an excellent Garden, containing upwards of an Acre, walled round, cloathed and flored with Fruit Trees; in the Occupation of Mr Godfrey Forster, Tenant at Will, at only per Annum

| | 15 0 0 | 21 0 0 |

Lot X

A FREEHOLD ESTATE, situate adjoining the preceding Lot; comprising an excellent well built Brick Dwelling House, containing Five Bedchambers, Parlour, and Dining Room, neatly wainscotted and finished, convenient Kitchen and Offices, Coach-house, Two Stall Stable, Fore Court, and Garden, walled, cloathed, and flored with Fruit Trees; in the Occupation of Mrs Simpson, Tenant at Will, at per Annum

| | [illegible] | 30 0 0 |

Lot XI

A FREEHOLD ESTATE, situate adjoining the preceding Lot; comprising an excellent well built Brick Dwelling House, containing Five Bedchambers, Parlour, and Dining Room, neatly wainscotted and finished, convenient Kitchen and Offices, Coach-house, Two Stall Stable, Fore Court and Garden, walled, cloathed and flored with Fruit Trees; in the Occupation of Mrs Sainthill, Tenant at Will, at per Annum

| | 24 0 0 | 50 0 0 |

CONDITIONS OF SALE

1st. The highest Bidder to be the Buyer, and if any Dispute arise between two or more Bidders, the Lot to be put up again.

2nd. No Person to advance less than 5l. at each Bidding.

3d. The Purchasers shall pay down immediately a Deposit of 20l. per Cent. in Part of the Purchase-Money, and sign an Agreement for Payment of the Remainder on or before the 26 of July, 1787; on having good Titles.

4th. The Purchaser of each Lot shall have a proper Conveyance, at his own Expence, on Payment of the Remainder of the Purchase-Money according to the 3d Condition; and be entitled to the Rents and Profits from Midsummer 1787, to which Time all Outgoings will be cleared.

5th. The largest Purchaser to have the Custody of the Original Title Deeds, on entering into the usual Deed of Covenants to the other Purchasers for producing the same; and such Purchasers to have attested Copies of such Title Deeds as they think fit, as their own Expence.

6th. There being a Duty on all Sales of Estates, etc. of Three-pence Halfpenny in the Pound, to be levied on the Buyers or Sellers, as may be thought most proper; the Lots comprised in the Particular are to be sold, subject to the Seller's paying one Moiety of the said Tax, and the Buyers the other, exclusive of the Sums the said Lots shall sell for.

Lastly. If the said Purchasers shall neglect or fail to comply with the above Conditions, the Deposit-Money to be forfeited, the Proprietor shall be at full Liberty to re-sell the said Lots, and the Deficiency (if any there should be by such second Sale) together with all Charges attending the same, to be made good by the Defaulter at this present Sale.

Appendix XIV
Some Wasters Recovered from the Factory Site

A selection of biscuit wasters recovered from the extreme south-west corner of the factory site during the 1969 excavations are shown (see Appendix XII). The wasters were located in a discontinuous layer up to approximately 300 mm (11.8 in) thick at a depth of approximately 1.22 m (4 ft). The layer covered an area of approximately 23 sq. m (254 sq. ft) and was very disturbed by nineteenth- and twentieth-century foundation and drain trenching.

Group 1. Various HANDLE SHAPES are illustrated as well as a small lid. The small (diameter 3.8 cm, 1.5 in) TEABOWL has a solid base without footrim. Bow miniature tewares do not usually have solid bases. The straight-sided beaker-shaped HANDLED CUP is relatively rare. Some surviving examples are decorated in underglaze blue with the 'image' pattern.

Group 2. Large numbers of biscuit KNIFE AND FORK HANDLES were recovered. Only two moulded designs were found amongst many plain ones. In one area large numbers of handles were found all broken in two in approximately the same place suggesting deliberate destruction by impact against a hard edge or spike as is traditional in the potting industry. The small fluted SAUCEBOAT became a waster because the body warped in the biscuit firing. The indented footrim of this piece is unusual and seems to be a feature of earlier sauceboats of this shape. The CANDLE NOZZLE with applied prunus decoration is very unusual and it is not clear what the rest of the piece comprised. The base of the nozzle has fired 'luting' slip still adherent (see Chapter 7, Plate 35).

Group 3. Upper left are two views of a small fragment of the BASE OF A TANKARD with a scratch 'R' mark on the base. No other pieces of the tankard were found and no other wasters with either a scratch 'R' or linear scratch (Chapter 6, Plate 23B) have come to light. Because scratch-marked Bow porcelain has distinctive qualities, particularly of the body, it has been suggested that it may have been produced at a different site. The finding of this biscuit waster amongst other waster material is important evidence that this class of Bow porcelain was made on the traditional site. The fragment has been subjected to chemical analysis (see Appendix XV). Three views of a leaf-moulded PICKLE DISH are shown and one of a virtually intact biscuit MINIATURE HANDLED CUP (height 3.5 cm, 1.4 in). The pointed base is noteworthy as this is not a feature of Bow full-sized cups and teabowls.

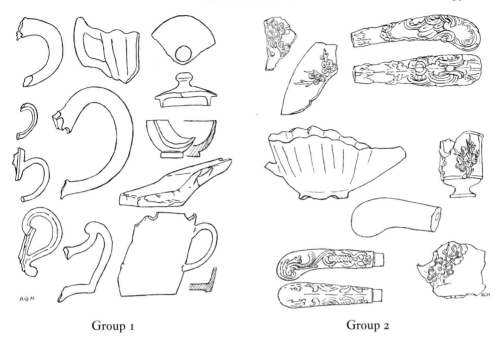

Group 1

Group 2

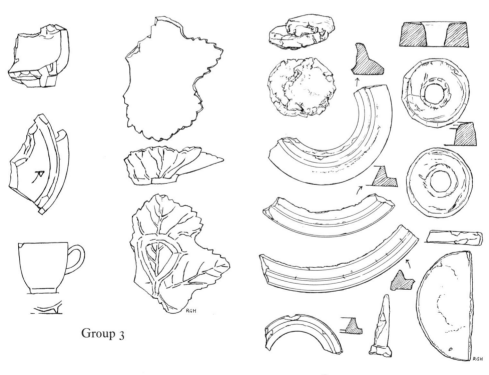

Group 3

Group 4

Group 4. KILN FURNITURE. Upper left are two fused fireclay pads probably used to separate saggars. The four semi-circular objects also shown in section are 'placing rings' used to support round objects such as bowls during biscuit firing. The rim of the inverted object would rest on the outer step of the ring before firing and could 'ride up' the slope above the step during shrinkage. The main purpose of these rings was to maintain the circular shape during biscuit firing. The material of the rings was either fine refractory or porcellaneous. The purpose of the circular objects shown at top right is uncertain. Large numbers were found and all were of porcellaneous material. The outer and inner sections were always conical in opposite directions. Cutting marks were often seen on the lower (greatest diameter) surface so the objects may represent the cut-off portion of a thrown or turned piece fired for an unknown reason. The object at bottom right is a large flat fireclay pad. Very large numbers of the round fireclay 'rims' shown at the bottom were found. These were used to support flatwares during glost or enamel firing in circular saggars pierced with three equally spaced holes for each object. The total number of objects that could be supported in one saggar seems to vary up to nine. Many of the pins had small areas of glaze and blue pigment on them and were presumably frequently reused. The pins entered the saggar from outside, the widened shoulder limiting the depth. This method of support was described by Cavaliere Cipriano Piccolpasso in his *Three Books of the Potter's Art* (1556–9, copy in the Victoria and Albert Museum), although the pins are of triangular rather than round section. Piccolpasso's work was essentially a description of the production of tin-glazed earthenware and it is of interest that triangular section pins were used by the tin-glaze potters in the Southwark and Lambeth areas. Tin-glazed plates from these potteries were traditionally fired face upwards. Because the weight of the piece deflected the pins downwards somewhat, the area of contact was often quite large resulting in considerable disfigurement. At Bow this lesson evidently was learned because, although some of the early flatwares are marred in this way, from about 1750–1 onwards all Bow flatwares are fired face down so that the three pins make a minimal contact with the edge of the piece. One pin only, found during the 1969 excavation, was of triangular section identical to those used south of the river. The kiln furniture illustrated here represents a very small selection of the finds, which will be the subject of future publications.

Appendix XV
Chemical Analysis of Bow Porcelain

The first Bow patent of 1744 describes the 'method of manufacturing a certain material, whereby a ware might be made' effectively the equivalent of oriental porcelain. The procedure described the initial production of a glass from 'pott ash' etc. and sand or flints which was fired and then ground to a fine powder. One part of the powder was mixed with two parts of washed 'unaker'. Unaker was the clay brought from America. No Bow porcelain analyses correspond with the likely composition of a body made according to the first patent. The second patent of 1748 describes, rather cryptically, the preparation of bone ashes which are made into 'bricks' with flint or sand, fired and then ground to a powder, the final composition being ground 'bricks' 2 parts and pipeclay 1 part. All published analyses of Bow porcelain correspond, in the main, to the last-mentioned formula with its important innovative use of bone ash. Bone ash itself consists of about 54% calcium and 41% phosphorus, less than 2% magnesium and no other element in excess of 0.3%. The phosphorus content of bone ash and therefore of bone china is a distinctive feature, as phosphorus is not an important constituent of any of the minerals normally used for the ceramic body. A qualitative test for phosphorus in the porcelain body was described by Dr A. J. Plenderleith in the *Burlington Magazine*, September 1927 ('The Material of the English Frit Porcelains', Part 3) and has been extensively applied. Josiah Wedgwood noted the probable Bow formulation in his 'Experiment' book entry for 13 February 1759: '4 parts bone ash, 4 parts Lynn sand, $\frac{1}{4}$ part gypsum or alabaster, $\frac{1}{4}$ part blue ball clay. This is the composition of Bow china but I am not certain of the proportions. In the early period of the manufactory they used to frit the bone ashes, sand and gypsum mixed up together and made into bricks, but have for some time past omitted that process and used them crude.' Until proved otherwise the use of gypsum (calcium sulphate, $CaSO_4.2H_2O$) in the Bow body must be regarded as highly improbable, as sulphates, for reasons not fully understood, cause faults in both body and glaze during firing. There are no published reports of the firing of experimental body mixes based on the Bow patents or on Josiah Wedgwood's information. The earliest report of the chemical analysis of Bow porcelain is contained in Sir A. H. Church's *English Porcelain of the Eighteenth Century* published in 1911 which gives the composition of biscuit fragments excavated in 1867 (Table 1). In the presentation of analysis the elemental composition is represented as the corresponding oxides rather than the elements themselves. The convention arose because in the classical methods of analysis most of the constituents were actually weighed as oxides and to a large extent the important elements in the china body are in the oxide form although this does not necessarily represent the true molecular structure. Church's analysis corresponds to the use of about 43% of bone ash. Rather tantalizingly Church remarks that 'the number of specimens free from bone ash was quite insignificant'. In 1922 Herbert Eccles and Bernard Rackham published a handbook of *Analysed Specimens of English Porcelain* and they give the analysis of an early form of sauceboat (Table 2), similar to one illustrated by Hurlbutt (op. cit., Pl. 5) and also No. 128, Pl. 30 in the *Catalogue of the English Ceramic Circle Exhibition 1948*. This analysis represents the use of over 45% of bone ash. The analyses reported in Tables 1 and 2 are derived from classical chemical methods. There has been considerable development in analytical methods since 1945 and one of the new non-destructive physical methods (X-ray fluorescence spectroscopy) has been applied to three specimens of Bow porcelain. The results (by courtesy of Dr Alwyn Cox) are shown in Tables 3–5. Although non-destructive, the method, which depends on the wavelength spectrum analysis of X-ray induced radiation in the surface layer of a substance, requires expensive apparatus and skilled operators and a 1 cm square glaze-free area of the ceramic body which must be ground optically flat. Its application to intact specimens is therefore somewhat limited at present. Table 3 gives the analysis of the biscuit waster marked with a scratch 'R' found in the 1969 excavation (see Appendix XIV). It shows a remarkable similarity to the analysis of the sauceboat given in Table 2 and is testimony to the authenticity of the early chemical analyses. Table 4 gives the analysis of an early enamel-decorated nappy plate similar to the one illustrated in Chapter 8, Plate 45. This does not show any important differences from the analysis of the scratch 'R' and early sauceboat specimens. The analysis of a blue powder-ground plate decorated with the usual Chinese river scene in reserves is given in Table 5. The plate is generally similar to the dish illustrated in Chapter 11, Plate 92 and dates from the period 1758–62. The analysis shows a notable change in the body composition of this later specimen. The proportion of bone ash is slightly reduced and the amount of calcium increased in relation to the phosphorus. There is a marked increase (about 6%) in the amount of silica in relation to the aluminium content which is reduced by about 3%. One possible interpretation of these changes is that the proportions of clay and bone ash in the body mix were reduced and the proportions of silica in the form of sand or flint increased. The increased calcium content might have derived from the increased silica. That would accord with the well-recognized deterioration in the Bow body which occurred some time after 1755, with increased fragility and decreased translucency, but points to the need for the analysis of a large number of specimens which can be dated with reasonable certainty.

SPECIMEN ANALYSES OF BOW PORCELAIN (see text for identity of specimens)

Table		1	2	3**	4**	5**
Na_2O	%	1.3	1.2	1.4	1.0	1.0
MgO	%	0.8	0.6	0.6	0.7	0.8
Al_2O_3	%	16.0*	8.4	7.8	8.3	4.8
SiO_2	%	40.0	43.6	43.8	38.9	49.1
P_2O_5	%	17.3	18.9	18.3	20.1	16.4
K_2O	%	0.6	0.9	1.2	0.9	1.4
CaO	%	24.0	24.5	25.8	29.1	25.8
PbO	%		1.75	0.74	0.53	0.44
Total	%	100.0	99.8	99.6	99.5	99.7

*The proportion of aluminium in Table 1 is unaccountably high.
**Each analysis represents the mean of five determinations.

Bibliography

Registers

Parishes near London:
1. Bow, St. Mary's Church
2. Bromley, St. Leonard
3. Chelsea, St. Luke (Chelsea Old Church)
4. Deptford Green, St. Nicholas
5. Greenwich, St. Alfege
6. Hornsey, St. Mary
7. Limehouse, St. Anne
8. Plumstead, St. Nicholas
9. Stepney, St. Dunstan
10. Stepney, St. George-in-the East
11. West Ham
12. Woolwich, St. Mary Magdalene

Parishes in the City of London:
1. St. Botolph-without-Aldgate
2. Christ Church, Newgate
3. St. Helen's Bishopsgate
4. St. Lawrence Jewry
5. St. Mary-le-Bow, Cheapside
6. St. Michael Bassishaw
7. St. Mildred Bread Street
8. St. Olave Old Jewry

Parishes in the Potteries:
1. Burslem
2. Bucknall
3. Norton-le-Moors
4. Stoke-on-Trent
5. Wolstanton

Other Parishes:
1. St. Helen's, Lancashire
2. Prescot, Lancashire

Local Documents

Bow Land Tax Returns 1741–66 (Central Library, Tower Hamlets, and Guildhall Library)
Burslem: Page from Vestry Minutes 1742
City Land Tax Returns *c.* 1744–50 (Guildhall Library)
Chelsea Rate Books 1748–70 (Chelsea Library, Manresa Road, SW3)
Limehouse Land Tax Returns, Volumes 18–37 inclusive (Guildhall Library)
West Ham Poor Rate Books (Stratford Library, Water Lane, E15)

Wills (Public Record Office, Chancery Lane)

Sarah Frye
Thomas Frye
Hillary Torriano
John Weatherby

Other Documents

Aqualate Papers (William Salt Library, Stafford).
Bankruptcy Order Books (Public Record Office).
Bow Account Book 1751–1755 (British Museum Add. MS 45905).
Bowcock Papers (British Museum).
Customs Books (Public Record Office).
Hoare's Bank, Archives.
Richard Parrot's Book (Newcastle-under-Lyme Museum).
Peers Family Papers (Oxford County Record Office).
Royal Exchange Assurance, Policy records (Guildhall Library).
W. S. Samuel papers, MS 17883 (Guildhall Library).
Sun Assurance Company, Policy records (Guildhall Library).
Case of the Undertaker of the Chelsea Manufacture of Porcelain Ware, Lansdowne MSS No. 829, fol. 21 (British Museum).

Contemporary Publications

Universal Pocket Companion, 1741.
London Directory, 1744–55.
R. Campbell, *The London Tradesman*, 1747.
Livery List of London, 1750.
Robert Dossie, *Handmaid of the Arts*, London, 1753.
W. Bristow, *Alphabetical List of Discharged Debtors*, London, 1761.
Universal Director (Mortimer's *Directory*), London, 1763.
Law List, 1787.
Gentleman's Magazine.
Musgrave's *Obituary.*

Bow References

Elizabeth Adams, *Some Links between Porcelain Factories of the Eighteenth Century, and the North West of England*, Paper read at Ceramics Summer School, University of Keele, 1969, privately printed.
Elizabeth Adams, 'The Bow Insurances and Related Matters', *E.C.C. Transactions*, Vol. 9, Pt. 1, 1973.

Elizabeth Adams, 'Ceramic Insurances in the Sun Company Archives, 1766–1774', *E.C.C. Transactions*, Vol. 10, Pt. 1, 1976.

J. A. Ainslie, 'Inscribed and Dated Bow', *Apollo*, January 1955.

Catalogue of the Well-known Collection of Bow Porcelain, the property of John A. Ainslie, Sotheby's, London, 7 March 1961.

Art Journal, Vol. XCII, New Series, pp. 239–3, 'Contents of lost Bow papers'.

Ralph Edwards, 'Thomas Frye 1710–1760', *Apollo*, February 1935.

Frank Hurlbutt, *Bow Porcelain*, London, 1926.

Hugh Tait, *Catalogue of the Bow Porcelain Special Exhibition 1744–1776*, British Museum, 1959.

Hugh Tait, 'Some Consequences of the Bow Porcelain Special Exhibition', Parts I–IV, *Apollo*, (February, April, June, October) 1960, Vol. LXXI, pp. 40–5, 93–8, 181–5 and Vol. LXXII, pp. 111–15.

Hugh Tait, 'The Bow Factory under Alderman Arnold and Thomas Frye (1747–1759)', *E.C.C. Transactions*, Vol. 5, Pt. 4, 1963.

A. J. Toppin, 'Bow porcelain, some recent excavations', *Burlington Magazine*, XL, 1922.

Geoffrey Wills, 'The Bow China Factory and Edward Heylyn', *Connoisseur*, Vol. CXXXIII, 1954.

Michael Wynne, 'Thomas Frye 1710–1762', *Burlington Magazine*, CXIV, 1972.

Pottery and Porcelain: General

W. Chaffers, *Marks and Monograms . . .*, 15th ed., London, 1957.

R. J. Charleston, ed., *English Porcelain*, London, 1968.

Herbert Eccles and Bernard Rackham, *Analysed Specimens of English Porcelain*, London (Victoria and Albert Museum), 1922.

Geoffrey Godden, *Illustrated Guide to Lowestoft Porcelain*, London, 1969.

Geoffrey Godden, 'Staffordshire Pioneer Bone-china', *Northern Ceramic Society Journal*, Vol. III, 1979.

W. B. Honey, *English Pottery and Porcelain*, revised by R. J. Charleston, London, 1962.

W. B. Honey, *Old English Porcelain*, 3rd ed. revised by Franklin D. Barrett, London, 1977.

Graham Hood, *Bonnin and Morris of Philadelphia; the first American Porcelain Factory 1770–1772*, University of North Carolina Press, 1972.

Ivor Noël Hume, *All the Best Rubbish*, London, 1974.

Arthur Lane, *English Porcelain Figures of the Eighteenth Century*, London, 1961.

Mrs D. MacAlister, ed., *William Duesbury's London Account Book*, E.C.C., London, 1931.

John Mallet, 'John Baddeley of Shelton . . . Pt. I.', *E.C.C. Transactions*, Vol. 6, Pt. 2, 1966; 'John Baddeley of Shelton . . ., Pt. II.', *E.C.C. Transactions*, Vol. 6, Pt. 3, 1967.

W. Mankowitz and R. G. Haggar, *The Concise Encyclopaedia of English Pottery and Porcelain*, London, 1957.

J. E. Nightingale, *Contributions towards the History of English Porcelain*, Salisbury, 1881.

Simeon Shaw, *Chemistry of Pottery*, London, 1837.

Simeon Shaw, *History of the Staffordshire Potteries*, Hanley, 1829.

B. M. Watney, *English Blue and White Porcelain of the Eighteenth Century*, 2nd ed., London, 1973.

Other Publications

Hugh Honour, *Chinoiserie. The Vision of Cathay*, London, 1961.

H. Ballou Morse, *The Chronicles of the East India Company Trading to China 1635–1834*, Vol. I, Oxford University Press, 1926.

Norma Perry, *Sir Everard Fawkener*, Voltaire Foundation, Banbury, Oxon, 1975. (Vol. 133 in the series, 'Studies on Voltaire and the Eighteenth Century', ed. Theodore Besterman).

H. J. Phillips, *The Thames in 1750*, London, 1951.

H. J. Phillips, *Mid-Georgian London*, London, 1964.

J. W. Sherwell, *The History of the Guild of Sadlers . . .*, 3rd and revised edition, London, 1956.

W. A. Thorpe, *English Glass*, 3rd edition, London, 1961.

Victoria County History—Middlesex, Vol. II, Oxford, 1967.

Victoria County History—Staffordshire, Vol. VIII, Oxford, 1963.

Philip L. White, ed., *Beekman Mercantile Papers, Vol. II 1746–1799*, New York Historical Society, New York, 1956.

Index